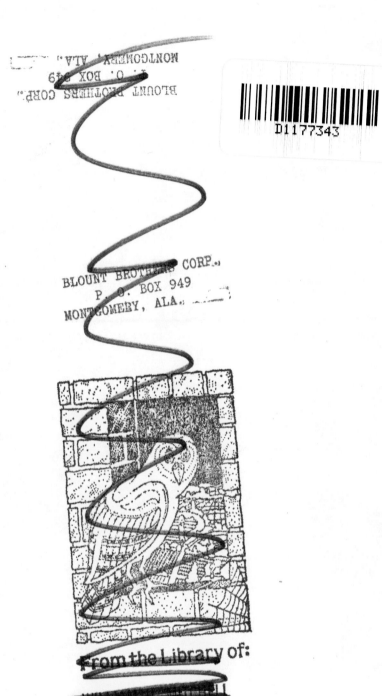

TheWoodBook Introduction

Now there is a single, complete source for information on a wide range of wood products. It is TheWoodBook.

Here, in a convenient, orderly volume is a storehouse of product information, specification guides, application and installation recommendations, plus span tables, coverage rates and many pages of design details. It is information tailored for those who design and work with wood.

The information is from the leading wood products associations, representing the full range of building materials for both residential and commercial construction. And now, TheWoodBook puts that information in one reference volume giving more information on more wood products than ever before available from a single source.

Information is arranged in standard construction information categories: Site Work, Wood, Thermal and Moisture Protection, and Finishes. Each is marked by a Division Page which lists the information to be found in that section. A complete Table of Contents follows this introductory section and an abbreviated Table of Contents is listed on each Division Page. A complete key word index is included at the back of the book to help find information and to cross-reference a particular subject.

TheWoodBook. It's an indispensable addition to your reference library. And it will be revised and reprinted annually to keep it that way.

TheWoodBook is published by Wood Products Publications, P.O. Box 1752, Tacoma, Washington 98401.

TheWoodBook is the registered trademark of Wood Products Publications.

© 1978 Wood Products Publications

ASSOCIATIONS

AMERICAN INSTITUTE OF TIMBER CONSTRUCTION (AITC)

The American Institute of Timber Construction represents the nation's structural glued laminating timber industry. Its members manufacture, fabricate, assemble, erect and/or design wood structural systems. Its program consists of licensing qualified manufacturers, quality control and inspection, and technical and design assistance to specifiers and users. AITC is headquartered in Englewood, Colorado. For literature or assistance, contact:

American Institute of Timber Construction
333 West Hampden Avenue
Englewood, Colorado 80110
(800) 525-1625 / (303) 761-3212 in Alaska, Colorado or Hawaii

AMERICAN PLYWOOD ASSOCIATION (APA)

Founded in 1936 as the Douglas Fir Plywood Association, the American Plywood Association today represents the manufacturers of approximately 80 percent of the softwood plywood produced in the U.S. APA's mission is threefold: testing and inspection, research and promotion. Association headquarters and main research laboratory are located in Tacoma, Washington. Regional field offices and quality testing laboratories are also maintained throughout the country. For information on services or literature, contact:

American Plywood Association
P.O. Box 2277
Tacoma, Washington 98401
(206) 272-2283

AMERICAN WOOD PRESERVERS INSTITUTE (AWPI)

The American Wood Preservers Institute represents more than 100 corporate members and more than two-thirds of the pressure-treating capacity in the U.S. With headquarters in McLean, Virginia and with five field offices around the country, AWPI is equipped to provide technical information and assistance to architects, engineers, designers, specifiers and others about the correct specification and use of pressure-treated wood products. For information or assistance, call or write:

American Wood Preservers Institute
1651 Old Meadow Road
McLean, Virginia 22101
(703) 893-4005 / (800) 336-0148

CALIFORNIA REDWOOD ASSOCIATION (CRA)

The San Francisco-based California Redwood Association conducts a broad range of promotional, technical and educational activities aimed at encouraging the proper specification, application and finishing of redwood products. Founded in 1916, the association today represents the leading redwood and plywood producers. Direct inquiries or requests for literature or technical assistance to:

California Redwood Association
One Lombard Street
San Francisco, California 94111
(415) 392-7880

COUNCIL OF FOREST INDUSTRIES OF B.C. (COFI)

In participating in TheWoodBook, the Council of Forest Industries of B.C. represents AFPA, Alberta Forest Products Association, CLMA, Cariboo Lumber Manufacturers' Association, ILMA, Interior Lumber Manufacturers' Association and the Northern Interior Lumber Sector. For information write:

Alberta Forest Products Association
204 11710 Kingsway Avenue
Edmonton, Alberta   T5G 0X5

Cariboo Lumber Manufacturers' Association
301 197 Second Avenue North
Williams Lake, British Columbia   V2G 1Z5

Interior Lumber Manufacturers' Association
295 333 Martin Street
Penticton, British Columbia   V2A 5K8

Northern Interior Lumber Sector
Council of Forest Industries of B.C.
51 550 Victoria Street
Prince George, British Columbia   V2L 2K1

NATIONAL FOREST PRODUCTS ASSOCIATION (NFPA)

The National Forest Products Association is a federation of 27 associations and several companies in the wood products industry. Its many mandates include developing design data for and securing code acceptance of wood products and construction systems. NFPA also conducts and supports programs to assure responsible management of forest resources. For a list of available literature or more information, contact:

National Forest Products Association
1619 Massachusetts Avenue NW
Washington, D.C. 20036
(202) 797-5800

RED CEDAR SHINGLE & HANDSPLIT SHAKE BUREAU (CEDAR BUREAU)

The Red Cedar Shingle & Handsplit Shake Bureau represents over 500 manufacturers in the Pacific Northwest. Formed in 1963 by the merger of the Red Cedar Shingle Bureau (1915) and the Handsplit Red Cedar Shake Association (1955), the Bureau conducts a grading, labeling and mill inspection program and provides product promotion and technical expertise to specifiers and users. Assistance or literature may be obtained by writing or calling:

Red Cedar Shingle & Handsplit Shake Bureau
Suite 275
515 116th Avenue NE
Bellevue, Washington 98004
(206) 453-1323

SOUTHERN FOREST PRODUCTS ASSOCIATION (SFPA)

Southern Forest Products Association's member mills account for approximately half of all Southern Pine lumber produced in the U.S. Founded in 1915 as the Southern Pine Association, SFPA is headquartered in New Orleans with field representatives in the East and Midwest, as well as the South. Among the association's major functions are the promotion and dissemination of design data and use recommendations and the obtaining of code acceptances for wood construction systems. Direct literature and technical assistance requests to:

Southern Forest Products Association
Box 52468
New Orleans, Louisiana 70152
(504) 443-4464

WESTERN WOOD PRODUCTS ASSOCIATION (WWPA)

The Western Wood Products Association in Portland, Oregon is the largest certified lumber grading agency in the nation. Its member mills in 12 western states account for approximately 60 percent of western and 40 percent of national softwood lumber production. WWPA was formed in 1964 by the consolidation of the West Coast Lumbermen's Association and the Western Pine Association. The association, in addition to quality control, provides technical assistance to users and specifiers of structural lumber. For such assistance, or for literature, write or call:

Western Wood Products Association
Yeon Building
Portland, Oregon 97204
(503) 224-3930

WOOD MOULDING AND MILLWORK PRODUCERS (WMMP)

The Portland, Oregon-based Wood Moulding and Millwork Producers serves as the trade association to the major moulding and millwork manufacturers. The association was known prior to 1977 as the Western Wood Moulding and Millwork Producers and since its founding in 1962 has set as its major objectives industry standardization and product promotion. For information on wood moulding and millwork products, contact:

Wood Moulding and Millwork Producers
1730 S.W. Skyline
P.O. Box 25278
Portland, Oregon 97225
(503) 292-9288

The Wood Book Contents

Abbreviations used:

AFPA—Alberta Forest Products Association
AITC—American Institute of Timber Construction
APA—American Plywood Association
AWPI—American Wood Preservers Institute
CRA—California Redwood Association
CLMA—Cariboo Lumber Manufacturers' Association
COFI—Council of Forest Industries
ILMA—Interior Lumber Manufacturers' Association
NFPA—National Forest Products Association
Cedar Bureau—Red Cedar Shingle and Handsplit Shake Bureau
SFPA—Southern Forest Products Association
WWPA—Western Wood Products Association
WMMP—Wood Moulding and Millwork Producers

(Continued on next page.)

THERMAL AND MOISTURE PROTECTION DIVISION

SHINGLES

Cedar Bureau—*Red Cedar Shingles
and Shakes*

FINISHES DIVISION

PANELING

CRA—*Redwood Interior Guide*

INDEX

Wood Products Publications, publisher of The WoodBook, has made every effort to secure accurate and current information about the wood products and systems referred to herein, but does not guarantee the accuracy of the printed material contained herein nor does it accept responsibility for any design or performance of material as actually constructed.

The Wood Book Information Categories

SITE WORK DIVISION

FOUNDATIONS

APA—*Concrete Forming and Wood Foundation Systems*

SITE FURNISHINGS

CRA—*Redwood Landscape Guide*

WOOD DIVISION

GENERAL INFORMATION

NFPA—*Wood Design Publications*

LAMINATED AND PROCESSED SHEETS

APA—*Plywood Specification and Grade Guide*
APA—*Plywood Floor Systems*
APA—*Plywood Roof Systems*

LUMBER

COFI—*Kiln-Dried Spruce-Pine-Fir*
SFPA—*Southern Pine Use Guide*
WWPA—*Product Use Manual*

PREFABRICATED STRUCTURAL WOOD

AITC—*Glulam Systems*

STOCK MILLWORK

WMMP—*Wood Moulding and Millwork*

WOOD TREATMENT

AWPI—*Pressure-Treated Wood*

THERMAL AND MOISTURE PROTECTION DIVISION

CLADDING/SIDING

APA—*Plywood Wall Systems*
CRA—*Redwood Plywood Guide*
CRA—*Redwood Exterior Guide*

SHINGLES

Cedar Bureau—*Red Cedar Shingles and Shakes*

FINISHES DIVISION

PANELING

CRA—*Redwood Interior Guide*

The WoodBook SiteWork

The**Wood**Book **SiteWork**

The APA Series

Construction

Concrete Forming & Wood Foundation Systems

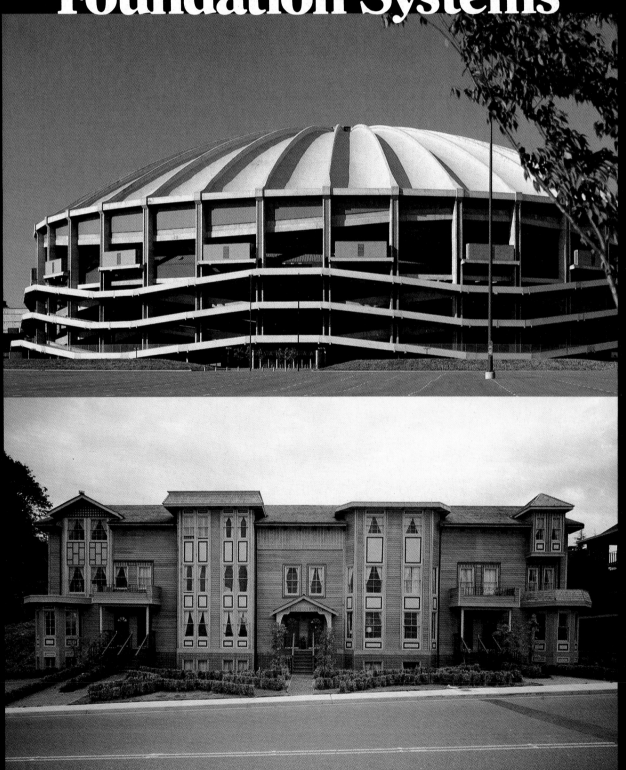

American Plywood Association

February 1978

2

FOUNDATIONS

Plywood

Introduction

When it comes to foundations and concrete forming, builders come to plywood. Why? Because of plywood's workability, durability, quality and economy. And, in the case of the AWWF, because it means an end to the off-season. Unlike conventional foundation systems, the AWWF can be built in all kinds of weather. And there's no waiting on subcontractors since the same carpenters who build the rest of the house can also install the foundation.

The basic elements of the AWWF are explained in the following pages. There's also a look at the Plen-Wood® system, the underfloor plenum heating and cooling system that saves time and money because it eliminates costly ducting. And there's grade and design information on plywood for concrete forming.

Plywood. There's no better material for foundations and forming.

NOTE: For information on plywood types, groups, grades, Identification Indexes and method of ordering, refer to APA's **Plywood Specification and Grade Guide,** C20.

SPECIFICATION GUIDE

Each panel of construction and/or concrete form plywood shall meet the requirements of the latest edition of U.S. Product Standard PS 1, and shall be identified with the appropriate grade-trademark of the American Plywood Association. All plywood which has any edge or surface permanently exposed to the weather or moisture shall be Exterior type.*

Panel thickness, grade, and Group or Identification Index shall be equal to or better than that shown on the drawings. Application shall be in accordance with recommendations of the American Plywood Association.

*An exception may be made in the case of plywood used for the All-Weather Wood Foundation, which may be Interior type with exterior glue provided it is pressure-preservative-treated in accordance with the American Wood Preservers Bureau AWPB-FDN Standard.

The All-Weather Wood Foundation

Advantages. Builders all across the country are switching to the All-Weather Wood Foundation because it offers advantages other foundation systems simply can't deliver.

Take scheduling, for example. Whether crawl space or full basement, the AWWF can be installed in all kinds of weather. There's no waiting for the ground to dry or for the rain to stop. There's less waiting on subcontractors since the AWWF can be installed by the same carpenters who build the rest of the house. And there's no delay for concrete or masonry delivery.

The AWWF can be installed easily, by a small crew, in less than a day. No special skills are required, just reasonable carpentry care. When it's up, there's no waiting while mortar or concrete cures.

And the AWWF is easier and more economical to finish inside. No furring is needed for installing insulation and drywall or paneling. Plumbing and wiring are simplified. Many builders report dollar savings in materials alone. Others cite the cumulative savings that result from the speed and ease of installation.

Prospective homeowners like the system because it provides dry, "non-basementy" basements. There's no clamminess or mustiness. And the wood framing makes it easier to install thicker batt-type insulation for greater energy savings.

CODE APPROVALS

The All-Weather Wood Foundation is an efficient structural system based on engineering calculations, field tests and experience. And it's recognized by the major building regulatory agencies. Approval information is contained in:

☐ International Conference of Building Officials, Research Committee Recommendation Report 2765

☐ 1976 Supplement to 1976 Basic Building Code of BOCA International

☐ 1976 Standard Building Code of the Southern Building Code Congress

☐ HUD Minimum Property Standards, 1973 Edition (both multi- and single-family housing)

☐ 1976 National Building Code of the American Insurance Association.

Elements of the System

The AWWF is basically a set of below-grade stud walls built of pressure-preservative-treated lumber and APA grade-trademarked plywood. The plywood-and-lumber walls act as deep girders to bridge soft spots in the soil and to absorb both normal backfilling pressure and unexpected stresses from earthquakes.

Plywood must be Exterior type or Interior type bonded with exterior glue and produced according to **Product Standard PS 1-74 for Construction and Industrial Plywood.** Plywood bearing the APA grade-trademark is produced according to PS 1. The lumber must be of a species and grade for which allowable unit stresses are given in the "National Design Specification for Stress Grade Lumber and Its Fastenings." It is also required to be grademarked by an approved inspection agency. Table 1 shows plywood and lumber requirements for a typical one-story house.

All plywood and framing within 8 inches of the ground is pressure-treated in accordance with the American Wood Preservers Bureau AWPB-FDN Standard and must bear the AWPB-FDN trademark. The treatment consists of impregnating preservative salts into the plywood and lumber under heat and pressure. The required 0.6 pcf preservative retention is 50 percent greater than codes require for normal ground-contact application. Stainless steel fasteners are recommended for below-grade application, including attachment of plywood sheathing and of the footer assembly.

A key element of the AWWF is moisture control. This is accomplished, first, by directing water away from the building with downspouts and splash blocks, and by sloping the backfill away from the building. In basement construction (Figure 1), plywood joints must be caulked full length with an appropriate

FIGURE 1 Basement Construction

Perimeter Foundation

Interior Bearing Wall

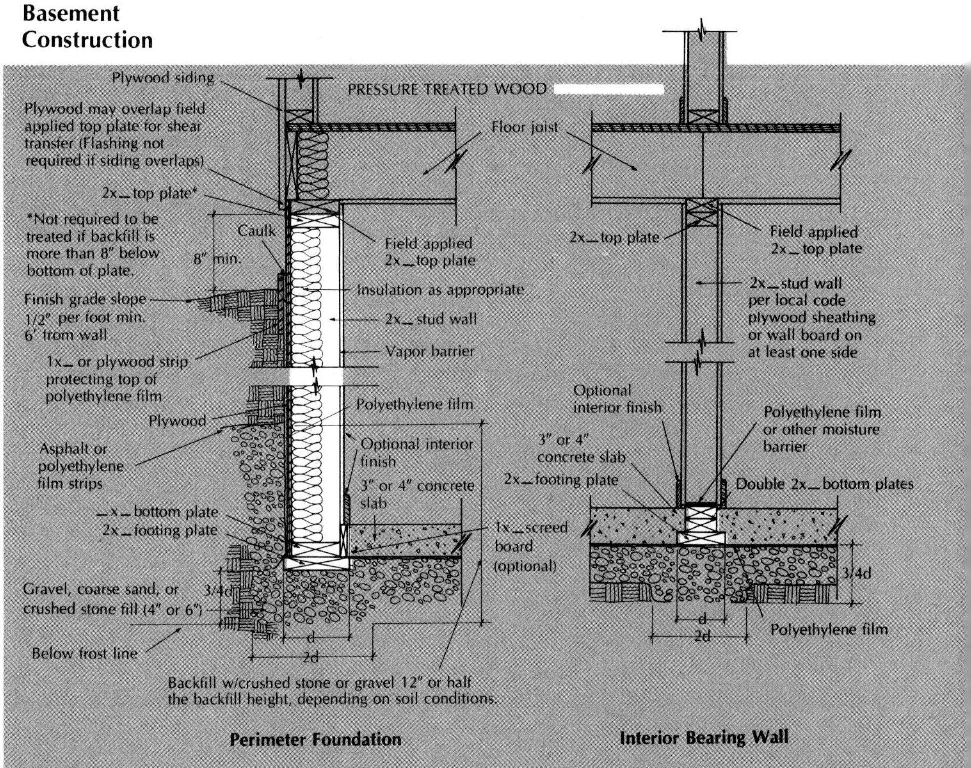

FIGURE 2 Crawl Space Construction

Perimeter Foundation

Interior Pier Support

compound. A 6-mil polyethylene film is also required. The polyethylene acts as a moisture deflector, directing moisture downward to a pervious gravel or crushed stone fill and footing where it is then disposed of through a sump. This simple, yet effective drainage system prevents a build-up of pressure against foundation walls and helps avoid leaks. Figure 2 shows typical AWWF crawl space construction.

The AWWF—whether full basement or crawl space—is adaptable to almost any home site and frame building design. While it is possible to build the entire foundation on the jobsite, accuracy and quality control often can be improved by fabricating sections in-shop.

For complete information on the AWWF—including details, fastener schedules and data for determining the foundation design of a typical house—write for **The All-Weather Wood Foundation: Why, What and How,** A400.

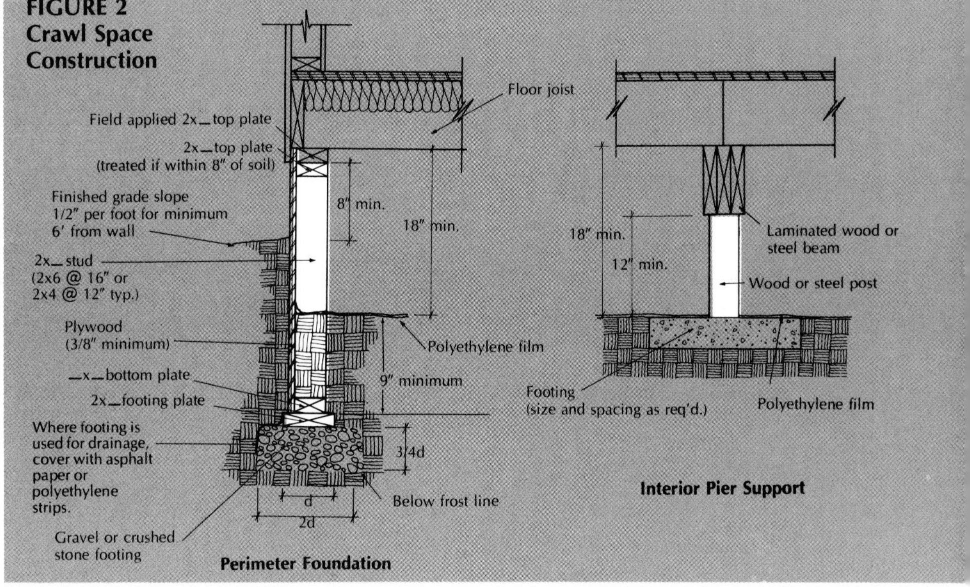

TABLE 1 Plywood and Framing Required for 32-Ft.-Wide, One-Story Basement House

Height of Backfill (Inches)	Stud* Size and Spacing	Footer Plate Size	Plywood (Face Grain Across Supports)
24	2 x 4 @ 12"	2 x 8	1/2" CDX 32/16
48	2 x 6 @ 16"	2 x 8	1/2" CDX 32/16
72	2 x 6 @ 12"	2 x 8	1/2" CDX 32/16
86	2 x 8 @ 16"	2 x 8	3/4" CDX 48/24

*Use Lodgepole Pine No. 2, Ponderosa Pine No. 2 or Northern Pine No. 2 for 24" and 48" backfill, and Douglas Fir No. 2 or Southern Pine No. 2 KD for 72" and 86" backfill. Check treater for availability of treatable species.

The Plen-Wood System

The Plen-Wood home heating and cooling system. It's a boon to builder and buyer alike because it cuts construction costs and is frugal with precious energy. And it's a ''natural'' in combination with the All-Weather Wood Foundation and the APA Glued Floor System.

The concept is simple. Instead of furnace ducts, the entire underfloor area of single-story residences is used as a plenum chamber from which warm or cool air is distributed to floor registers and the rooms above. A down-flow furnace keeps the air in the plenum under slight pressure to assure uniform distribution of conditioned air. The plenum itself is simply an insulated crawl space sealed with a 6-mil polyethylene vapor barrier.

The system saves money because it eliminates costly ducting. As much as $330 per house can be saved over the cost of conventional concrete slab construction in some areas of the country, according to cost-comparison estimates of the National Association of Home Builders Research Foundation.

The Plen-Wood system is also easy to build. No special skills or techniques are required. Standard, readily available materials are used throughout. And the system allows greater design flexibility. Ceilings don't have to be designed to accommodate heating and cooling ducts. Sloping, vaulted or beamed ceilings may be used throughout the house. Attic space is freed for other uses.

HVAC contractors generally recommend the same size equipment for the Plen-Wood as required for conventionally ducted systems. Since it works by convection, conduction and radiation, a more uniform floor-to-ceiling temperature is produced and maintained. As a result, many Plen-Wood homeowners report

optimum comfort at lower thermostat settings . . . and significant energy savings. Another positive sales feature: the natural comfort of resilient wood floors.

Although the single-layer APA Glued Floor System will usually contribute to even greater cost savings, the Plen-Wood may also be constructed with conventional subflooring. And while ideal in combination with the AWWF for an all-wood system, foundation walls may also be conventionally constructed.

The Plen-Wood system has been successfully used in thousands of homes in every climatic region of the country and, with minor variations, meets the model building codes. Some local codes require soil treatment.

For complete design data and installation information, contact the American Plywood Association.

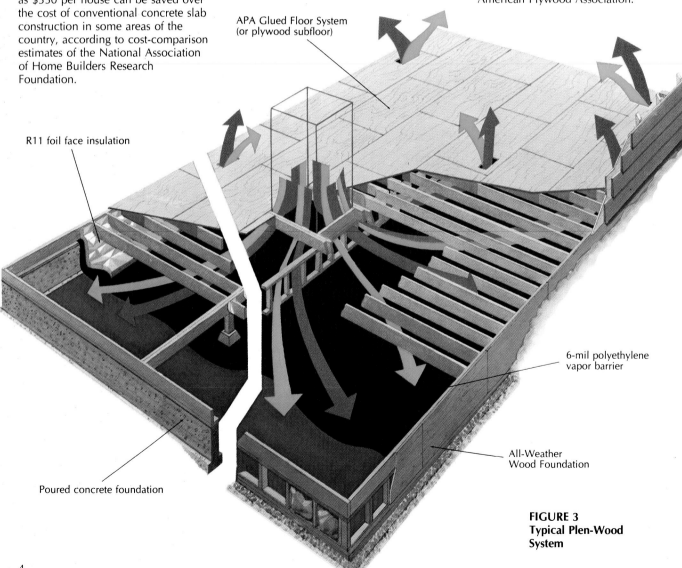

APA Glued Floor System
(or plywood subfloor)

R11 foil face insulation

6-mil polyethylene
vapor barrier

All-Weather
Wood Foundation

Poured concrete foundation

FIGURE 3
Typical Plen-Wood
System

Plywood for Concrete Forming

There's no material more widely used for concrete forming than plywood. And no better material for the job—whether it's foundations, floors, walls, roof systems, columns, bridges, or dams.

Plywood produces smooth concrete surfaces. It offers many reuses. It's easy to work with ordinary carpentry skills and tools. It holds nails and fastening devices without splitting near panel edges. It may be bent easily for curved forms and liners. Yet it's stiff to minimize deflection during pouring. Plywood's natural insulating qualities help provide more consistent curing conditions. The large panel size and light weight reduce form construction and stripping time. And various surface textures are available for imparting attractive and unusual concrete textures.

Although nearly any Exterior type plywood can be used for concrete forming, a special panel called PLYFORM® is manufactured specifically for the purpose. PLYFORM can be manufactured in two classes—Class I and Class II—with Class I the strongest, stiffest and most widely available. PLYFORM can also be manufactured with a High Density Overlaid (HDO) surface, and in STRUCTURAL I panels. HDO PLYFORM has an exceptionally smooth, hard surface for the smoothest possible concrete finishes and the maximum number of pours. STRUCTURAL I PLYFORM is stronger and stiffer than PLYFORM Class I or II and is sometimes used for high pressures where face grain is parallel to supports. Additional plywood grades designed for concrete forming include special overlays and proprietary panels.

TABLE 2 Grade-Use Guide for Concrete Forms (a)

Use These Terms When You Specify Plywood	Description	Typical Grade-Trademarks	Veneer Grade	
			Faces	Inner plies
B-B PLYFORM Class I & II (b) APA	Specifically manufactured for concrete forms. Many reuses. Smooth, solid surfaces. Mill-oiled unless otherwise specified.	B-B PLYFORM CLASS I (APA) EXTERIOR PS 1-74 000	B	C
High Density Overlaid PLYFORM Class I & II (b) APA	Hard, semi-opaque resin-fiber overlay heat-fused to panel faces. Smooth surface resists abrasion. Up to 200 reuses. Light oiling recommended between pours.	HDO · PLYFORM-I · EXT-APA · PS 1-74	B	C Plugged
STRUCTURAL I PLYFORM (b) APA	Especially designed for engineered applications. All Group 1 species. Stronger and stiffer than PLYFORM Class I and II. Recommended for high pressures where face grain is parallel to supports. Also available with High Density Overlay faces.	STRUCTURAL I B-B PLYFORM CLASS I (APA) EXTERIOR PS 1-74 000	B	C or C Plugged

(a) Commonly available in ⅝" and ¾" panel thickness (4'x8' size).
(b) Check dealer for availability in your area.

Form Construction

Site-built forms are usually most economical when plywood is intended for a single use. Some forming plywood may later be reused for subflooring, sheathing, or temporary jobsite needs. **Site-built wall forms** are usually fabricated on the ground, then tilted into place. In some cases forms are built right on the footings. Studs are erected and plywood then nailed to the inside. As few and as small nails as possible should be used: 5d for ⅜-inch and 6d for ¾-inch plywood. Plywood slab forms should be nailed at least at each corner of the panel. Do not butt panels too tightly, especially on the first pour. **High wall forms** are often preframed. Wales may be installed with clips or special brackets. To eliminate leakage and to produce a smoother joint, horizontal joints may be backed up by headers or nailing strips. **Low wall forms** may require no wales at all. Studs may provide sufficient bracing, depending on the spacing of form ties. **Column forms** are often framed with 2x4s and anchored at the base. Columns may be built in place or as a complete column box to be set in place.

The required plywood thickness and the size and spacing of framing for concrete forms depends on the maximum concrete pressure. For column and wall forms, this pressure is governed by such factors as pour rate, concrete temperature, slump and density, cement type, method of vibration and height of forms. (See APA's **Plywood for Concrete Forming** for methods of estimating pressures.) Once the maximum pressure has been determined, the plywood thickness and support spacing can be selected using Table 3.

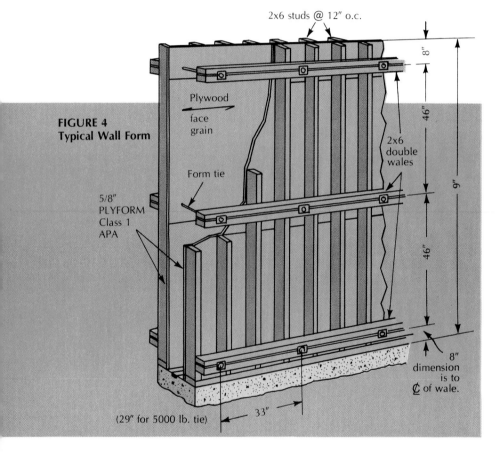

**FIGURE 4
Typical Wall Form**

2x6 studs @ 12" o.c.

Plywood face grain

Form tie

5/8" PLYFORM Class 1 APA

2x6 double wales

8"

46"

9"

46"

8" dimension is to ℄ of wale.

(29" for 5000 lb. tie) 33"

TABLE 3 Allowable Pressures on PLYFORM Class I (psf) for Architectural Applications
(Deflection limited to 1/360th of the span)
FACE GRAIN ACROSS SUPPORTS*

Support Spacing (inches)	Plywood Thickness (inches)					
	1/2	5/8	3/4	7/8	1	1-1/8
4	3265	4095	5005	5225	5650	6290
8	970	1300	1650	2005	2175	2420
12	410	575	735	890	1190	1370
16	175	270	370	475	645	750
20	100	160	225	295	410	490
24			120	160	230	280
32					105	130
36						115

*Plywood continuous across two or more spans.

Care and Handling

Reasonable care yields maximum reuse. Wooden wedges reduce damage when stripping forms. Don't use metal bars or prys. Double-head nails also cut damage and speed stripping. To prevent damage to working surfaces, lower, do not drop forms. After stripping, clean and scrape panels with a wide, blunt blade, then oil and stack on a level surface protected from the weather. Prime all edges, cuts and blemishes. Use stickers to permit normal drying.

For complete concrete forming design tables, engineering data, application examples and care and handling information, write for **Plywood for Concrete Forming**, V345.

Additional Information

For additional information on the All-Weather Wood Foundation, plywood for concrete forming and other plywood systems and applications, request any of the publications listed below. Single copies are available without charge by writing the American Plywood Association, P.O. Box 2277, Tacoma, Washington 98401.

The All-Weather Wood Foundation: Why, What and How, A400
Plywood for Concrete Forming, V345
Plywood Residential Construction Guide, Y405
Plywood Commercial/Industrial Construction Guide, Y300
Plywood Systems: Floors, B430
AWWF: A Builder's Checklist, B405
Plywood Concrete Form Surfaces, Coatings And Treatments, Z394

APA: THE MARK OF QUALITY

The American Plywood Association's grade-trademarks are used by qualified member mills to identify plywood that has been manufactured to meet the requirements of **U.S. Product Standard PS 1-74 for Construction and Industrial Plywood.** Information covered in this and all APA publications is based upon the use of plywood of known quality. Always insist on plywood bearing the **Mark of Quality**—the APA grade-trademark.

Our field representatives can help. For additional assistance in specifying plywood, get in touch with your nearest American Plywood Association field service representative. Call or write:

ATLANTA
Paul D. Colbenson
P. O. Box 90550
Atlanta, Georgia 30364
(404) 762-6649

CHICAGO
Vernon D. Haskell
120 East Ogden Avenue
Room 204
Hinsdale, Illinois 60521
(312) 323-5787

DALLAS
A. M. Leggett
10010 Miller Road
Suite 105
Dallas, Texas 75238
(214) 348-0643

LOS ANGELES
Long Beach, California
(213) 439-8616

NEW YORK
Englewood Cliffs, New Jersey
(201) 567-7238

SAN FRANCISCO
Philip L. Benfield
P. O. Box 3536
Fremont, California 94538
(415) 657-5959

WASHINGTON, D.C.
Paul G. Nystrom
4121 Chatelain Road
Room 203
Annandale, Virginia 22003
(703) 750-3993

The plywood use recommendations contained in this brochure are based on the American Plywood Association's continuing program of laboratory testing, product research and comprehensive field experience. However, quality of workmanship and the conditions under which plywood is used vary widely. Because the Association has no control over these elements, it cannot accept responsibility for plywood performance or designs as actually constructed.

Plywood cuts costs. Not quality.

AMERICAN PLYWOOD ASSOCIATION

P. O. Box 2277 / Tacoma, WA 98401

Form No. C60

3A5

Redwood
Landscape Guide

California
Redwood
Association

California redwood is an excellent wood for landscape structures. In conjunction with the extensive outdoor areas often associated with condominiums, community centers, shopping centers, children's play yards, and common-ownership spaces, the lower-cost garden grades of redwood offer economy in large-scale uses. Decks, benches, fences, screens, arbors, planters, retaining walls. and play equipment—all are uses well suited to garden-grade redwood. Here are some of the reasons.

Durability. Redwood heartwood contains natural extractives that give it high resistance to insects and decay.

Stability. No other wood has less shrinkage than redwood, and this stability means minimum tendency to warp, twist, or cup when exposed to heat and weather, and little tendency to weather check.

Finish retention. Finishes last longer on redwood because of its stability and absence of pitches and resins.

Redwood Garden Grades

The garden grades of redwood contain knots, are usually more highly figured and patterned than the clear upper grades, and are not ordinarily kiln dried. They are described below.

Construction Heart. An excellent heart-wood grade recommended for general construction. It is resistant to insects and decay. It allows knots approximately ½ the width of the face, and some manufacturing imperfections if they do not cause waste. Seasoning checks, slight shake, and medium crook are permitted.

Construction Common. Similar to Construction Heart, except that sapwood is permitted.

Merchantable. Allows knots slightly larger than those allowed in Construction Heart. Loose knots and knotholes occur in some pieces. This grade can be recut economically for many uses.

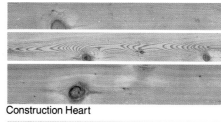

Construction Heart

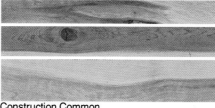

Construction Common

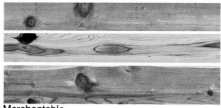

Merchantable

Application and Design Suggestions

Heartwood (Construction Heart or Merchantable selected for total heartwood content) should be used for members on or in the ground (within 6 inches of the ground for loadbearing structural members), or where the wood will come into contact with soil and alternate cycles of wetting and drying, as in planter boxes and green-house stock.

Sapwood-containing grades can be used for any application where the wood is in little danger of attack by decay or insects, and where the contrasting color tones of the cinnamon-colored heartwood and cream-colored sapwood form a positive design factor.

Fences. There is probably no such thing as a purely decorative fence. A fence will always function in some way—by controlling or admitting sunlight or air, or by acting as either a physical or visual barrier. Most fences are built with 4×4 posts, 2×4 stringers, and 1-inch-thick boards. If heavier fence boards are used, such as 2×4's, stringers and posts should be proportionately heavier.

Post holes should be about 2 feet deep for a 5-foot fence, 2½ feet deep for a 6-foot fence, and 3½ for an 8-foot fence.

Posts set in concrete should be filled in around the bottoms with earth or gravel before pouring, to keep the concrete from sealing off the bottom of the post and preventing drainage.

Hilly Site. On a sloping site, some fence designs look best when allowed to follow the natural contours of the land. Examples are split rail and post-and-rail fences, or their many variations. Solid or louvered fences should be stepped down in sections.

Garden Grade Lumber Sizes

The table gives the nominal and surfaced sizes for garden grades of redwood.

Unseasoned Boards, Strips, Dimension

Thicknesses								
Nominal	$3/4$	1^*	$1^1/4$	$1^1/2$	2^*	3	4	6
Surfaced S1S or S2S	$11/16$	$25/32$	$1^1/16$	$1^5/16$	$1^9/16$	$2^9/16$	$3^9/16$	$5^5/8$

Widths					
Nominal	3	4	6	8	10	12
Surfaced	$2^9/16$	$3^9/16$	$5^5/8$	$7^1/2$	$9^1/2$	$11^1/2$

*These items are frequently surfaced at $3/4$" net and $1^5/8$" net respectively.

Suggested Span Allowances

The following tables are based on *non-stress-graded* redwood used in a single span. Abnormal loading such as planter boxes will require shorter spans or larger beams and joists.

Where requirements are more exacting or engineered design is required by local codes, it is recommended that *structural* grades of redwood lumber be used and the allowable spans be calculated based upon the recommended design values listed for each structural grade in *Standard Specifications for Grades of California Redwood Lumber,* published by the Redwood Inspection Service, One Lombard Street, San Francisco, California 94111.

Suggested Beam Spans

for non-stress-graded Construction Heart and Construction Common redwood lumber with live load of 40 lbs. per sq. ft. and dead load of 10 lbs. per sq. ft.

Beam Size	Beam Span			
	6′ deck width	8′ deck width	10′ deck width	12′ deck width
4×6	4′-6″	4′-0″	3′-6″	3′-0″
4×8	6′-0″	5′-0″	4′-6″	4′-0″
4×10	7′-6″	6′-6″	6′-0″	5′-6″

Deflection limited to L/360

Suggested Joist Spans

for non-stress-graded Construction Heart and Construction Common redwood lumber with live load of 40 lbs. per sq. ft.

Joist Size		Joist Span
2×6	16″ o.c.	6′-0″
	24″ o.c.	5′-0″
2×8	16″ o.c.	9′-0″
	24″ o.c.	7′-6″
2×10	16″ o.c.	12′-0″
	24″ o.c.	10′-0″

(o.c. means "on center")

Deflection limited to L/240

Suggested Decking Spans

for non-stress-graded Construction Heart and Construction Common redwood lumber with live load of 40 lbs. per sq. ft.

Size	Span
2×4, 2×6	24″

Deflection limited to L/180

Decks. In deck construction, two important considerations are large knots and the type of grain the lumber contains.

In load-bearing applications (deck floor, bench seat), large knots should be placed over joists or other supports. This may mean laying the decking down loosely on a trial basis to check the best arrangement of pieces.

Vertical grain lumber is sawn at right angles to the tree's annual growth rings, so that the rings form an angle of 45 degrees or more with the surface of the piece. Flat grain lumber is sawn tangent to the growth rings. Flat grain boards should be laid "bark-side" up to avoid excessive raised grain and splinters.

Vertical Grain

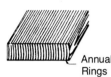

Annual Rings

Flat Grain

Bark Side

Pith Side

When nailing near the end or edge of a piece, predrill the nail hole or blunt the tip of the nail slightly to avoid splitting the wood.

Specifications

Specifiers of redwood can assure themselves of obtaining the exact product they desire by including the necessary elements in the specification. A sample specification for decking follows:

"Decking shall be Construction Common redwood, 2×4, S4S, graded in accordance with *Standard Specifications for Grades of California Redwood Lumber*, published by the Redwood Inspection Service."

Storage

Lumber should be stored under cover and off the ground, in such a way that it lies flat. Lumber that sags in storage or is propped against a wall may warp or bend permanently.

Finishes

CRA recommends the application of a water repellent on all exterior redwood, and especially on sapwood-containing grades. Water repellent retards natural weathering, reduces the effects of moisture, and helps protect the wood from dirt and grime. It can serve as a finish in itself, or as an undercoat for further finishes such as a pigmented stain or wood bleach. In the event that no other finish is used, a second application of water repellent is recommended on the completed structure. Water repellent will modify the natural weathering process, eliminating the dark initial stage, and will help stabilize the color at a buckskin tan. When using water repellent, be sure to follow manufacturer's directions carefully and read the warnings on the label.

Clear film-forming finishes are not recommended for exterior use on redwood lumber.

Nails and Fastenings

Noncorrosive nails and fastenings should be used outdoors to prevent the stain streaks that can occur with plain iron, steel, or cement-coated nails. Recommended nails are stainless steel or aluminum alloy. *Top quality, hot-dipped* galvanized nails will also perform well if the galvanized coating is not damaged during nailing.

Related Literature

The California Redwood Association publishes a series of data sheets on garden applications of redwood, available from the CRA address below. These include data sheets on fences, decks, garden shelters, garden work centers, retaining walls, patio paving, benches, and planter boxes. A comprehensive guide to exterior finishes is available.

For detailed information on redwood interior paneling and redwood siding and trim, see CRA Data Sheet 3A7, *Redwood Interior Guide* (in Wood Book), and Data Sheet 3A4, *Redwood Exterior Guide* (in Wood Book). For information on redwood plywood, see CRA Data Sheet 3A9, *Redwood Plywood Guide* (in Wood Book).

The CRA trademark is your assurance of quality. The California Redwood Association is a non-profit organization maintained by the principal redwood producers. Its interests extend from the growth and protection of quality timber for the future and the best utilization of current forest crops, to research, and the dissemination of information on the use of redwood.

California Redwood Association

One Lombard Street
San Francisco, California 94111
Telephone: (415) 392-7880

CRA Member Company Sales Offices

Arcata Redwood Company
P.O. Box 218, Arcata, CA 95521
Georgia-Pacific Corporation
Fort Bragg Division-Redwood
90 West Redwood Ave., Fort Bragg, CA 95437
Harwood Products Company
P.O. Box 609, Willits, CA 95490
Masonite Corporation, Western Lumber Division
P.O. Box 97, Calpella, CA 95418
Miller Redwood Company
P.O. Box 247, Crescent City, CA 95531
Simpson Timber Company
900 Fourth Ave., Seattle, WA 98164
The Pacific Lumber Company
1111 Columbus Ave., San Francisco, CA 94133

Redwood—a renewable resource.

The**Wood**Book **Wood**

available from
National Forest Products Association
1619 Mass. Ave., N.W. Washington, D. C. 20036

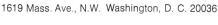

WOOD DESIGN PUBLICATIONS

National Design Specification For Wood Construction

1977 Edition

Nationally recognized guide for wood structural design. Includes general requirements, design provisions and formulas, and data on sawn lumber, structural glued laminated timbers, round timber piles, panel products and wood fastenings. A supplement provides design values for structural lumber, glued laminated softwood and hardwood timbers. *Price $5.00.*

Wood Structural Design Data

1978 Edition

(Not available until January 1978)

Technical manual on design of typical wood structural members. Includes physical and mechanical properties of structural lumber, design information and load tables for wood beams, wood columns, plank and laminated floors and roofs, and maximum spans for floor joists. *Price $10.00.*

Span Tables for Joists and Rafters

1977 Edition

Simplified system for determining allowable joist and rafter spans. Includes bending stress and modulus of elasticity values for all species and grades of 2-inch framing lumber customarily used in construction. *Price $3.00.*

Wood Construction Data Series

Seven manuals containing design and construction information on the following subjects:
WCD #1 — Manual for House Framing. *Price $1.00*
WCD #2 — Random Length Decking. *Price $1.00*
WCD #3 — Design of Wood Formwork for Concrete Structures. *Price $1.00*
WCD #4 — Plank and Beam Framing for Residential Construction. *Price $1.00*
WCD #5 — Heavy Timber Construction Details. *Price $1.00*
WCD #6 — Design of Wood Structures for Permanence. *Price $1.00*
WCD #7 — Insulation of Wood-Frame Structures. *Price $1.00*

Construction Cost Saver Series

Six pamphlets describing ways to achieve optimum efficiency in the use of wood framing where cost considerations are of major significance.
Cost Saver #1 — Pre-Planning—Key to Savings. *Price $.25*
Cost Saver #2 — Use of 24', 28' and 32' House Depths. *Price $.25*
Cost Saver #3 — Use of Full Span Capability of Lumber Joists. *Price $.25*
Cost Saver #4 — Exterior Wall Framing. *Price $.25*
Cost Saver #5 — The All-Weather Wood Foundation System. *Price $.25*
Cost Saver #6 — Keeping Energy Saving Construction Costs Down. *Price $.25*

The All-Weather Wood Foundation System--Design, Fabrication and Installation Manual

Detailed information on the design and construction of basement and crawl-space foundations from pressure-treated wood. The manual presents structural design recommendations, fabrication standards, and on-site preparation and installation procedures. *Price $3.00.*

The APA Series

General

Plywood Specification & Grade Guide

Grade of veneer on panel face

Grade of veneer on panel back

A-C

Species Group number — GROUP 2 **APA**

Designates the type of plywood — EXTERIOR

Product Standard governing manufacture — PS 1-74 000

Mill number

Grade of veneer on panel face

Grade of veneer on panel back

C-D

Identification Index — 2 4 / 0 **APA**

Designates the type of plywood — INTERIOR

Product Standard governing manufacture — PS 1-74 000

Type of glue used if other than interior — EXTERIOR GLUE

Mill number

Grade of veneer on panel face
Grade of veneer on panel back
Designates the type of plywood   Product Standard governing
Exterior or Interior   manufacture

A-B · G-1 · EXT-APA · PS 1-74 000

Species Group number   Mill number

Short Form Plywood Specification

Each panel of construction and industrial plywood shall meet the requirements of the latest edition of U.S. Product Standard PS 1 and shall be identified with the appropriate grade-trademark of the American Plywood Association. All plywood which has any edge or surface permanently exposed to the weather shall be Exterior type. (An exception may be made in the case of plywood used for the All-Weather Wood Foundation, which may be Interior type with exterior glue provided it is pressure-preservative-treated in accordance with the American Wood Preservers Bureau AWPB-FDN Standard.)

Application shall be in accordance with the recommendations of the American Plywood Association. (See appropriate APA publications.)

American Plywood Association
February 1978

6

LAMINATED
Plywood

Guide to Engineered Grades of Plywood

SPECIFIC GRADES AND THICKNESSES MAY BE IN LOCALLY LIMITED SUPPLY.
SEE YOUR DEALER BEFORE SPECIFYING.

	Grade Designation	Description and Most Common Uses	Typical Grade-trademarks	Veneer Grade			Most Common Thicknesses (inch)				
				Face	Inner Plies	Back					
Interior Type	C-D INT-APA	For wall and roof sheathing, subflooring, industrial uses such as pallets. Most commonly available with exterior glue. Specify exterior glue where construction delays are anticipated and for treated-wood foundations. (6)	C-D 32/16 INTERIOR PS 1-74 000 APA / C-D 24/0 INTERIOR PS 1-74 000 APA EXTERIOR GLUE	C	D	D	5/16	3/8	1/2	5/8	3/4
	STRUCTURAL I C-D INT-APA and STRUCTURAL II C-D INT-APA	Unsanded structural grades where plywood strength properties are of maximum importance: structural diaphragms, box beams, gusset plates, stressed-skin panels, containers, pallet bins. Made only with exterior glue. See (5) for species group requirements. Structural I most commonly available.	STRUCTURAL I C-D 24/0 INTERIOR PS 1-74 000 APA EXTERIOR GLUE	C(3)	D(3)	D(3)	5/16	3/8	1/2	5/8	3/4
	UNDERLAYMENT INT-APA	For underlayment or combination subfloor-underlayment under resilient floor coverings, carpeting in homes, apartments, mobile homes. Specify exterior glue where moisture may be present, such as bathrooms, utility rooms, or where construction is delayed, as in site-built floors. Touch sanded. Also available in tongue-and-groove. (1) (5)	UNDERLAYMENT GROUP 1 INTERIOR PS 1-74 000 APA	C Plugged	C(4) & D	D		3/8	1/2	5/8	3/4
	C-D PLUGGED INT-APA	For built-ins, wall and ceiling tile backing, cable reels, walkways, separator boards. Not a substitute for UNDERLAYMENT as it lacks UNDERLAYMENT's indentation resistance. Touch-sanded. Also made with exterior glue. (1) (5)	C-D PLUGGED GROUP 2 INTERIOR PS 1-74 000 APA	C Plugged	D	D	5/16	3/8	1/2	5/8	3/4
	2·4·1 INT-APA	Combination subfloor-underlayment. Quality base for resilient floor coverings, carpeting, wood strip flooring. Use 2-4-1 with exterior glue in areas subject to moisture or where construction is delayed, as in site-built floors. Unsanded or touch-sanded as specified. Can be special ordered in Exterior type for porches, patio decks, roof overhangs, exterior balconies. Available in tongue-and-groove. (2)	2·4·1 T&G GROUP 1 INTERIOR PS 1-74 000 APA	C Plugged	C(4) & D	D	1-1/8				
Exterior Type	C-C EXT-APA	Unsanded grade with waterproof bond for subflooring and roof decking, siding on service and farm buildings, crating, pallets, pallet bins, cable reels, treated-wood foundations. (6)	C-C 42/20 EXTERIOR PS 1-74 000 APA	C	C	C	5/16	3/8	1/2	5/8	3/4
	STRUCTURAL I C-C EXT-APA and STRUCTURAL II C-C EXT-APA	For engineered applications in construction and industry where full Exterior type panels are required. Unsanded. See (5) for species group requirements.	STRUCTURAL I C-C 32/16 EXTERIOR PS 1-74 000 APA	C	C	C	5/16	3/8	1/2	5/8	3/4
	UNDERLAYMENT C-C Plugged EXT-APA / C-C PLUGGED EXT-APA	For underlayment or combination subfloor-underlayment under resilient floor coverings where severe moisture conditions may be present, as in balcony decks. Use for tile backing, refrigerated or controlled atmosphere rooms, pallets, fruit pallet bins, reusable cargo containers, tanks and boxcar and truck floors and linings. Touch-sanded. Also available in tongue-and-groove. (1) (5)	UNDERLAYMENT C-C PLUGGED GROUP 2 EXTERIOR PS 1-74 000 APA / C-C PLUGGED GROUP 3 EXTERIOR PS 1-74 000 APA	C Plugged	C(4)	C		3/8	1/2	5/8	3/4
	B-B PLYFORM CLASS I & CLASS II EXT-APA	Concrete form grades with high reuse factor. Sanded both sides. Mill-oiled unless otherwise specified. Special restrictions on species. Available in HDO and STRUCTURAL I. Class I most commonly available. (2)	B-B PLYFORM CLASS I EXTERIOR PS 1-74 000 APA	B	C	B				5/8	3/4

(1) Available in Group 1, 2, 3, 4, or 5.

(2) Made only from certain wood species to conform to APA specifications.

(3) Special improved grade for structural panels.

(4) Special construction to resist indentation from concentrated loads.

(5) Also available in STRUCTURAL I (all plies limited to Group 1 species) and STRUCTURAL II (all plies limited to Group 1, 2, or 3 species).

(6) Made in many different species combinations. Specify by Identification Index.

Veneer Grades

N Smooth surface "natural finish" veneer. Select, all heartwood or all sapwood. Free of open defects. Allows not more than 6 repairs, wood only, per 4x8 panel, made parallel to grain and well matched for grain and color.

A Smooth, paintable. Not more than 18 neatly made repairs, boat, sled, or router type, and parallel to grain, permitted. May be used for natural finish in less demanding applications.

B Solid surface. Shims, circular repair plugs and tight knots to 1 inch across grain permitted. Some minor splits permitted.

C Plugged Improved C veneer with splits limited to 1/8 inch width and knotholes and borer holes limited to 1/4 x 1/2 inch. Admits some broken grain. Synthetic repairs permitted.

C Tight knots to 1-1/2 inch. Knotholes to 1 inch across grain and some to 1-1/2 inch if total width of knots and knotholes is within specified limits. Synthetic or wood repairs. Discoloration and sanding defects that do not impair strength permitted. Limited splits allowed. Stitching permitted.

D Knots and knotholes to 2-1/2 inch width across grain and 1/2 inch larger within specified limits. Limited splits allowed. Stitching permitted. Limited to Interior grades of plywood.

Guide to Appearance Grades of Plywood[1]

SPECIFIC GRADES AND THICKNESSES MAY BE IN LOCALLY LIMITED SUPPLY.
SEE YOUR DEALER BEFORE SPECIFYING.

Interior Type

Grade Designation[2]	Description and Most Common Uses	Typical Grade-trademarks	Face	Inner Plies	Back	1/4	3/8	1/2	5/8	3/4
N-N, N-A N-B INT-APA	Cabinet quality. For natural finish furniture, cabinet doors, built-ins, etc. Special order items.	N·N·G·1 INT·APA·PS 1·74 / N·A·G·2 INT·APA·PS 1·74	N	C	N, A, or B					3/4
N-D-INT-APA	For natural finish paneling. Special order item.	N·D·G·3 INT·APA·PS 1·74	N	D	D	1/4				
A-A INT-APA	For applications with both sides on view, built-ins, cabinets, furniture, partitions. Smooth face; suitable for painting.	A·A·G·4 INT·APA·PS 1·74	A	D	A	1/4	3/8	1/2	5/8	3/4
A-B INT-APA	Use where appearance of one side is less important but where two solid surfaces are necessary.	A·B·G·4 INT·APA·PS 1·74	A	D	B	1/4	3/8	1/2	5/8	3/4
A-D INT-APA	Use where appearance of only one side is important. Paneling, built-ins, shelving, partitions, flow racks.	A-D GROUP 1 INTERIOR APA PS 1·74 000	A	D	D	1/4	3/8	1/2	5/8	3/4
B-B INT-APA	Utility panel with two solid sides. Permits circular plugs.	BB·G·3 INT·APA·PS 1·74	B	D	B	1/4	3/8	1/2	5/8	3/4
B-D INT-APA	Utility panel with one solid side. Good for backing, sides of built-ins, industry shelving, slip sheets, separator boards, bins.	B-D GROUP 3 INTERIOR APA PS 1·74 000	B	D	D	1/4	3/8	1/2	5/8	3/4
DECORATIVE PANELS—APA	Rough-sawn, brushed, grooved, or striated faces. For paneling, interior accent walls, built-ins, counter facing, displays, exhibits.	DECORATIVE · B·D · G·1 INT·APA · PS 1·74	C or btr.	D	D	5/16	3/8	1/2	5/8	
PLYRON INT-APA	Hardboard face on both sides. For counter tops, shelving, cabinet doors, flooring. Faces tempered, untempered, smooth, or screened.	PLYRON INT·APA	C & D					1/2	5/8	3/4

Exterior Type

Grade Designation[2]	Description and Most Common Uses	Typical Grade-trademarks	Face	Inner Plies	Back	1/4	3/8	1/2	5/8	3/4
A-A EXT-APA	Use where appearance of both sides is important. Fences, built-ins, signs, boats, cabinets, commercial refrigerators, shipping containers, tote boxes, tanks, ducts. (3)	AA·G·3 EXT·APA·PS 1·74	A	C	A	1/4	3/8	1/2	5/8	3/4
A-B EXT-APA	Use where the appearance of one side is less important. (3)	AB·G·1 EXT·APA·PS 1·74	A	C	B	1/4	3/8	1/2	5/8	3/4
A-C EXT-APA	Use where the appearance of only one side is important. Soffits, fences, structural uses, boxcar and truck lining, farm buildings. Tanks, trays, commercial refrigerators. (3)	A-C GROUP 1 EXTERIOR APA PS 1·74 000	A	C	C	1/4	3/8	1/2	5/8	3/4
B-B EXT-APA	Utility panel with solid faces. (3)	BB·G·1 EXT·APA·PS 1·74	B	C	B	1/4	3/8	1/2	5/8	3/4
B-C EXT-APA	Utility panel for farm service and work buildings, boxcar and truck lining, containers, tanks, agricultural equipment. Also as base for exterior coatings for walls, roofs. (3)	B-C GROUP 2 EXTERIOR APA PS 1·74 000	B	C	C	1/4	3/8	1/2	5/8	3/4
HDO EXT-APA	High Density Overlay plywood. Has a hard, semi-opaque resin-fiber overlay both faces. Abrasion resistant. For concrete forms, cabinets, counter tops, signs, tanks. (3)	HDO 60/60 B·B PLYFORM I · EXT·APA · PS 1·74	A or B	C or C plgd	A or B		3/8	1/2	5/8	3/4
MDO EXT-APA	Medium Density Overlay with smooth, opaque, resin-fiber overlay one or both panel faces. Highly recommended for siding and other outdoor applications, built-ins, signs, displays. Ideal base for paint. (3)(5)	MDO · BB · G·4 · EXT·APA · PS 1·74	B	C	B or C		3/8	1/2	5/8	3/4
303 SIDING EXT-APA	Proprietary plywood products for exterior siding, fencing, etc. Special surface treatment such as V-groove, channel groove, striated, brushed, rough-sawn. Stud spacing indicated on grade stamp.	303 SIDING 6-W GROUP 4 16 oc SPAN EXTERIOR APA PS 1·74 000	(4)	C	C		3/8	1/2	5/8	
T 1-11 EXT-APA	Special 303 panel having grooves 1/4'' deep, 3/8'' wide, spaced 4'' or 8'' o.c. Other spacing optional. Edges shiplapped. Available unsanded, textured and MDO.	303 SIDING O/C T 1-11 19/32 INCH GROUP 2 24 oc SPAN EXTERIOR APA PS 1·74 000	C or btr.	C	C			19/32	5/8	
PLYRON EXT-APA	Hardboard faces both sides, tempered, smooth or screened.	PLYRON EXT·APA	C					1/2	5/8	3/4
MARINE EXT-APA	Ideal for boat hulls. Made only with Douglas fir or western larch. Special solid jointed core construction. Subject to special limitations on core gaps and number of face repairs. Also available with HDO or MDO faces.	MARINE A·A EXT·APA PS 1·74	A or B	B	A or B	1/4	3/8	1/2	5/8	3/4

(1) Sanded both sides except where decorative or other surfaces specified.
(2) Available in Group 1, 2, 3, 4, or 5 unless otherwise noted.
(3) Also available in STRUCTURAL I (all plies limited to Group 1 species) and STRUCTURAL II (all plies limited to Group 1, 2, or 3 species).
(4) C or better for 5 plies; C Plugged or better for 3 plies.
(5) Also available as a 303 siding.

Guide to Identification Index on Engineered Grades

| Thickness (inch) | C-D INT - APA
C-C EXT - APA | | | NOTES: |
	Group 1 & Structural I	Group 2* or 3, & Structural II*†	Group 4**†	
5/16	20/0	16/0	12/0	* Panels with Group 2 outer plies and special thickness and construction requirements, or STRUCTURAL II panels with Group 1 faces, may carry the Identification Index numbers shown for Group 1 panels.
3/8	24/0	20/0	16/0	
1/2	32/16	24/0	24/0	** Panels made with Group 4 outer plies may carry the Identification Index numbers shown for Group 3 panels when they conform to special thickness and construction requirements detailed in PS 1.
5/8	42/20	32/16	30/12	
3/4	48/24	42/20	36/16	
7/8	--------	48/24	42/20	† Check local availability.

Key Definitions:

Type:

Plywood is manufactured in two types: Exterior type with 100% waterproof glueline and Interior type with highly moisture-resistant glueline. Interior type plywood may be bonded with exterior or interior glue, although most is made with exterior glue. Specify Exterior type plywood for all permanent outdoor applications and those subject to continuing moist conditions or extreme high humidity. For other applications, Interior type may be used.

Group:

Wood from more than 70 species of varying strength may be used in plywood manufacture. The species are grouped on the basis of stiffness and strength, and divided into five classifications — Groups 1 through 5. Stiffest and strongest woods are in Group 1. The group number in the American Plywood Association grade-trademark refers to the weakest species used in face and back, except in decorative and sanded panels ⅜ inch thick or less. These are identified by the face species group. PS 1 lists species in all groups.

Appearance Grades:

Within each type of plywood are grade designations based on an appearance grading system for the veneer. Grades are N, A, B, C, and D, with N and A veneers the best looking. Panel grades are generally designated by veneer grade of panel face and back and by glueline (i.e., interior or exterior). PS 1 details allowable growth characteristics and repairs.

Engineered Grades:

Engineered grades are designed for demanding construction applications where properties such as nail bearing, shear, compression, tension, etc., are of maximum importance and appearance is secondary to strength.

C-D INTERIOR and the more commonly available C-D INTERIOR WITH EXTERIOR GLUE (CDX) are Interior type panels for uses such as sheathing. They will withstand considerable exposure to outdoor moisture conditions during construction, but must not be mistaken for Exterior plywood. STRUCTURAL I C-D is limited to Group 1 species throughout. STRUCTURAL II C-D permits Group 1, 2, or 3 species. Both are bonded with exterior glue.

Identification Index:

The basic unsanded grades of plywood — C-D sheathing, C-C Exterior, and STRUCTURAL I and II C-C and C-D — carry an Identification Index of two numbers in the American Plywood Association grade-trademark, for example 24/0 or 32/16. The left-hand number refers to maximum recommended spacing of roof framing in inches when the panel is used as roof sheathing. The right-hand number

refers to maximum spacing of floor framing when the panel is used for subflooring. In each case, face grain is across supports and panel is continuous across two or more spans.

IMPORTANT NOTE: The spans referred to in the Index numbers are accepted by most major building codes. Local interpretations may vary, however. So make sure your specifications comply with the local code under which you are building.

Class I, Class II:

Applies only to Plyform grade for concrete form plywood. Indicates species mix permitted. Plyform Class I is limited to Group 1 faces, Group 1 or 2 crossbands, and Group 1, 2, 3, or 4 center ply. Plyform Class II is limited to Group 1 or 2 faces (Group 3 under certain conditions) and Group 1, 2, 3, or 4 inner plies.

Method of Ordering:

Appearance grades: Designate finished thickness, grade, Group number, type, APA grade-trademark, dimensions, number of pieces:
¼" A-A, Group 1, Interior, APA grade-trademarked, 48" x 96", 100 pcs.

Textured sidings: Designate thickness, 303, stud spacing, texture, pattern, APA grade-trademark, dimensions, number of pieces:
⅝" 303-16 o.c., rough-sawn Texture 1-11, grooves 4" o.c., APA grade-trademarked, 48" x 96", 100 pcs. Note manufacturer's trade name and appearance grade if desired.

Engineered grades: Designate thickness, grade, Identification Index (or Group number), type, APA grade-trademark, dimensions, number of pieces:
⅜"C-D 24/0, Interior, APA grade-trademarked, 48" x 96", 100 pcs. Note "exterior glue" if desired.
⅝"[1] UNDERLAYMENT, Group 1, Interior, APA grade-trademarked, 48"[2] x 96", 100 pcs.

Concrete form: Designate thickness, grade, Class, APA grade-trademark, dimensions, number of pieces. Concrete form panels are mill-oiled unless otherwise specified:
⅝" B-B Plyform Class I Exterior, APA grade-trademarked, 48" x 96", 100 pcs.

(1) As provided for in U.S. Product Standard PS 1 and accepted by the model codes and HUD/FHA, mills may substitute ¹⁹/₃₂" panels for nominal ⅝", and ²³/₃₂" panels for nominal ¾". These thicknesses are acceptable over the spans specified for their respective nominal thicknesses.
(2) Most tongue-and-groove panels are manufactured to have a 47½" *net* face width, although mills vary. Check with your supplier.

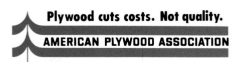

P.O. Box 2277 / Tacoma, Washington 98401
(206) 272-2283

Form No. C20

Construction

Plywood Floor Systems

American Plywood Association

February 1978

6

LAMINATED

Plywood

Introduction

Plywood floors have long been synonymous with fast, quality, economical construction—in homes, apartments, commercial buildings, factories, warehouses. Plywood provides a smooth, solid structural base for finish flooring. The large panel size speeds construction and reduces the number of joints for improved sound and fire control. Plywood's light weight makes it easy to handle and install. And its cross-laminated construction produces stiff floors that easily distribute concentrated loads.

Years of APA® research on ways to achieve better floors with plywood have produced a number of superior floor systems. These systems are explained in the following pages, along with information on special floors, fire-rated floors and sound-resistant floor assemblies. No matter what your floor need, there's a plywood system that will provide optimum comfort, strength and economy.

NOTE: For information on plywood types, groups, grades, Identification Indexes and method of ordering, refer to APA's **Plywood Specification and Grade Guide,** C20.

SPECIFICATION GUIDE

Each panel of construction plywood shall meet the requirements of the latest edition of U.S. Product Standard PS 1, and shall be identified with the appropriate grade-trademark of the American Plywood Association. All plywood which has any edge or surface permanently exposed to the weather or moisture shall be Exterior type.*

Panel thickness, grade, and Group or Identification Index shall be equal to or better than that shown on the drawings. Application shall be in accordance with recommendations of the American Plywood Association.

*An exception may be made in the case of plywood used for the All-Weather Wood Foundation, which may be Interior type with exterior glue provided it is pressure-preservative-treated in accordance with the American Wood Preservers Bureau AWPB-FDN Standard.

TABLE 1
Guide to Engineered Grades of Plywood for Floors
Specific grades and thicknesses may be in locally limited supply. See your dealer for availability before specifying.

Use These Terms When You Specify Plywood	Description and Most Common Uses	Typical Grade-Trademarks	Most Common Thicknesses (inch)				
Interior Type							
C-D INT-APA	For subflooring. Most commonly made with exterior glue. Specify exterior glue where construction delays are anticipated.	C-D 32/16 (APA) INTERIOR PS 1* 000 EXTERIOR GLUE	5/16	3/8	1/2	5/8	3/4
STRUCTURAL I C-D INT-APA, STRUCTURAL II C-D INT-APA	Unsanded structural grades where plywood strength properties are of maximum importance: structural diaphragms, stressed skin panels. Made only with exterior glue.	STRUCTURAL I C-D 32/16 (APA) INTERIOR PS 1* 000	5/16	3/8	1/2	5/8	3/4
UNDERLAYMENT INT-APA	For underlayment or combination subfloor-underlayment under resilient floor coverings, carpeting in homes, apartments, mobile homes. Specify exterior glue where moisture may be present, such as bathrooms, utility rooms. Touch sanded. Also available with tongue and groove and exterior glue.	UNDERLAYMENT GROUP 1 (APA) INTERIOR PS 1* 000		3/8	1/2	5/8 19/32*	3/4 23/32*
2-4-1 INT-APA	Combination subfloor-underlayment. Quality base for resilient floor coverings, carpeting, wood-strip flooring. Use 2-4-1 with exterior glue in areas subject to moisture. Unsanded or touch sanded as specified. Also available with tongue and groove and exterior glue.	2-4-1 (APA) GROUP 1 INTERIOR PS 1* 000			1-1/8		
Exterior Type							
C-C EXT-APA	Unsanded grade with waterproof bond for subflooring.	C-C 48/24 (APA) EXTERIOR PS 1* 000	5/16	3/8	1/2	5/8	3/4
UNDERLAYMENT C-C PLUGGED EXT-APA, C-C PLUGGED EXT-APA	For underlayment or combination subfloor-underlayment under resilient floor coverings where severe moisture conditions may be present, as in balcony decks. Touch sanded. Also available with tongue and groove.	UNDERLAYMENT C-C PLUGGED GROUP 3 (APA) EXTERIOR PS 1* 000		3/8	1/2	5/8 19/32*	3/4 23/32*

*As provided for in U.S. Product Standard PS 1 and accepted by the model codes and HUD/FHA, mills may substitute 19/32" panels for nominal 5/8" and 23/32" panels for nominal 3/4". These thicknesses are acceptable over the spans specified for their respective nominal thicknesses.

Combined Subfloor–Underlayment

Combined subfloor-underlayment construction provides the structural qualities of subflooring and a good substrate for direct application of non-structural finish flooring in a single panel. The system saves time and money while delivering strength, stiffness and durability.

Combined subfloor-underlayment goes down quickly and stays flat. It is dimensionally stable. And, as with all underlayment grades of plywood, the special inner-ply construction provides excellent resistance to dents, punctures and concentrated loads. Floor coverings look better longer over combined subfloor-underlayment.

The recommendations in Table 2 are for combined subfloor-underlayment that will receive direct application of tile, carpeting, linoleum or other non-structural finish flooring. Plywood is assumed continuous over two or more spans with face grain across supports. Panel edges should be tongue-and-groove or blocked with 2-inch lumber. Most T&G panels are made in net widths of 47-1/2 inches. When other than 48 inches, the net width is shown below the body of the APA grade-trademark. Specify subfloor-underlayment panels with exterior glue in areas where moisture will be present, as in bathrooms and utility rooms.

Although suitable for direct application of finish flooring, an additional thin layer of underlayment is often used under tile or linoleum so finish floor levels are flush throughout. This added layer also renews any surfaces that may have been scuffed or roughened during construction. Plywood underlayment also produces a measurable increase in stiffness. Nail-gluing may be worthwhile because it provides the most stiffness from the added layer.

Special conditions may impose heavy traffic and concentrated loads that require subfloor-underlayment construction in excess of the minimums shown.

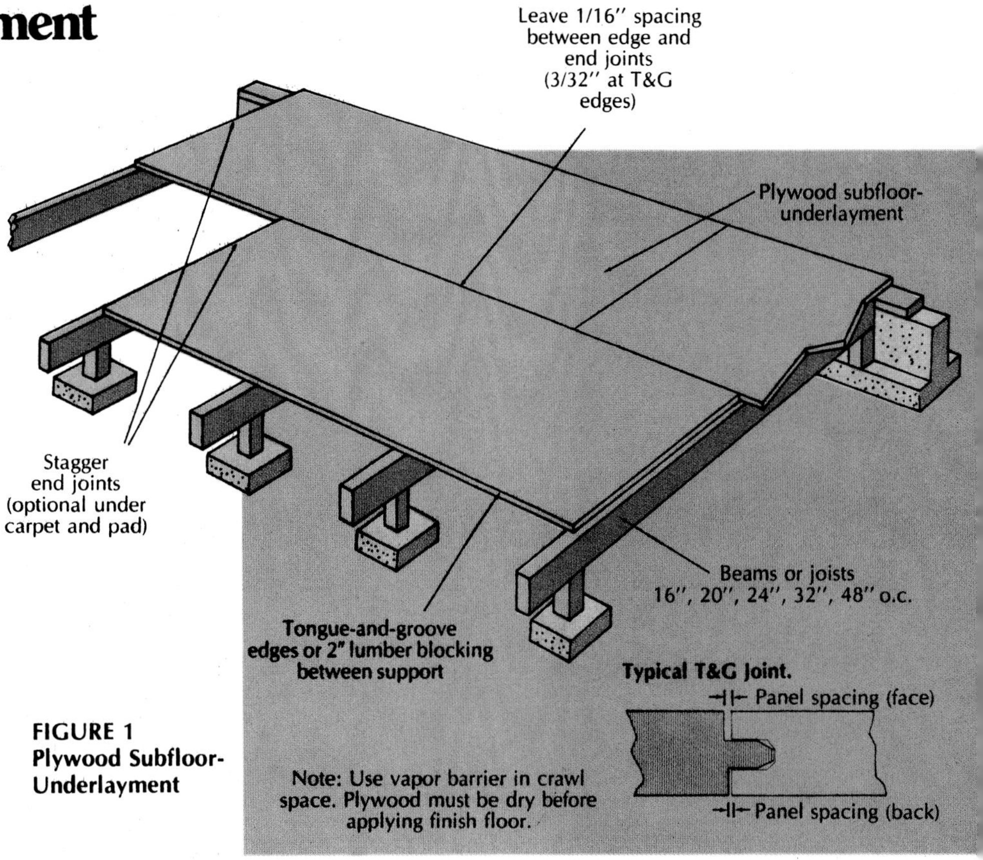

INSTALLATION

Panels should be installed with at least 1/16-inch space around the edges and ends. The T&G joint is designed so that the upper plies of the panel will be spaced to avert ridging if the panel picks up moisture and expands. Joints should be left

Leave 1/16″ spacing between edge and end joints (3/32″ at T&G edges)

Plywood subfloor-underlayment

Stagger end joints (optional under carpet and pad)

Tongue-and-groove edges or 2″ lumber blocking between support

Beams or joists 16″, 20″, 24″, 32″, 48″ o.c.

Typical T&G Joint.
Panel spacing (face)
Panel spacing (back)

Note: Use vapor barrier in crawl space. Plywood must be dry before applying finish floor.

**FIGURE 1
Plywood Subfloor-Underlayment**

TABLE 2
Combined Subfloor-Underlayment

| Plywood Grade (a) | Plywood Species Group | Maximum Support Spacing | | | | | | | | Nail Spacing (inches) | |
| | | 16″ o.c. | | 20″ o.c. | | 24″ o.c. | | 32″ or 48″ o.c. | | | |
		Panel Thickness	Deformed Shank Nail Size	Panel Thickness	Deformed Shank Nail Size	Panel Thickness	Deformed Shank Nail Size	Panel Thickness	Deformed Shank Nail Size	Panel Edges	Intermediate
UNDERLAYMENT INT-APA (with interior or exterior glue), UNDERLAYMENT EXT-APA (C-C Plugged EXT-APA)	1	1/2″	6d	5/8″(b)	6d	3/4″(c)	6d	—	—	6	10
	2 & 3	5/8″(b)	6d	3/4″(c)	6d	7/8″	8d	—	—	6	10
	4	3/4″(c)	6d	7/8″	8d	1″	8d	—	—	6	10
2-4-1	1,2 & 3	(2-4-1 specifications are so written that panels from all species groups have equal properties.)						1-1/8″	8d (or 10d common smooth shank if supports well seasoned)	6	(d)

(a) For certain types of flooring such as wood block or terrazzo, sheathing grades of plywood may be used.
(b) May be 19/32″.
(c) May be 23/32″.
(d) 10″ for 32″ o.c., 6″ for 48″ o.c. supports.

3

slightly open, not tightly butted. Normally, a space of about 3/32 inch (the width of a 6d box nail) between the upper plies of the panels will be enough for the T&G joint. If wet conditions are anticipated, up to 1/16 inch of additional spacing at both sides and ends is advisable. The joint space should be filled just prior to application of any resilient finish floor.

Seasoned lumber is recommended for floor supports. Unless joists are of thoroughly seasoned material and have remained dry during construction, countersink nail heads 1/16 inch below the surface of the underlayment just prior to laying finish flooring to avoid nail popping. Otherwise, nails should be driven flush or slightly set. To minimize the effects of framing shrinkage, deformed-shank nails of the recommended size should be used. Avoid using cement-coated nails. Do not fill over nail heads. Fill joints and sand if resilient flooring is to be applied. For thin vinyl flooring, light sanding may be required over the entire surface.

2-4-1® SUBFLOOR-UNDERLAYMENT

A variation of single-layer subfloor-underlayment, 1-1/8-inch 2-4-1 is one of the fastest, simplest and most economical wood floor systems ever devised. 2-4-1 makes an ideal surface for any type of finish floor covering—vinyl tile, linoleum, wall-to-wall carpeting or hardwood flooring.

2-4-1 is an Interior type panel. Most manufacturers offer it with exterior glue for use where prolonged moisture during construction is anticipated. 2-4-1 can also be manufactured on special order in Exterior type for special uses, such as exterior decks. Panels are available with square edges or with a precisely engineered tongue-and-groove joint that eliminates the need for blocking.

The advantages of 2-4-1 are many. Labor costs are reduced because fewer pieces are required. The thick panels allow wider support spacing—32 or 48 inches on center. 2-4-1 is a dry material—no shrinkage

means fewer callbacks, particularly when used with on-site gluing techniques. 2-4-1 provides comfortable resiliency underfoot, a positive sales feature in new home construction. The thick panel and T&G joint contribute to good thermal and acoustical values. And attractive, economical exposed-beam ceilings can be achieved below 2-4-1 floors. Some manufacturers produce panels with grooved and/or textured veneers to serve as combination floor/ceiling or roof/ceiling panels.

Recommendations call for either 2x joists 32 inches on center or 4x girders spaced 48 inches. The 32-inch support system may prove to be the least expensive way to install 2-4-1 in most areas of the country. With the combination of dry, dimensionally stable 2-4-1 and dry lumber framing, it is possible to build a floor assembly that is virtually free from nail popping and callback problems. Modern nail-gluing techniques are highly recommended because they stop the squeak caused by nail popping. The glue also adds stiffness to the floor system.

The 48-inch support system may be constructed with 2x joists spiked together, with 4x lumber, with lightweight steel beams or with wood-steel floor trusses. Girders of doubled 2x members should have top edges aligned to permit smooth panel end joints.

INSTALLATION

When 2-4-1 is nailed in place, the face grain of the panels should run across the framing members and, wherever possible, a panel should cover two or more spans. End joints should be staggered. Joints between panels should not be driven tight. Leave 1/16-inch spacing at end and T&G joints. When the floor covering is thin resilient tile, fill any cracks wider than 1/16 inch and sand joints lightly if they are not absolutely flush.

Under resilient tile when joists are not kiln dried, set all nails 1/8-inch but do not fill. Set nails just prior to laying the resilient flooring to take advantage of any framing seasoning that may have taken place. Besides ordinary and deformed-shank nails, several power-driven nails and other fasteners of various configurations are approved for fastening 2-4-1.

Plywood Subflooring

Plywood also may be used for subfloors beneath a separate underlayment. Plywood subflooring has long been recognized by the major regional building codes and HUD/FHA. These acceptances follow the recommendations given in Table 3. Most state and local code acceptances are similar.

The limiting factor in the design of plywood floors is deflection under concentrated loads at panel edges. The Identification Indexes in Table 3 are the minimum recommended for the spans indicated. These values apply to C-D INT-APA, STRUCTURAL I and II C-D INT-APA, C-C EXT-APA and STRUCTURAL I and II C-C EXT-APA grades only, and are based on the performance of plywood floors under both static and transient concentrated loads, particularly traffic loads. The spans assume plywood continuous over two or more spans with face grain across supports.

The allowable uniform loads vary between panels. However, all panels marked with Identification Index numbers will carry over 160 psf on their maximum span before reaching the usual deflection limit of 1/360 of the span.

C-D INT with exterior glue (CDX) may be used where moisture is expected or where durability is required during construction delays. Where permanent exposure to the weather or moisture will be required, only Exterior type plywood should be used.

Because particular panels (e.g., 3/4-inch 36/16, 5/8-inch 30/12, 1-1/8-inch Groups 1 and 2, 1-1/4-inch Groups 3 and 4 and STRUCTURAL II of all thicknesses) may be difficult to obtain locally, it is advisable to check availability with your dealer, or

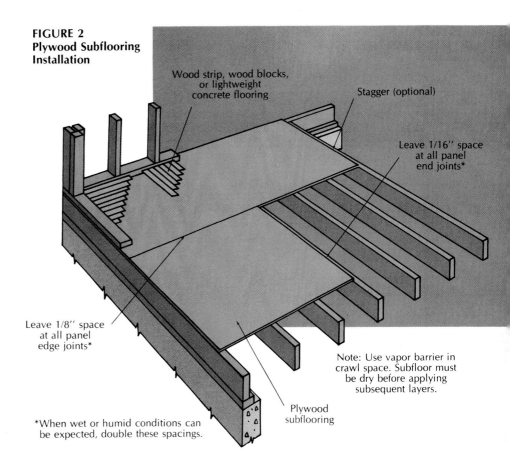

FIGURE 2
Plywood Subflooring Installation

Wood strip, wood blocks, or lightweight concrete flooring

Stagger (optional)

Leave 1/16" space at all panel end joints*

Leave 1/8" space at all panel edge joints*

Note: Use vapor barrier in crawl space. Subfloor must be dry before applying subsequent layers.

Plywood subflooring

*When wet or humid conditions can be expected, double these spacings.

include an alternate panel in specifications.

INSTALLATION

Edges shall be tongue-and-groove or supported with blocking for square-edge panels, unless (1) a separate underlayment layer is installed with its joints offset from those in the subfloor, or (2) a minimum of 1-1/2 inches of lightweight concrete is applied over the plywood, or (3) 25/32-inch wood strip flooring is installed at right angles to joists. The minimum thickness of

TABLE 3
Plywood Subflooring

Panel Identification Index	Plywood Thickness (inch)	Maximum Span (inches)	Nail Size & Type	Nail Spacing (inches)	
				Panel Edges	Intermediate
30/12	5/8(e)	12(a)	8d common	6	10
32/16	1/2, 5/8	16(b)	8d common (c)	6	10
36/16	3/4(e)	16(b)	8d common	6	10
42/20	5/8, 3/4, 7/8	20(d)	8d common	6	10
48/24	3/4, 7/8	24	8d common	6	10
1-1/8" Groups 1 & 2	1-1/8 (e)	48	10d common	6	6
1-1/4" Groups 3 & 4	1-1/4 (e)	48	10d common	6	6

(a) May be 16" if 25/32" wood strip flooring is installed at right angles to joists.
(b) May be 24" if 25/32" wood strip flooring is installed at right angles to joists.
(c) 6d common nail permitted if plywood is 1/2".
(d) May be 24" if 25/32" wood strip flooring is installed at right angles to joists, or if a minimum 1-1/2" of lightweight concrete is applied over plywood.
(e) Check dealer for availability.

Plywood Underlayment

the underlayment should be 1/4 inch for subfloors with an Identification Index up to 48/24, and 3/8 inch for thicker panels on 48-inch spans.

For many commercial construction applications, heavier than usual traffic and concentrated loads may require larger framing members and thicker plywood. In these areas, Identification Indexes greater than the minimums shown in Table 3 are suggested. Where joists are 16 inches on center, panels with an Identification Index of 42/20 or 48/24 will give additional stiffness. For beams or joists 24 or 32 inches on center, 1-1/8-inch plywood is ideal.

Underlayment grades of plywood have a solid, touch-sanded surface for direct application on non-structural finish flooring such as carpeting, linoleum or tile. And special inner-ply construction to resist dents and punctures from concentrated loads. Plywood underlayment is also the most dimensionally stable of underlayment panel materials and eliminates excessive swelling and subsequent buckling or humps around nails.

Any unevenness that may exist in a subfloor is easily bridged by plywood underlayment. The plywood needed to bridge an uneven floor will depend on roughness and loads applied. Flooring manufacturers recognize 1/4-inch plywood as an underlayment where the subfloor is

relatively smooth, as with plywood subfloors, especially in remodeling work.

For best results, be sure to specify the grade and thickness shown in Table 4. Where floors may be subject to unusual moisture conditions, use UNDERLAYMENT INT-APA with exterior glue, UNDERLAYMENT EXT-APA, or C-C Plugged EXT-APA. (C-D Plugged is not an adequate substitute for Underlayment grade since it does not insure equivalent dent resistance.) Extra attention also should be given to smoothness of faces, and especially to panel edges, when thin vinyl flooring is used.

FIGURE 3
Plywood Underlayment Installation

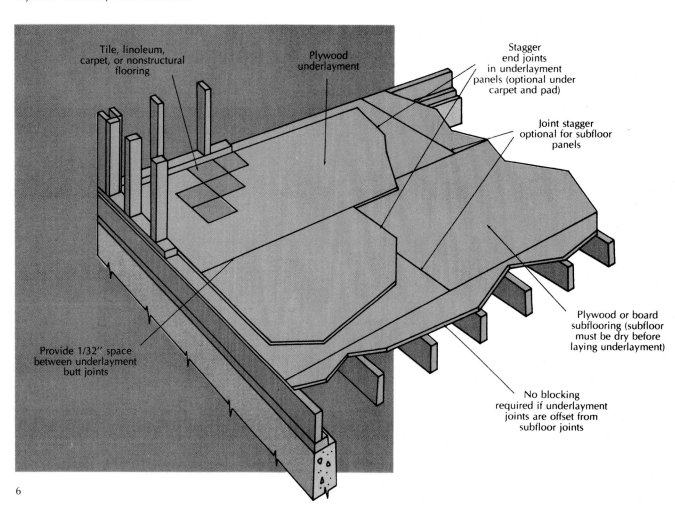

Tile, linoleum, carpet, or nonstructural flooring

Plywood underlayment

Stagger end joints in underlayment panels (optional under carpet and pad)

Joint stagger optional for subfloor panels

Provide 1/32" space between underlayment butt joints

Plywood or board subflooring (subfloor must be dry before laying underlayment)

No blocking required if underlayment joints are offset from subfloor joints

INSTALLATION

For maximum stiffness under non-structural flooring such as carpeting, linoleum or tile, install plywood underlayment with face grain across supports and with end joints over framing. Apply underlayment just prior to laying the finish floor, or protect it against water or physical damage until the finish floor is installed. Stagger panel end joints with respect to each other and offset all joints with respect to those of the subfloor. Space panel ends and edges about 1/32 inch.

Fill and thoroughly sand edge joints of panels to receive resilient floor covering, except carpet. Fill any damaged or open areas, such as joints or splits, and thoroughly sand any surface roughness, particularly at joints and around nails. Do not fill nail holes.

Unless subfloor and joists are of thoroughly seasoned material and have remained dry during construction, countersink nail heads 1/16 inch below the surface of the underlayment just prior to laying finish floors to avoid nail popping. Staples should be countersunk 1/32 inch.

TABLE 4
Plywood Underlayment

Plywood Grades and Species Group	Application	Minimum Plywood Thickness (inch)	Fastener Size and Type (set nails 1/16")	Fastener Spacing (inches)	
				Panel Edges	Intermediate
Groups 1, 2, 3, 4, 5 UNDERLAYMENT INT-APA (with interior, or exterior glue) UNDERLAYMENT EXT-APA C-C Plugged EXT-APA	Over plywood subfloor.	1/4	18 Ga. staples or 3d ring-shank nails (a) (b)	3	6 each way
	Over lumber subfloor or other uneven surfaces.	3/8	16 Ga. staples (a)	3	6 each way
			3d ring-shank nails (b)	6	8 each way
Same grades as above, but Group 1 only.	Over lumber floor up to 4" wide. Face grain must be perpendicular to boards.	1/4	18 Ga. staples or 3d ring-shank nails	3	6 each way

(a) Crown width 3/8" for 16 ga., 3/16" for 18 ga. staples, length sufficient to penetrate completely through, or at least 5/8" into, subflooring.
(b) Use 3d ring-shank nail also for 1/2" plywood and 4d ring-shank nail for 5/8" or 3/4" plywood.

APA Glued Floor System

The APA Glued Floor System is an ideal way to provide extra stiff, noise-resistant, economical floors—in homes, apartments, schools, townhouses, commercial buildings and factory-built modular units. Best of all, perhaps, the Glued Floor System when properly constructed solves the builder's worst floor problem—callbacks to repair floors with squeaks, bounce or nail popping.

The system is based on thoroughly tested gluing-techniques and field-applied construction adhesives that firmly and permanently adhere a layer of structural plywood underlayment to wood joists. The glue bond is so strong that floor and joists behave like integral T-beam units. The glue carries the stress, not the nails. And squeaks from shrinking lumber

and nail popping are virtually eliminated. Floor stiffness can be increased up to 90 percent over conventional floor construction, or greater when the tongue-and-groove joints are glued as well. The system is normally used with combined subfloor-underlayment, although it is also applicable to two-layer floors.

Field-glued floors go down quickly, even in cold weather, using ordinary construction materials and techniques. The system may allow increased joist spacing, or sometimes a reduced joist size, because of the composite action of floor and framing. No bridging is required. And only about one-fifth as many nails are required when combined subfloor-underlayment is used.

Perfection of the Glued Floor System was made possible by the development of improved construction adhesives which permit effective field gluing, even in below-freezing weather. These adhesives are not to be confused with ordinary drywall glues. Only glues which conform to Performance Specification AFG-01, developed by APA to assure dependable quality construction, are recommended for use with the system. A number of adhesive brands meeting the requirements of AFG-01 are available from building supply dealers. Always follow the specific application recommendations of the manufacturer.

Combined subfloor-underlayment plywood panel thicknesses typically are 1/2, 5/8 or 3/4 inch, depending on joist spacing. Although T&G is used most often, square edge may be used if 2x4 blocking is placed under panel edge joints between joists. Plywood is also glued to the blocking.

FIGURE 4
APA Glued Floor System

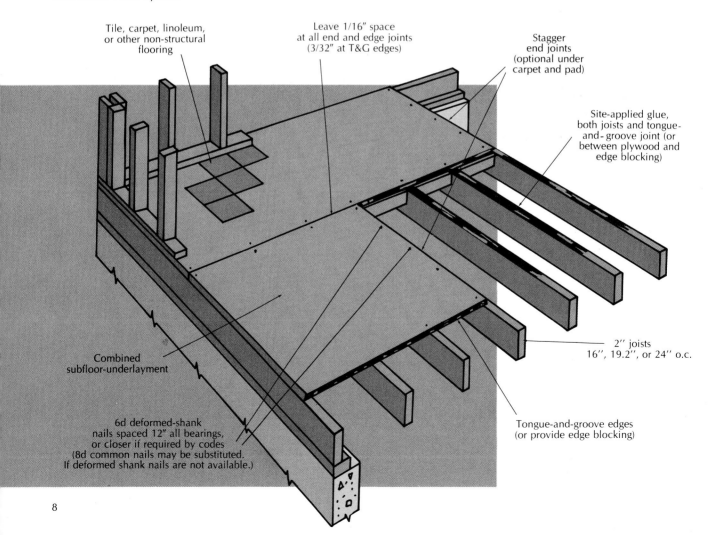

Tile, carpet, linoleum, or other non-structural flooring

Leave 1/16" space at all end and edge joints (3/32" at T&G edges)

Stagger end joints (optional under carpet and pad)

Site-applied glue, both joists and tongue-and-groove joint (or between plywood and edge blocking)

Combined subfloor-underlayment

6d deformed-shank nails spaced 12" all bearings, or closer if required by codes (8d common nails may be substituted. If deformed shank nails are not available.)

2" joists 16", 19.2", or 24" o.c.

Tongue-and-groove edges (or provide edge blocking)

INSTALLATION

For a single-layer floor, UNDERLAYMENT APA T&G plywood is placed across joists with end joints staggered. Leave 1/16-inch space at all end and edge joints (3/32-inch at T&G edges). Before each panel is placed, a bead of glue is applied to the joists with a caulking gun. The T&G joint also is glued. The plywood panel is then nailed with 6d deformed-shank nails spaced 12 inches at all supports. (8d common smooth nails may be substituted, although these are more likely to "pop.") It is very important to complete all nailing of panels within glue manufacturers' specified assembly time to assure proper bonding.

For complete details of the APA Glued Floor System, including joist span tables and application procedures, write for **Plywood Systems: Floors,** Form B430.

TABLE 5
Plywood Recommendations
for APA Glued Floor System

Joist Spacing	Flooring Type	Plywood Thickness and Grade		
		1/2"	5/8"	3/4"
16"	Resilient Flooring	UNDER-LAYMENT Group 1	UNDER-LAYMENT Group 1, 2, 3 (a)	UNDER-LAYMENT Group 1, 2, 3, 4(b)
	Separate Under-layment or Structural Finish Flooring	C-D 32/16	C-D 32/16, 42/20	C-D 36/16, 42/20, 48/24
19.2"	Resilient Flooring		UNDER-LAYMENT Group 1 (a)	UNDER-LAYMENT Group 1, 2, 3 (b)
	Separate Under-layment or Structural Finish Flooring		C-D 42/20	C-D 42/20, 48/24
24"	Resilient Flooring			UNDER-LAYMENT Group 1(b)
	Separate Under-layment or Structural Finish Flooring			C-D 48/24

(a) UNDERLAYMENT grade may be 19/32".
(b) UNDERLAYMENT grade may be 23/32".

Recommended plywood grades are UNDERLAYMENT INT-APA or UNDER-LAYMENT with exterior glue for subfloor-underlayment combinations: C-D INT-APA or C-D with exterior glue for subfloor when used with a separate underlayment or with structural finish flooring. Specify exterior glue where panels may be exposed to moisture during or after construction, as in bathrooms and utility rooms. UNDERLAYMENT C-C PLUGGED EXT-APA is available for applications where particularly severe moisture conditions may be present, such as balcony decks. Common plywood thickness versus joist spacing combinations are given in the table above. (7/8" or 1" UNDERLAYMENT of any Group, or C-D with appropriate Identification Index numbers, may be substituted for the lesser thicknesses if desired.)

TABLE 6
Allowable Clear Spans for APA
Glued Floor System (Partial List)

Species-Grade	Joist Size	1/2" Plywood Joists @ 16"	5/8" Plywood(a) Joists @ 16"	3/4" Plywood(b) Joists @ 16"	3/4" Plywood(b) Joists @ 24"
DOUGLAS FIR-LARCH - NO. 1	2x6	10'-11"	11'-2"	11'-5"	9'-5"
	2x8	14-2	14-5	14-8	12-5
	2x10	17-10	18-2	18-4	15-10
	2x12	21-6	21-10	22-1	19-3
DOUGLAS FIR-LARCH - NO. 2	2x6	10-6	10-6	10-6	8-7
	2x8	13-10	13-10	13-10	11-3
	2x10	17-7	17-7	17-7	14-5
	2x12	21-2	21-5	21-5	17-6
DOUGLAS FIR SOUTH - NO. 1	2x6	10-2	10-5	10-8	9-1
	2x8	13-2	13-6	13-9	12-0
	2x10	16-7	16-11	17-2	15-4
	2x12	20-0	20-4	20-7	18-5
HEM - FIR-NO. 1	2x6	10-3	10-3	10-3	8-5
	2x8	13-5	13-7	13-7	11-1
	2x10	16-11	17-3	17-4	14-2
	2x12	20-5	20-9	21-0	17-2
HEM - FIR-NO. 2	2x6	9-4	9-4	9-4	7-7
	2x8	12-4	12-4	12-4	10-0
	2x10	15-8	15-8	15-8	12-10
	2x12	19-1	19-1	19-1	15-7
MOUNTAIN HEMLOCK NO. 2	2x6	9-6	9-6	9-6	7-9
	2x8	12-4	12-7	12-7	10-3
	2x10	15-6	15-10	16-0	13-1
	2x12	18-8	19-0	19-3	15-11
SOUTHERN PINE KD-NO. 1	2x6	10-11	11-2	11-5	9-8
	2x8	14-2	14-5	14-8	12-9
	2x10	17-10	18-2	18-5	16-3
	2x12	21-6	21-10	22-1	19-9
SOUTHERN PINE KD-NO. 2	2x6	10-7	10-8	10-8	8-8
	2x8	13-8	14-0	14-0	11-6
	2x10	17-3	17-6	17-10	14-8
	2x12	20-10	21-1	21-4	17-9
SOUTHERN PINE KD-NO. 3	2x6	8-0	8-0	8-0	6-7
	2x8	10-7	10-7	10-7	8-8
	2x10	13-6	13-6	13-6	11-0
	2x12	16-5	16-5	16-5	13-5

(a) UNDERLAYMENT grade may be 19/32".
(b) UNDERLAYMENT grade may be 23/32".

Special Floor Systems

LIGHTWEIGHT CONCRETE OVER PLYWOOD

Lightweight concrete over plywood is an excellent way to reduce vibrations and sound transmission between floors while simultaneously improving fire resistance—important considerations in apartment construction.

Plywood is an excellent base for lightweight concrete. Panels marked 42/20 may be used where joists are 24 inches on center. (See ICBO Report No. 1007.) An Identification Index of 32/16 is the recommended minimum for supports 16 inches on center.

For additional information on the acoustical advantages of lightweight concrete over plywood, write for APA's **Plywood Construction for Noise Control,** Form W460.

HEAVY-DUTY FLOORS

Above-grade plywood floors may be designed to support forklift trucks in areas of heavy loading or to support relatively high loads imposed by warehouse shelving or stacked storage. Heavy-duty plywood floors also make excellent mezzanine decks and vibration-free surfaces for mounting computer equipment.

Tables 7 and 8 give plywood and framing recommendations for uniform and concentrated (i.e., forklift traffic) loads. Structural edge support must be provided where high concentrated loads occur. Where no lift-truck use is expected, 2-inch wood framing is adequate.

PLYWOOD FLOOR DIAPHRAGMS

Plywood floors strengthen and stiffen buildings against wind loading and earthquakes. Generally, the regular nailing schedule for plywood floors provides all the resistance required. Where greater resistance is needed, or for special designs, the plywood floor may be designed as a structural diaphragm.

Plywood underlayment can perform as an integral part of a diaphragm. This is an important factor when remodeling commercial structures. The use of plywood underlayment as a diaphragm has enabled old buildings to be upgraded to meet urban renewal requirements.

For additional information, write for **Plywood Diaphragm Construction,** Form U310.

STRESSED-SKIN AND SANDWICH PANELS

Stressed-skin panels are structural components with plywood skins rigidly glued to lumber framing. They may be two-sided panels with plywood top and bottom skins, one-sided panels with only a top skin, or T-flange panels with a lumber flange replacing the plywood bottom skin. Plywood face grain is usually parallel to supports. In all three, efficient use of materials results from the composite action of the plywood and its framing.

The rigid, fully structural adhesives that give stressed-skin floor panels their unique properties of strength and stiffness are considerably more difficult to handle than the construction adhesives used in the APA Glued Floor System. The panels, therefore, must be shop fabricated under careful quality control.

Sandwich panels may have honeycomb paper or plastic foam cores with edge framing members. They are always two-sided panels with both plywood top and bottom skins. A typical floor panel might have 1/2-inch top skin and 3/8-inch bottom skin. Check local building codes for requirements relating to thermal protection of plastic foam. Plywood of sufficient thickness provides a thermal barrier that satisfies the requirements of some codes.

For additional information, write for **Design of Plywood Stressed-Skin Panels,** Form U813, and **Design of Plywood Sandwich Panels,** Form U814.

TABLE 7
Plywood Recommended for Uniform Loads for Heavy Duty Floors
(Deflection limited to 1/240th of span)

Uniform Live Load (psf)	Center-to-Center Support Spacing (Inches)(Nominal 2-Inch-Width Supports Unless Noted)					
	12 (a)	16 (a)	20 (a)	24 (a)	32	48 (b)
50	32/16	32/16	42/20	48/24	2-4-1	2-4-1
100	32/16	32/16	42/20	48/24	2-4-1	1½ (c)
150	32/16	32/16	42/20	48/24	2-4-1	1¾ (d) 2 (c)
200	32/16	42/20	42/20	2-4-1	1⅛ (d) 1⅜ (c)	2 (d) 2½ (c)
250	32/16	42/20	48/24	2-4-1	1⅜ (d) 1½ (c)	2¼ (d)
300	32/16	48/24	2-4-1	2-4-1	1½ (d) 1⅝ (c)	2¼ (d)
350	42/20	48/24	2-4-1	1⅛ (d) 1⅜ (c)	1½ (d) 2 (c)	
400	42/20	2-4-1	2-4-1	1¼ (d) 1⅜ (c)	1⅝ (d) 2 (c)	
450	42/20	2-4-1	2-4-1	1⅜ (d) 1½ (c)	2 (d) 2¼ (c)	
500	48/24	2-4-1	2-4-1	1½ (c)	2 (d) 2¼ (c)	

(a) A-C Group 1 sanded panels may be substituted for Identification Index panels (1/2" for 32/16; 5/8" for 42/20; 3/4" for 48/24).
(b) Nominal 4" wide supports.
(c) Group 1 face and back, any species inner plies, sanded or unsanded, single layer.
(d) STRUCTURAL I, sanded or unsanded, single layer.

TABLE 8
Thickness of Plywood to Carry Fork-Truck Traffic
Grade is STRUCTURAL I A-C except where 2-4-1 is noted

Tire Tread Print Width	Load per Wheel (Pounds)	Center-to-Center Support Spacing (Minimum 6-Inch-Wide Supports)			
		12"	16"	20"	24"
3 in.	500	2-4-1	2-4-1	2-4-1	2-4-1
	1000	1-1/4"	1-1/4"	1-1/4"	1-1/4"
	1500	1-1/2"	1-3/4"	1-3/4"	1-3/4"
	2000	2"	2"	2-1/4"	2-1/4"
5 in.	1000	2-4-1	2-4-1	1-1/8"	1-1/8"
	1500	1-1/8"	1-1/8"	1-1/4"	1-1/4"
	2000	1-1/4"	1-1/2"	1-1/2"	1-3/4"
	2500	1-1/2"	2"	2"	2"
	3000	1-3/4"	2"	2-1/4"	2-1/4"
7 in.	2000	1-1/8"	1-1/8"	1-1/4"	1-1/4"
	3000	1-1/4"	1-1/2"	1-1/2"	1-3/4"
	4000	1-3/4"	1-3/4"	1-3/4"	2"
	5000	2"	2"	2-1/4"	2-1/2"
	6000	2-1/4"	2-1/2"	2-3/4"	3"
9 in.	3000	1-1/4"	1-1/4"	1-1/4"	1-1/4"
	4000	1-1/2"	1-1/2"	1-3/4"	1-3/4"
	5000	1-3/4"	1-3/4"	2"	2"
	6000	2"	2"	2-1/4"	2-1/4"
	7000	2-1/4"	2-1/4"	2-3/4"	2-3/4"

PREFRAMED PLYWOOD FLOORS

Shop-fabricated preframed plywood floors can speed job-site erection and reduce the required number of workmen for both residential and non-residential construction. In-plant fabrication, either by production line or station jig procedures, also allows better quality control, year-round assembly without weather-caused delays, and materials availability through planned ordering techniques.

Preframed plywood panels may be nail-glued with the same construction adhesives as those used in the APA Glued Floor System or fabricated with mechanical fasteners only. And because of plywood's inherent rigidity and impact resistance, finished components transport better than those of alternative materials. Boom trucks or light cranes are usually required for panel erection.

For additional information, contact the American Plywood Association.

CANTILEVERED IN-LINE JOISTS

The cantilever system is structurally more efficient than conventional simple-span joists. Stresses on the suspended joists are reduced because the span is shorter than it would be if the joist were to span from wall plate to center support. Bending stresses in the over-hanging joist are also reduced due to the negative moment induced by the overhang.

This structural advantage sometimes permits the use of joists one size smaller than would be required in the conventional system. Even when no reduction in joist size is possible, cantilevered joists and plywood are stiffer than a system of simple-span joists.

Additional information is contained in APA's **Cantilevered In-Line Joist System,** Form Z417.

PLYWOOD STAIR TREADS AND RISERS

A growing number of builders and manufacturers are using plywood for treads and risers of both site-fabricated and prefabricated stairs. Plywood treads perform well in closed-riser stairways because of plywood's cross-grain stiffness. Risers support the front and back of the tread, creating a very short effective span.

Plywood tread grade and thickness recommendations are contained in APA's **Plywood Systems: Floors,** Form B430.

PLYWOOD FLOORS OVER CONCRETE

A system of plywood over sleepers imbedded in mastic has been successfully installed over concrete slabs. Tongue-and-groove plywood was used to eliminate blocking between sleepers at plywood panel edges and to allow air circulation beneath the floor. Use only Exterior type plywood or Interior plywood with exterior glue. A vapor barrier is essential directly above or below the slab. Preservative treatment of the sleepers is recommended when the slab is on or below grade, although plywood normally will not require treatment.

LONG SPAN FLOORS

For floor spans longer than 16 feet, plywood subfloors may be installed directly to fabricated members such as glulams, plywood "I" beams or box beams, open-web wood or steel joists and steel beams.

These members are normally spaced 24 inches on center or more, so plywood at least 3/4 inch thick is generally required. For supports 24 inches on center, 48/24 plywood subflooring carries 160 psf at a deflection of 1/360 of the span. For supports 32 inches on center, a deflection of 1/360 of the span is reached at 180 psf loading with 1-1/8-inch 2-4-1.

METAL JOISTS

Builders electing to use metal framing systems may readily attach plywood directly to framing with special fasteners available for this purpose.

For additional information, write APA for **Plywood Over Metal Framing,** Form A330.

SPECIAL FLOOR SURFACING

Hardboard overlaid plywood (Plyron®) is sometimes used as a finish floor, especially for industrial installation. (Check your local dealer for availability.) High Density Overlaid (HDO) panels with a special heavy-duty screen-grid surface sometimes are used for skid-resistant, long-wearing surfaces under foot traffic. A number of liquid coatings also are available for floor surfacings. Some are suitable for balconies, porches, patio decks and other exterior applications.

Fire, Noise And Insulation Notes

FIRE-RESISTANT FLOORS

Over 30 lumber-and-plywood floor-ceiling (or roof-ceiling) systems are listed in the 1976 UL Fire Resistance Index and are accepted as rated constructions by building codes. In these assemblies, materials such as gypsumboard, plaster and mineral acoustical tile provide primary fire protection. The plywood floor acts to retard flame passage and temperature rise, as well as to reinforce joists after the effectiveness of the ceiling has been lost.

In most assemblies, a double layer of plywood (1/2 inch and 5/8 inch) is used, although several have a single layer of 5/8 inch or thicker. Some model codes accept 1-1/2-inch lightweight concrete under certain conditions in lieu of the top layer of plywood for one-hour floor-ceiling

assemblies. Any finish floor material may be used. One assembly (L513) permits an economical 24-inch joist spacing with a single-layer 3/4-inch glued plywood floor. T&G joints are glued and protected with a gypsum pad stapled from below into the plywood. Diagonal bridging between joists is not required.

For additional information, write for **Plywood Construction for Fire Protection,** Form W305.

PLYWOOD AND ACOUSTICS

Excellent noise control levels can be achieved in wood frame structures with plywood floors. Performance standards for floors are based on criteria established by FHA. Tests have shown that wood joist floors with various combinations of materials provide recommended reduction in both sound transmission and impact noise.

Insulation, suspended ceilings, separate ceiling framing and overlays of lightweight concrete all achieve high ratings. For each of them, of course, control of detailing and quality of workmanship are critical.

For complete details, write **Plywood Construction for Noise Control,** Form W460.

INSULATING PLYWOOD FLOORS

Wood is a natural insulator. Add to that the ease of insulating a wood frame-plywood floor system and you have sturdy, economical construction that easily meets or exceeds the HUD Minimum Property Standards (MPS).

For additional information, write for APA's **Plywood Systems: Floors,** Form B430.

Additional Information

For additional information on plywood floor systems and other plywood applications, request any of the publications listed below. Single copies are available without charge by writing the American Plywood Association, P.O. Box 2277, Tacoma, Washington 98401.

Plywood Systems: Floors, B430
Plywood Residential Construction Guide, Y405
Plywood Commercial/Industrial Construction Guide, Y300
Plywood Diaphragm Construction, U310
Plywood Construction for Fire Protection, W305
Plywood Construction for Noise Control, W460
Engineered 24″ Framing and Plywood, B420
Plywood Design Specification, Y510
Design of Plywood Stressed-Skin Panels, U813
Design of Plywood Sandwich Panels, U814
Cantilevered In-Line Joist System, Z417
Plywood Over Metal Framing, A330
Plywood for Remodeling: Commercial, Industrial and Institutional, B380

APA: THE MARK OF QUALITY

The American Plywood Association's grade-trademarks are used by qualified member mills to identify plywood that has been manufactured to meet the requirements of **U.S. Product Standard PS 1 74 for Construction and Industrial Plywood.** Information covered in this and all APA publications is based upon the use of plywood of known quality. Always insist on plywood bearing the **Mark of Quality**—the APA grade-trademark.

Our field representatives can help. For additional assistance in specifying plywood, get in touch with your nearest American Plywood Association field service representative. Call or write:

ATLANTA
Paul D. Colbenson
P. O. Box 90550
Atlanta, Georgia 30364
(404) 762-6649

CHICAGO
Vernon D. Haskell
120 East Ogden Avenue
Room 204
Hinsdale, Illinois 60521
(312) 323-5787

DALLAS
A. M. Leggett
10010 Miller Road
Suite 105
Dallas, Texas 75238
(214) 348-0643

LOS ANGELES
Long Beach, California
(213) 439-8616

NEW YORK
Englewood Cliffs, New Jersey
(201) 567-7238

SAN FRANCISCO
Philip L. Benfield
P. O. Box 3536
Fremont, California 94538
(415) 657-5959

WASHINGTON, D.C.
Paul G. Nystrom
4121 Chatelain Road
Room 203
Annandale, Virginia 22003
(703) 750-3993

Plywood cuts costs. Not quality.

AMERICAN PLYWOOD ASSOCIATION

P. O. Box 2277 / Tacoma, WA 98401

Form No. C50

The APA Series
Construction

Plywood Roof Systems

American Plywood Association

February 1978

6

LAMINATED

Plywood

Introduction

For roofs, whether residential, commercial, or industrial, APA® grade-trademarked plywood offers numerous benefits.

Plywood works with almost any support system—wood or steel trusses, ordinary joist and purlin systems, glulam or timber framing. Plywood lends itself to panel-by-panel installation, to preframed systems and special components, and to diaphragm construction for high wind and earthquake resistance. Plywood roof systems with excellent fire ratings are possible. And plywood roofs are easily insulated.

The following pages contain design data for several plywood roof systems, including diaphragms, special components and plywood under special coatings. There's also information on plywood roof assemblies with wind- and fire-resistive ratings.

APA grade-trademarked plywood. The build-a-better-roof material.

IDENTIFICATION INDEX

The basic unsanded grades of plywood—C-D sheathing, C-C Exterior and STRUCTURAL I and II C-C and C-D—carry an Identification Index of two numbers, such as 24/0 or 32/16, in the American Plywood Association grade-trademark. The left-hand number refers to the maximum recommended center-to-center spacing in inches of roof framing when the panel is used as roof sheathing. The right-hand number refers to the maximum recommended center-to-center spacing of floor framing when the panel is used for subflooring. In each case, face grain is across supports and the panel is continuous across two or more spans.

The spans referred to in the Index numbers are accepted by most major building codes. Local interpretations may vary, however, so be sure your specifications comply with the local code under which you are building.

NOTE: For a tabular "Guide to Identification Index on Engineered Grades" and for additional information on plywood types, groups, grades and method of ordering, refer to APA's **Plywood Specification and Grade Guide, C20.**

SPECIFICATION GUIDE

Each panel of construction plywood shall meet the requirements of the latest edition of U.S. Product Standard PS 1, and shall be identified with the appropriate grade-trademark of the American Plywood Association. All plywood which has any edge or surface permanently exposed to the weather or moisture shall be Exterior type.*

Panel thickness, grade, and Group or Identification Index shall be equal to or better than that shown on the drawings. Application shall be in accordance with recommendations of the American Plywood Association.

*An exception may be made in the case of plywood used for the All-Weather Wood Foundation, which may be Interior type with exterior glue provided it is pressure-preservative-treated in accordance with the American Wood Preservers Bureau AWPB-FDN Standard.

TABLE 1
Guide to Engineered Grades of Plywood for Roofs
Specific grades and thicknesses may be in locally limited supply. See your dealer before specifying.

Use These Terms When You Specify Plywood	Description and Most Common Uses	Typical Grade-Trademarks	Most Common Thicknesses (inch)				
INTERIOR TYPE							
C-D INT-APA	Roof sheathing grade. Most commonly made with exterior glue. Specify exterior glue when construction delays are anticipated.	C-D 32/16 (APA) INTERIOR PS 1/4 000 EXTERIOR GLUE	5/16	3/8	1/2	5/8	3/4
STRUCTURAL I C-D INT-APA, STRUCTURAL II C-D INT-APA	Unsanded structural grades where plywood strength properties are of maximum importance: structural diaphragms, box beams, gusset plates, stressed-skin panels. Made only with exterior glue.	STRUCTURAL I C-D 32/16 (APA) INTERIOR PS 1/4 000	5/16	3/8	1/2	5/8	3/4
2-4-1 INT-APA	For heavy-timber roof construction. Use 2-4-1 with exterior glue in areas subject to moisture. Unsanded or touch-sanded as specified. Also available with tongue-and-groove edges.	2-4-1 GROUP 1 (APA) INTERIOR PS 1/4 000	1-1/8				
EXTERIOR TYPE							
C-C EXT-APA	Full Exterior type panel with waterproof bond for roof decking. Unsanded. Minimum C-grade veneers throughout.	C-C 48/24 (APA) EXTERIOR PS 1/4 000	5/16	3/8	1/2	5/8	3/4
STRUCTURAL I C-C EXT-APA, STRUCTURAL II C-C EXT-APA	For engineered applications in construction and industry where full Exterior type panels are required. Unsanded.	STRUCTURAL I C-C 48/24 (APA) EXTERIOR PS 1/4 000	5/16	3/8	1/2	5/8	3/4

NOTE: Exterior type sanded panels are sometimes used for roof decks under special coatings. See Table 6 and the section "Plywood Under Special Coatings," page 8.

Plywood Roof Sheathing

Plywood roof sheathing can be used under any type of shingle or roofing material. It covers fast with minimal waste. Plywood's stability during temperature fluctuations makes it particularly suitable for built-up roofs. And plywood provides a "tight," durable, rack-resistant roof deck under asphalt or wood shingles and shakes.

Allowable uniform live loads (applied loads such as snow) given in Table 2 assume plywood continuous across two or more spans with face grain across supports. Values assume 5 psf dead load (weight of plywood and roofing material). Uniform load deflection limit is 1/180 of the span under live load plus dead load; 1/240 of the span under live load only. Loads are based on the minimum assumed properties of all Identification Index grades. In some cases, such as the 48/24 index, higher loads are permissible if C-C EXT or STRUCTURAL I grades are specified. Special conditions, such as heavy concentrated loads, may require construction in excess of the minimums indicated.

INSTALLATION

Plywood sheathing over roof trusses spaced 24 inches on center is widely recognized as the most economical construction for residential roofs and has become the industry standard. When support spacing exceeds the maximum allowable length of an unsupported edge (Table 2, Column 4) for either residential or commercial

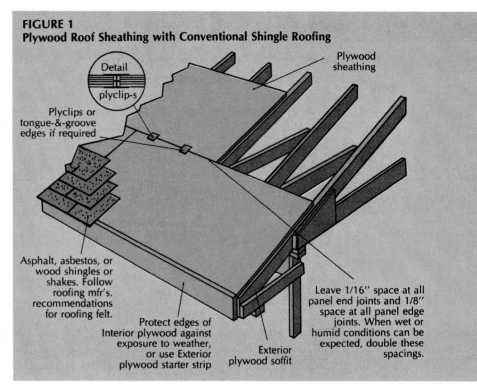

FIGURE 1
Plywood Roof Sheathing with Conventional Shingle Roofing

Plywood sheathing

Detail plyclip-s

Plyclips or tongue-&-groove edges if required

Asphalt, asbestos, or wood shingles or shakes. Follow roofing mfr's. recommendations for roofing felt.

Protect edges of Interior plywood against exposure to weather, or use Exterior plywood starter strip

Exterior plywood soffit

Leave 1/16" space at all panel end joints and 1/8" space at all panel edge joints. When wet or humid conditions can be expected, double these spacings.

roof decks, provide blocking, tongue-and-groove edges, or other edge support, such as Plyclips.® Use two Plyclips for 48-inch or greater spans; one for lesser spans.

Space panel ends 1/16 inch and panel edges 1/8 inch. Special Plyclips with spacer-webs are available to help assure proper spacing at panel edges. (See Figure 1.) Where wet or humid conditions prevail, double these spacings. Use

6d common smooth, ring-shank or spiral thread nails for plywood 1/2 inch thick or less; 8d for plywood to 1 inch thick. For 1-1/8-inch 2-4-1® panels, use 8d ring-shank or spiral thread or 10d common smooth nails. Space nails 6 inches at panel edges and 12 inches at intermediate supports for spans less than 48 inches. For spans 48 inches or greater, space nails 6 inches at all supports.

TABLE 2
Maximum Allowable Uniform Live Loads for Roof Decking
(C-D INT-APA, C-C EXT-APA, STRUCTURAL I and II C-D INT-APA, and STRUCTURAL I and II C-C EXT-APA grades only)

Identification Index	Plywood Thickness (inches)	Maximum Span (inches)	Unsupported Edge-Max. Length (inches)	Allowable Live Loads (psf)									
				Spacing of Supports Center-to-Center (inches)									
				12	16	20	24	30	32	36	42	48	60
12/0	5/16	12	12	150									
16/0	5/16, 3/8	16	16	160	75								
20/0	5/16, 3/8	20	20	190	105	65							
24/0	3/8, 1/2	24	20, 24 (b)	250	140	95	50						
32/16	1/2, 5/8	32	28	385	215	150	95	50	40				
42/20	5/8, 3/4, 7/8	42	32		330	230	145	90	75	50	35		
48/24	3/4, 7/8	48	36			300	190	120	105	65	45	35	
48/24 (a)	3/4, 7/8	48	36				225	125	105	75	55	40	
2-4-1	1-1/8	72	48				390	245	215	135	100	75	45
1-1/8" Grp. 1 & 2	1-1/8	72	48				305	195	170	105	75	55	35
1-1/4" Grp. 3 & 4	1-1/4	72	48				355	225	195	125	90	65	40

(a) Loads apply only to C-C EXT-APA, STRUCTURAL I C-D INT-APA, and STRUCTURAL I C-C EXT-APA, Check availability of these grades before specifying.
(b) Maximum unsupported length 20 inches for 3/8 inch plywood, 24 inches for 1/2 inch plywood.

PLYWOOD NAIL HOLDING

Extensive laboratory and field tests, reinforced by more than 25 years of experience, offer convincing proof than even 5/16-inch plywood will hold shingle nails securely and permanently in place, even under hurricane-force winds. A normal wood-shingled roof will average more than 6 nails per square foot. Each nail need carry no more than 11 pounds. Plywood sheathing only 5/16 inch thick shows a withdrawal resistance averaging 50 pounds for a single 3d shingle nail in laboratory and field tests of wood shingles after 5 to 8 years exposure. Given shape and height factors, actual suction or lifting action, even during hurricanes, will not normally exceed 25 psf up to 30-foot heights. Field experience also shows that asphalt shingles consistently tear through at the nail head before the nail pulls out of the plywood.

EXTERIOR PLYWOOD SOFFITS

For plywood grade and span recommendations for closed and open soffits, refer to APA's **Plywood Wall Systems,** C30.

Although the recommendations given in Table 2 have proven fully satisfactory for 3-, 4- and 5-ply built-up roofs, many roofing manufacturers require that spans be reduced slightly when roofing is to be guaranteed by a performance bond. A consensus of their recommendations is given in Table 3. Panel spacing, and nail size and spacing, are the same as those recommended for plywood sheathing.

TABLE 3
Spans for 20-year Bonded Roofs

Allowable Grades for All Indexes	Panel Identification Index	Plywood Thickness (inch)	Maximum Spacing of Supports (inches)	Edge Support Plyclips (number as shown) Blocking, Tongue-&-Groove or Other
STR. I & II C-C EXT-APA	24/0	3/8, 1/2	16	1
STR. I & II C-D INT-APA C-D INT-APA	32/16	1/2, 5/8	24	1
C-C EXT-APA	42/20	5/8, 3/4, 7/8	32	1
C-D INT-APA w/ext. glue	48/24	3/4, 7/8	48	2

Preframed Roofs

Preframed plywood panels can save time and labor in commercial structures and at the same time deliver diaphragm strength to resist loads from wind or earthquake. In preframing, roof sections of plywood fastened to lumber stiffeners are fabricated using production line techniques. Preframed panels may be assembled either at the site or in a shop. No elaborate fabrication equipment is needed. Connections are simply nailed or stapled.

Plywood recommendations in Table 4 are based on face grain parallel to supports with all panel edges supported by Plyclips, tongue-and-groove edges, solid blocking, or framing. Dead load is assumed at 5 psf. Deflection limits are 1/180 of the span for total load; 1/240 for live load only. Allowable loads for sanded panels other than STRUCTURAL I are based on use of Group 1 faces. Reduce applicable loads by 5 percent for Group 2, 10 percent for Group 3, and 13 percent for Group 4. Unless otherwise noted, panels are assumed to have the minimum number of plies allowed by PS 1.

The basic 4x8-foot preframed units may be installed individually on an in-place purlin system. Larger panels—typically 8x20 to 8x30 feet—are assembled by on-site ground crews. These larger panels, with a purlin preattached to one edge, are then erected with a forklift. Stiffener load-span recommendations and details of typical assemblies are contained in APA's **Build A Better Roof,** Form A310. Use nails and Plyclips, and space panels, per recommendations given for roof sheathing.

Long Span Systems

Plywood sheathing gives excellent performance in long span roof systems with either metal or wood framing. Both preframed plywood panel systems and direct application of sheathing to secondary or primary framing are common approaches, with bay spacing and type of framing governing the choice.

Experience shows that 3/4-inch plywood over supports 48 inches on center will yield maximum economies. Plywood with an Identification Index of 48/24 is good for 35 psf snow load and meets the requirements for most bonded roofs. Fire-retardant-treated plywood decking and steel or treated wood joists enjoy fire insurance rates comparable to unprotected metal roofs. Figure 2 shows typical connections for open-web flat roof trusses with wood chords and wood or steel webs. Wood "I" joists with plywood webs are also widely available.

FIGURE 2
Typical Connections/Open-Web Joists

Nailer Bolted to Steel Joist

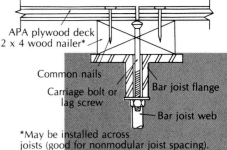

APA plywood deck
2 x 4 wood nailer*
Common nails
Carriage bolt or lag screw
Bar joist flange
Bar joist web
*May be installed across joists (good for nonmodular joist spacing).

Plywood Nailed to Open-Web Flat Chord Wood Truss

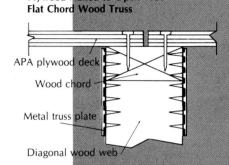

APA plywood deck
Wood chord
Metal truss plate
Diagonal wood web

Plywood Nailed to Open-Web Wood/Steel Truss

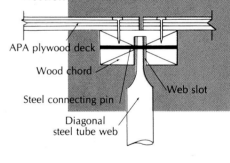

APA plywood deck
Wood chord
Steel connecting pin
Web slot
Diagonal steel tube web

TABLE 4
Allowable Live Loads for Plywood Roof Sheathing with Face Grain Parallel to Supports

SURFACE	Number and Length of Spans	STRUCTURAL I Grades		Grades Other Than STRUCTURAL I	
		Identification Index and Thickness (inches)	Maximum Allowable Uniform Live Load (psf)	Identification Index and Thickness (inches)	Maximum Allowable Uniform Live Load (psf)
UNSANDED	Four @ 12"	24/0—3/8	35	24/0—1/2 (a) / 24/0—1/2 (b)	50 / 160
	Three @ 16"	32/16—1/2 (b) / 32/16—1/2 (c)	115 / 75	24/10—1/2 (b) / 32/16—1/2 (b)	65 / 70
	Two @ 24"	32/16—1/2 (c) / 32/16—1/2 (b) / 42/20—5/8 / 48/24—3/4	25 / 40 / 80 / 110	32/16—1/2 (b) (d) / 32/16—5/8 (b) / 42/20—5/8 (c) / 42/20—5/8 (b) / 42/20—3/4 / 48/24—3/4 / 48/24—7/8	25 / 45 / 30 / 45 / 50 / 50 / 120
	One @ 48"	1-1/8	45	2-4-1	25 (f)
SANDED (e)	Four @ 12"	3/8	80	3/8 / 1/2	50 / 195
	Three @ 16"	3/8 / 1/2	30 / 135	1/2 / 5/8	80 / 190
	Two @ 24"	1/2 / 5/8	45 / 105	5/8 / 3/4	65 / 115
	One @ 48"	1-1/8	55	1-1/8	30

(a) Three-ply and four-ply construction.
(b) Five-ply construction only.
(c) Four-ply construction.
(d) Solid blocking recommended.
(e) Sanded panels other than STRUCTURAL I assumed to be Group 1.
(f) 35 psf with solid blocking at panel ends.

Plywood Roof Diaphragms

With only slight design modifications, any plywood roof deck system described in the previous sections will also function as a diaphragm to resist high wind and seismic loading. And when a series of floor, wall and roof diaphragms are properly tied together, the entire building functions as a unit against lateral loads.

A diaphragm's ability to function effectively as a beam, transferring lateral loads to shear walls, is related to the quality of the connections. Nailing is critical since shears are transmitted through these fasteners. Common nails provide required bearing capacity. Other nail types may be used when their lateral bearing values are considered in the design. Load-carrying capacity is highest when the diaphragm is blocked.

Table 5 gives plywood and fastening recommendations for diaphragm roofs. Plywood and framing are assumed designed for perpendicular loads. To design a plywood diaphragm, follow these steps.

1. Determine lateral loads and resulting shears.
2. Determine nailing schedule (Table 5). Consider load direction with respect to joints.
3. Compute chord stress due to bending moment. Provide adequate splices. Check deflection. Check anchorage of boundary framing (e.g., chords) to walls.

TABLE 5
Recommended Shear in Pounds per Foot for Horizontal Plywood Diaphragms with Framing of Douglas Fir, Larch or Southern Pine (c) for Wind or Seismic Loading

APA Grade-Trademarked Plywood	Common Nail Size	Min. Nail Penetration in Framing (inches)	Minimum Plywood Thickness (inch)	Min. Width of Framing Member	Blocked Diaphragms — Nail Spacing at Boundaries (All Cases) Continuous Edges Parallel to Load (Cases 3, 4, 5, & 6) (a) 6"	4"	2½"	2"	Unblocked Diaphragms — Nails Spaced 6" Max. at Supported Edges (a) Case 1 (No Unblocked Edges or Continuous Joints Parallel to Load)	Cases 2, 3, 4, 5 & 6
					Other panel edges 6"	6"	4"	3"		
STRUCTURAL I C-D INT-APA or STRUCTURAL I C-C EXT-APA	6d	1-1/4	5/16	2	185	250	375	420	165	125
				3	210	280	420	475	185	140
	8d	1-1/2	3/8	2	270	360	530	600	240	180
				3	300	400	600	675	265	200
	10d	1-5/8	1/2	2	320	425	640 (b)	730 (b)	285	215
				3	360	480	720	820	320	240
C-D INT-APA, C-C EXT-APA, STRUCTURAL II C-D INT-APA STRUCTURAL II C-C EXT-APA sheathing and other APA grades except Species Group 5	6d	1-1/4	5/16	2	170	225	335	380	150	110
				3	190	250	380	430	170	125
			3/8	2	185	250	375	420	165	125
				3	210	280	420	475	185	140
	8d	1-1/2	3/8	2	240	320	480	545	215	160
				3	270	360	540	610	240	180
			1/2	2	270	360	530	600	240	180
				3	300	400	600	675	265	200
	10d	1-5/8	1/2	2	290	385	575 (b)	655 (b)	255	190
				3	325	430	650	735	290	215
			5/8	2	320	425	640 (b)	730 (b)	285	215
				3	360	480	720	820	320	240

(a) Space nails 12 in. on center along intermediate framing members.
(b) Reduce tabulated allowable shears 10 percent when boundary members provide less than 3-inch nominal nailing surface.
(c) For framing other species: (1) Find species group of lumber in table 13, NFPA Nat'l Design Spec. (2) Find shear value from table for nail size, and for STRUCTURAL I plywood (regardless of actual grade). (3) Multiply value by 0.82 for Lumber Group III or 0.65 for Lumber Group IV.
Notes: Design for diaphragm stresses depends on direction of continuous panel joints with reference to load, not on direction of long dimensions of plywood sheet. Continuous framing may be in either direction for blocked diaphragms.

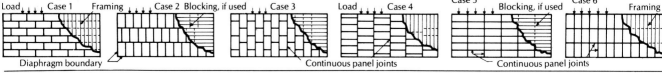

Load   Case 1   Framing   Case 2   Blocking, if used   Case 3   Load   Case 4   Case 5   Blocking, if used   Case 6   Framing

Diaphragm boundary   Continuous panel joints   Continuous panel joints

Special Roof Systems

GLUED STRUCTURAL COMPONENTS

Glued plywood components are structural assemblies that offer great design freedom to commercial building planners. High strength-to-weight ratios, efficient use of materials, uniform size and quality resulting from production-line manufacture, and fast close-in time are only a few considerations that make structurally glued plywood components an important factor in modern commercial construction.

Stressed-skin panels. The stressed-skin panel is one of the most useful of the glued plywood components. Efficient and easy to handle, the stressed-skin panel (Figure 3) has a plywood skin glued to the top of longitudinal framing members. The skin and framing act as a single structural unit in carrying loads. When designed with a bottom skin and filled with insulative material, the stressed-skin panel also provides good thermal values and a ready-to-finish ceiling.

The most practical roof spans for this type of plywood component are 12 to 32 feet. Design procedures for both single- and double-skin panels are available. For complete information, write for APA's **Plywood Design Specification, Supplement 3,** Form U813.

Folded plates. Plywood folded plates rely on shape rather than mass for strength and stiffness. The plywood acts not only as sheathing, but as an integral part of a "shell roof system" that eliminates the need for heavy framing. Folded plates can be used for spans up to 100 feet or more. Plywood thickness is governed by rafter spacing and shear adjacent to the rafter supports. Rafters are sized to span between chord members.

Radial folded plates are an extension of the rectangular folded plate concept and require no center support. Chords radiate from an apex and are supported at or near the perimeter of the building.

For detailed information, write for APA's **Fabrication of Plywood Folded Plates,** Form V900.

Space planes. These are a family of plywood roofs incorporating combinations of plates, usually triangular or polygonal. The planes interact to support vertical loads without beams or trusses. Essentially, they are shell structures in which the webs or skins carry the shear to the framing at their boundaries by means of diaphragm action. The chords usually are not parallel.

Plywood box beams. Box beams, constructed of nailed and glued or pressure-glued lumber and plywood, develop an extremely high strength-to-weight ratio. Shop-fabricated glued beams can be used to span distances up to 80 feet or more. They consist of one or more vertical plywood webs laminated to seasoned lumber flanges. Vertical stiffeners at intervals along the beam's length distribute concentrated loads and prevent web buckling. For detailed information, write APA for **Plywood Design Specification, Supplement 2,** Form S812.

**FIGURE 3
Typical One-Sided Stressed-Skin Panel**

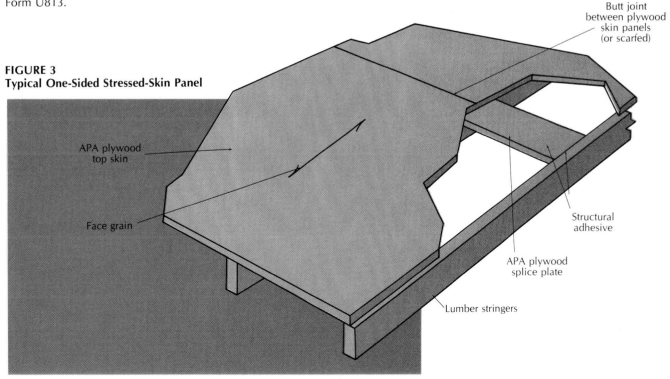

Butt joint between plywood skin panels (or scarfed)

APA plywood top skin

Face grain

Structural adhesive

APA plywood splice plate

Lumber stringers

PLYWOOD UNDER SPECIAL COATINGS

New chemical coatings for roofs have increased the range of design possibilities, particularly in larger commercial structures with contoured or steeply pitched roof surfaces that may be exposed to view.

The plywood thickness and span recommendations in Table 6 assume installation with face grain perpendicular to supports and liquid coating applied directly to plywood. Check local building codes for any required deviation from recommendations. Allowable roof live load is based on the same deflection criteria as described for Table 2.

Only Exterior type plywood is recommended for use under special coatings for roofs. Where the coating requires a very smooth base, use A-C EXT-APA or B-C EXT-APA plywood.

Where maximum smoothness is not essential, use C-C Plugged EXT-APA. Tongue-and-groove plywood (1/2 inch or thicker) or lumber blocking at panel edges is recommended. Leave 1/16-inch space between panel ends and edges. Where wet or humid conditions prevail, double these spacings. If high performance coatings are to be used for finish, check coating manufacturer's recommendations for panel joint treatment. Use minimum 6d deformed-shank nails for 5/8- and 3/4-inch plywood and 8d deformed-shank nails for 7/8-inch plywood. For curved surfaces, use deformed-shank nails only. Space nails 6 inches along panel ends and edges; 12 inches along intermediate supports. Nail type, size and spacing may vary for plywood diaphragm designs.

FIRE-RATED CONSTRUCTION

There are three basic categories of fire-rated wood roof construction—protected, heavy timber and fire-retardant-treated—that are recognized by building codes and insurance rating bureaus.

Protected construction. Protected construction includes any normal wood-and-plywood assembly with a fire-resistive material—e.g., gypsumboard, plaster, mineral acoustical tile—added to give primary protection to the joists. The plywood slows flame passage and temperature rise while reinforcing the joists against collapse under load.

The plywood stressed-skin assembly illustrated in Figure 4 is the thinnest one-hour combustible assembly which has passed Underwriters Laboratories tests. The layers of fiber insulation board and Type X gypsumboard may be applied in the field. One-half-inch plywood

TABLE 6
Allowable Plywood Thicknesses and Maximum Spans for Roof Decks Under Special Coatings

Grade	Plywood Thickness (inch)	Maximum Support Spacing (inches)			Allowable Live Roof Load (psf)
		Group 1	Groups 2 & 3	Group 4	
A-C, B-C, C-C PLUGGED (EXT-APA)	3/8	22	20	16	60
	1/2	30	24	22	45
	5/8	36	30	28	45
	3/4	44	36	32	35
	7/8	48	44	42	35

FIGURE 4
One-Hour Combustible Roof/Ceiling Assembly
(U.L. Design L504)

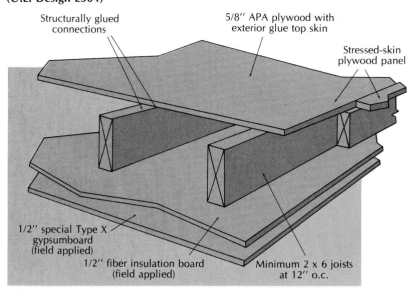

Structurally glued connections

5/8″ APA plywood with exterior glue top skin

Stressed-skin plywood panel

1/2″ special Type X gypsumboard (field applied)

1/2″ fiber insulation board (field applied)

Minimum 2 x 6 joists at 12″ o.c.

construction is identified as such by an appropriate label, it is rated on a parity with non-combustible construction by many insurance rating bureaus. Hence, it qualifies for lower insurance rates.

The roof may be simply a treated 3/4-inch plywood deck over treated wood joists or trusses, or steel supports. A stressed-skin panel with treated lumber stringers and 3/4-inch plywood top skin may also be used. The bottom skin may be treated plywood or gypsumboard. The stressed-skin panel may be supported by untreated wood beams if they are

may be substituted for the 1/2-inch insulation board. For detailed information on this and more than 30 other approved protected roof construction assemblies incorporating plywood, refer to UL Fire Resistance Index.

Heavy timber. Until recent years, roof decks qualifying for the heavy timber rating had to consist of planks at least 2 inches thick, or laminated planks at least 3 inches wide on edge. APA's 1-1/8-inch-thick 2-4-1 plywood with exterior glue is now accepted by all major codes as an alternative to planks, based on comparative fire tests. Typically, 2-4-1 has tongue-and-groove edges and panels are attached to supports spaced 4 feet on center (Figure 5). A heavy timber rating has been given by ICBO to square-edge 2-4-1 plywood when applied with face grain parallel to minimum 4x6 supports spaced 48 inches on center in the preframed panelized roof. In this case, all plywood edges are supported by framing.

Treated construction. Fire-retardant-treated roofs lend themselves to a variety of support systems—wood framing, long-span trusses, steel or concrete supports, or laminated beams—and are a good way to get large clear-span interiors. FRT construction qualifies for lower flame spread and smoke generation ratings, thus reducing its fire hazard classification. When treated

TABLE 7
Maximum Allowable Uniform Live Loads for 3/4″ Thick FRT Roof Decking
(C-D INT-APA with exterior glue, C-C EXT-APA, STRUCTURAL I and II C-D INT-APA, and STRUCTURAL I and II C-C EXT-APA grades only)

FACE GRAIN PERPENDICULAR TO SUPPORTS

Identification Index	Allowable Live Loads (psf)						
	Spacing of Supports Center-to-Center (inches)						
	20	24	30	32	36	42	48
48/24	250	160	100	85	55	40	30
48/24 (a)		185	115	100	60	45	35

FACE GRAIN PARALLEL TO SUPPORTS

Identification Index	Allowable Live Loads (psf)		
	Spacing of Supports Center-to-Center (inches)		
	12	16	24
48/24	295	125	40
48/24 (b)		270	90

(a)Loads apply only to C-C EXT-APA, STRUCTURAL I C-D INT-APA, and STRUCTURAL I C-C EXT-APA. Check availability of these grades before specifying.
(b)Loads apply only to STRUCTURAL I C-D INT-APA, and STRUCTURAL I C-C EXT-APA. Check availability of these grades before specifying.

FIGURE 5
Plywood Heavy Timber Roof Construction

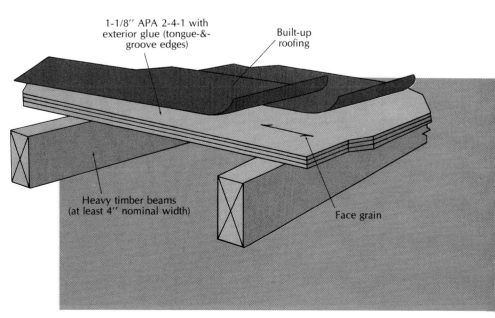

1-1/8″ APA 2-4-1 with exterior glue (tongue-&-groove edges)

Built-up roofing

Heavy timber beams (at least 4″ nominal width)

Face grain

FIGURE 6
Fully-Wind-Resistive Roof Assembly
(NM 510)

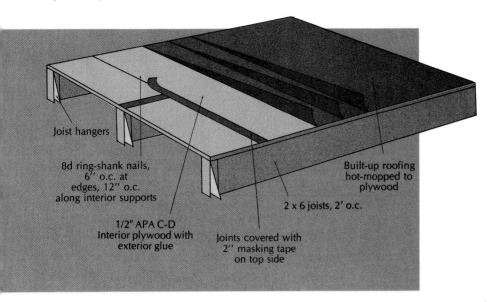

Joist hangers

8d ring-shank nails,
6" o.c. at
edges, 12" o.c.
along interior supports

1/2" APA C-D
Interior plywood with
exterior glue

Joints covered with
2" masking tape
on top side

2 x 6 joists, 2' o.c.

Built-up roofing
hot-mopped to
plywood

spaced at least 8 feet on center. The allowable live loads for 3/4-inch FRT plywood sheathing with an Identification Index of 48/24 are given in Table 7.

WIND-RATED CONSTRUCTION

Wind ratings are based on the roof system's performance in wind uplift tests. Systems meeting UL requirements are assigned a semi-wind-resistive (Class 30 or 60), or fully-wind-resistive classification (Class 90). Many of the fire-rated assemblies also can qualify for these ratings. Heavy timber usually is accorded semi-wind-resistive recognition.

Two plywood roof systems have earned fully-wind-resistive or Class 90 ratings and are recognized in 47 states. This means each system has passed a test that simulates winds of 174 miles per hour. One of the systems is shown in Figure 6. The other is a panelized roof deck of 1/2-inch C-D Interior plywood with exterior glue on 2x4 stiffeners spanning 8 feet between purlins framed into glulam beams. A built-up asphalt roof is hot-mopped to the surface.

INSULATING PLYWOOD ROOFS

Insulating plywood roof decks is simpler, quicker and less expensive than other decks. With plywood's flat surface, non-rigid batt insulation can be applied on the underside of the deck, and built-up roofing on top, without further preparation that costs

time and money. Most metal roof systems, on the other hand, require special rigid insulation on top of the deck to provide the smooth surface needed for hot-mopping. The plywood deck with batt insulation also provides better sound absorption values, an important consideration in commercial, industrial and institutional construction.

A wood frame/plywood roof deck system can be insulated through a variety of effective techniques. Figure 7 shows four-plywood roof decks—three with insulation and one without.

FIGURE 7
"U" Values of Plywood Roof Decks

No Insulation

Outside air

Inside air

⅜" built-up roof
½" plywood

Winter	Summer
0.578	0.472

Reflective Insulation (a)

Foil insulation

Air space
Air space

No. of equal air spaces	Winter	Summer
(a) Foil sheets assumed 1	0.268	0.096
reflective both sides 2	0.186	0.067
except exposed bottom. 3	0.114	0.064

Additional Information

For additional information on plywood roof systems, request any of the publications listed below. Single copies are available without charge by writing the American Plywood Association, P. O. Box 2277, Tacoma, Washington 98401.

Build A Better Roof, A310
Plywood Commercial/Industrial Construction Guide, Y300
Plywood Diaphragm Construction, U310
Plywood Construction for Fire Protection, W305
Plywood Design Specification, Y510
    Supplement 2: Design of Plywood Beams, S812
    Supplement 3: Design of Plywood Stressed-Skin Panels, U813
Fabrication of Plywood Folded Plates, V900
Plywood Over Metal Framing, A330
Plywood for Remodeling: Commercial, Industrial and Institutional, B380

APA: THE MARK OF QUALITY

The American Plywood Association's grade-trademarks are used by qualified member mills to identify plywood that has been manufactured to meet the requirements of **U.S. Product Standard PS 1-74 for Construction and Industrial Plywood.** Information covered in this and all APA publications is based upon the use of plywood of known quality. Always insist on plywood bearing the **Mark of Quality**—the APA grade-trademark.

Rigid Insulation

Rigid insulation board

		Winter	Summer
Fiberboard or			
expanded	1 in.	0.222	0.204
perlite	1½ in.	0.169	0.159
(k = 0.36)			
Fiberglass or			
molded bead	1 in.	0.175	0.163
polystyrene	1½ in.	0.129	0.123
(k = 0.25)			
Extruded	1 in.	0.149	0.140
polystyrene	1½ in.	0.108	0.104
(k = 0.20)			
Polyurethane	1 in.	0.113	0.108
(k = 0.14)			

Flexible Insulation

Flexible batt insulation

Air space

	Winter	Summer
R11 with		
no air space (b)	0.079	0.076
R11 with		
dead air space (b)	0.073	0.070
R19 with		
no air space	0.048	0.047
(b) min. 2x6		
joists required		

Our field representatives can help. For additional assistance in specifying plywood, get in touch with your nearest American Plywood Association field service representative. Call or write:

ATLANTA

Paul D. Colbenson
P. O. Box 90550
Atlanta, Georgia 30364
(404) 762-6649

CHICAGO

Vernon D. Haskell
120 East Ogden Avenue
Room 204
Hinsdale, Illinois 60521
(312) 323-5787

DALLAS

A. M. Leggett
10010 Miller Road
Suite 105
Dallas, Texas 75238
(214) 348-0643

LOS ANGELES

Long Beach, California
(213) 439-8616

NEW YORK

Englewood Cliffs, New Jersey
(201) 567-7238

SAN FRANCISCO

Philip L. Benfield
P. O. Box 3536
Fremont, California 94538
(415) 657-5959

WASHINGTON, D.C.

Paul G. Nystrom
4121 Chatelain Road
Room 203
Annandale, Virginia 22003
(703) 750-3993

Plywood cuts costs. Not quality.

AMERICAN PLYWOOD ASSOCIATION

P. O. Box 2277 / Tacoma, WA 98401   Form No. C40

Kiln-Dried Spruce-Pine-Fir

For Single-Family Homes

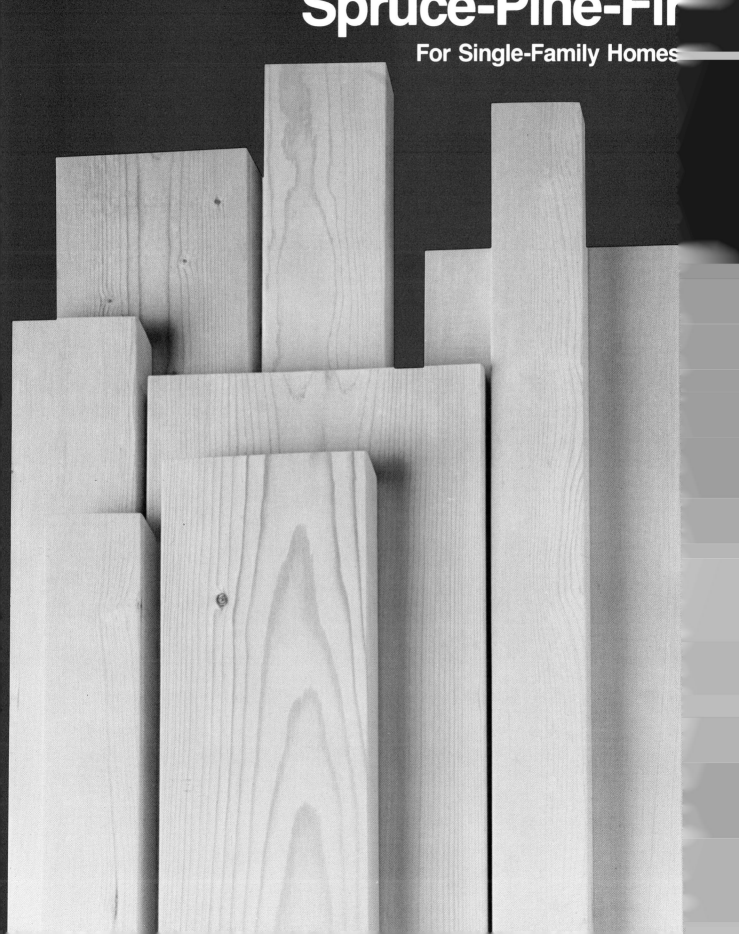

Kiln-Dried Spruce-Pine-Fir

A multi-purpose framing lumber for single-family homes

Of all the wood species manufactured into lumber in Canada, the Spruce-Pine-Fir group is foremost in both supply and production volume.

Spruce-Pine-Fir is found in abundance and produced in volume in the western Canadian provinces of British Columbia and Alberta. Standing timber inventory is estimated at more than 176 billion cubic feet. This forest reserve is carefully harvested on a perpetual yield basis, thus assuring a plentiful supply of dimension lumber for the foreseeable future. Because of its accessibility, assured continuity of supply and high quality, the Spruce-Pine-Fir group accounts for a major percentage of Canada's exports of commercial softwood lumber.

The principal species included in the Spruce-Pine-Fir group are White spruce (*Picea glauca*), Engelmann spruce (*Picea engelmannii*), Lodgepole pine (*Pinus contorta*), and Alpine fir (*Abies lasiocarpa*). Minor species include Red and Black spruce, Balsam fir and Jack pine.

Species comprising the Spruce-Pine-Fir group share a number of common characteristics. The trees generally attain heights of up to 100 feet and diameters up to 3 feet, and yield high grade, tight knotted lumber. The wood is of medium strength and weight. Colouring ranges from creamy white to pale yellow with a clean appearance. In contrast with other commercial softwoods of a darker shade, Spruce-Pine-Fir is distinctly a 'white wood', with little colour distinction between springwood and summerwood.

One of the most important characteristics of Spruce-Pine-Fir lumber is that it is uniformly seasoned in dry kilns to a moisture content of 19% or less. Kiln-drying makes the lumber less susceptible to decay, stain and insect attack and thus enhances its appearance. The wood's dimensional stability is markedly improved by the drying process and problems such as warping, twisting, checking, shrinkage and nail popping are virtually eliminated.

In general, the wood is straight grained and smooth textured with good working, nail holding, gluing, and finishing properties. Characteristics of the Spruce-Pine-Fir group make it a particularly versatile lumber for framing applications in all types of single-family residential construction. In addition to its widespread use in on-site construction for joists, rafters, beams and studs, Spruce-Pine-Fir is also used extensively in the mobile home and prefabricated housing industries.

Canadian Spruce-Pine-Fir has ALS approval

All kiln-dried Spruce-Pine-Fir produced in Canada is manufactured and graded under the National Lumber Grades Authority (NLGA) rule, which is approved and enforced by the

Standard timber-frame construction using Spruce-Pine-Fir is the most efficient and economic system for residential construction.

Canadian Lumber Standards Administrative Board. The Canadian NLGA grading rule is also recognized by the American Lumber Standards Committee and accepted by the Federal Housing Administration and the authorities administering all major model building codes including the Basic Building Code, the National Building Code, the Southern Standard Building Code and the Uniform Building Code.

Grades of Spruce-Pine-Fir dimension lumber are identical with those in use throughout the United States and conform to all applicable requirements of American Softwood Lumber Standard PS 20-70.

Sizes and Grades of Spruce-Pine-Fir

As an assurance of its assigned grade, all Spruce-Pine-Fir dimension lumber carries an official grademark. The grademark shows the registered symbol of the certifying agency; the mill identity, usually by number; the grading rule used; the grade; and the species or species group. In addition, some indications relating to size and moisture content may be added to the regular mark.

The NLGA grading rule requires that kiln-dried Spruce-Pine-Fir CLS lumber be planed on all four sides to precise dimensions. Edges are usually eased for safe handling. Spruce-Pine-Fir is available in a range of nominal widths and thicknesses (see table) in lengths of 6' to 16' and occasionally longer (studs to 10' only). It is normally shipped in packages of a single size and uniform length consisting of a mix of No. 2 grade and better.

The NLGA rule classifies dimension lumber into two width categories and five end-use categories. Under this grading rule, all grades are uniformly graded the full length of the piece and may be cut to shorter lengths without lowering the grade. The categories and grades are:

Structural Light Framing (2″ to 4″ Thick, 2″ to 4″ Wide)

Select Structural No. 1	Intended primarily for use where high strength, stiffness and good appearance are desired.
No. 2	Recommended for most general construction uses.
No. 3	Appropriate for use in general construction where appearance is not a factor.

Light Framing (2″ to 4″ Thick, 2″ to 4″ Wide)

Construction	Recommended and widely used for general framing purposes. Pieces are of good appearance but graded primarily for strength and
Standard	serviceability.
Utility	Recommended and widely used where a combination of good strength and economical construction is desired for such purposes as studding, blocking, plates, bracing, and rafters.

Stud (2″ to 4″ Thick, 2″ to 6″ Wide)

Stud	Special purpose grade intended for studs.

Structural Joists and Planks (2″ to 4″ Thick, 5″ and Wider)

Select Structural No. 1	Intended primarily for use where high strength, stiffness and good appearance are desired.
No. 2	Recommended for most general construction uses.
No. 3	Appropriate for use in general construction where appearance is not a factor.

Appearance Framing (2″ to 4″ Thick, 2″ and Wider)

Appearance	For use in general housing and light construction where lumber permitting knots but of high strength and fine appearance is desired.

Available Sizes of Kiln-Dried CLS Spruce-Pine-Fir

Nominal Size (in.)	Surfaced Green Net Size (in.)	Surfaced Dry Net Size (in.)
2 x 2	1⁹/₁₆ x 1⁹/₁₆	1½ x 1½
2 x 3	1⁹/₁₆ x 2⁹/₁₆	1½ x 2½
2 x 4	1⁹/₁₆ x 3⁹/₁₆	1½ x 3½
2 x 6	1⁹/₁₆ x 5⅝	1½ x 5½
2 x 8	1⁹/₁₆ x 7½	1½ x 7¼
2 x 10	1⁹/₁₆ x 9½	1½ x 9¼
2 x 12	1⁹/₁₆ x 11½	1½ x 11¼
3 x 4	2⁹/₁₆ x 3⁹/₁₆	2½ x 3½
3 x 6	2⁹/₁₆ x 5⅝	2½ x 5½
3 x 8	2⁹/₁₆ x 7½	2½ x 7¼
3 x 10	2⁹/₁₆ x 9½	2½ x 9¼
3 x 12	2⁹/₁₆ x 11½	2½ x 11¼
4 x 4	3⁹/₁₆ x 3⁹/₁₆	3½ x 3½
4 x 6	3⁹/₁₆ x 5⅝	3½ x 5½
4 x 8	3⁹/₁₆ x 7½	3½ x 7¼
4 x 10	3⁹/₁₆ x 9½	3½ x 9¼
4 x 12	3⁹/₁₆ x 11½	3½ x 11¼

The light weight and excellent nailing properties of the Spruce-Pine-Fir species group are well suited to production line manufacturing techniques.

This brochure is intended to convey to builders and specifiers the inherent qualities of Spruce-Pine-Fir lumber manufactured by the members of the signatory industry associations. It should be noted that previously published data on Spruce-Pine-Fir design values are in the process of re-evaluation by means of in-grade testing. Early results indicate that it might be possible to increase design values for Spruce-Pine-Fir lumber in the future. On completion of the test program, new data will be published.

Additional information about kiln-dried Spruce-Pine-Fir is available from the following forest products associations which represent the major Canadian producers.

Alberta Forest Products Association,
204-11710 Kingsway Avenue,
Edmonton, Alberta T5G 0X5

A.F.P.A.® 00
S — P — F   1
S-DRY

Cariboo Lumber Manufacturers' Association,
301-197 Second Avenue North,
Williams Lake, British Columbia V2G 1Z5

CLMA® 1   S-DRY 1
1   S — P — F

Interior Lumber Manufacturers' Association,
295-333 Martin Street,
Penticton, British Columbia V2A 5K8

ILMA® S-DRY 1
00   S — P — F

Northern Interior Lumber Sector,
Council of Forest Industries of British Columbia,
514-550 Victoria Street,
Prince George, British Columbia V2L 2K1

COFI®   S-P-F
S-DRY
100   No 1

SOUTHERN PINE
use guide

Southern Pine has long been a preferred species for homes and other structures because of its high strength, resistance to wear and ability to hold fastenings. Under the American Softwood Lumber Standard, it has become an even more efficient, more economical material for engineered and conventional buildings.

The broad range of uses covered by recommendations in this guide...timbers, light framing, exposed beam roof systems, paneling, siding, millwork, trim, patio decks, scaffolding, stadium seats, bridges, highway structures, piers and wharves and many more...demonstrates a versatility unique among woods. Southern Pine's resistance to blemish or scarring is as valuable with paneling as with boardwalks. The ease with which it takes treatment is as useful with patio decks as with pole-frame structures.

mr manufacturer

SFPA is a nonprofit organization of lumber manufacturers in 12 Southern states: Virginia, North and South Carolina, Georgia, Florida, Tennessee, Alabama, Mississippi, Louisiana, Arkansas, Texas, and Oklahoma. More than 150 member mills produce roughly half of all the Southern Pine lumber in the U.S. The Association has more than 80 active member companies and 150 associate members.

OBJECTIVES: SFPA carries out program services in marketing, forest resources and safety, serves as a spokesman for the industry in public, educational, technical and governmental forums. The marketing objectives are:

1. **Provide retail dealers, homebuilders, architects, specifiers and other users, including students, with information, tools and services to effectively sell and encourage the use of members' principal lumber products.**
2. **Create favorable market conditions for SFPA member lumber products in nonresidential and industrial construction.**
3. **Encourage and assist the development and use of more efficient engineered wood framing and foundation systems.**

FIELD SERVICES: SFPA maintains fieldstaff representatives throughout the South, East and Midwest to assist specifiers and customers.

PUBLICATIONS: SFPA publishes and distributes a wide range of pamphlets, books and other materials in support of its many program services. Its periodicals include the weekly "SFPA Newsletter" and "Trade Barometer" as well as reference services on transportation for the membership. In addition, SFPA makes available a slide presentation to assist retail dealer countermen in understanding and selling Southern Pine.

pp product presentation

Southern Pine

Southern Pine is a general group of four principal tree species of longleaf, slash, shortleaf and loblolly, grown in a geographic range from Virginia to Texas.

Availability of Trees and Wood

People are increasingly dependent on trees for basic necessities and pleasures. By the year 2000, the population of the United States is expected to exceed 300 million. Availability of wood products must be doubled by then to adequately house Americans and meet other material needs. Not only lumber, plywood and other building materials but also clothing, containers, chemicals, paper and a host of household essentials must be derived from the forests in ever larger volume. Recreational demands on the forests will rise, too, as opportunities to enjoy the outdoors continue to shrink in congested metropolitan areas.

Many more trees will be needed to meet these various demands and maintain the scenic quality of the nation's landscape. The South—with 192 million acres of forestland—offers a potential for timber growth not enjoyed by other regions, and here a resource development project of immense scope is in the making.

To assure an adequate supply of timber for our future needs, SFPA has initiated one of the most ambitious programs in history in its "Trees Forever" program. This program recognizes that it will be necessary to double timber growth in the South before the end of the century if we are to meet anticipated population growth. This can be accomplished only through massive extension of sound forestry practices to small private ownerships.

Quantities and Grades

The Southern lumber industry has changed considerably in the last decade, particularly in regard to the volume, grades and sizes of products manufactured. Production of Southern Pine has increased from less than 6 billion board feet in 1962 to more than 8 billion board feet in 1973.

One of the most significant trends in Southern Pine sizes is the change from board production to 2″ dimensional sizes.

Production of Southern Pine Sizes

ITEM	1963	1967	1971	1976
1″ to 1½″	52%	36%	17%	14%
2″ Dimension	43%	59%	82%	84%

Reasons for this trend are: **1.** Demand for Southern Pine dimension framing. In 1976, 78% of the Southern Pine shipped was for light construction and residential use. **2.** Production considerations and market prices make 2″ dimensional sizes more economical to produce. The trend in sizes of dimension produced has also shown changes which are reflected in the following.

Sizes of Dimension Southern Pine Produced

SIZE	1963	1967	1971	1976
Studs	—	4%	11%	11%
2x4	12%	15%	27%	26%
2x6	12%	17%	17%	20%
2x8	9%	11%	11%	10%
2x10	6%	8%	12%	12%
2x12	3%	3%	3%	5%

Higher grades have also shown a decrease, and therefore are not always readily available. This should be considered in specifying these grades.

Grades of Southern Pine Produced

GRADE/SIZE	1963	1967	1971	1976
C & Btr				
1½″ & less	15%	12%	17%	13%
D				
1½″ & less	14%	13%	11%	12%
Select Structural				
2″ Nominal	—	—	—	—
No. 1				
1½″ & less	—	—	4%	4%
2″ Nominal	20%	15%	11%	12%
No. 2				
1½″ & less	50%	54%	51%	53%
2″ Nominal	58%	54%	49%	52%
No. 3				
1½″ & less	20%	19%	17%	18%
2″ Nominal	18%	19%	19%	17%
Stud			10%	11%
Construction			1%	—
Standard	(2x4 only)		4%	2%
Utility			4%	1%
Economy			1%	3%

ABCs OF THE AMERICAN SOFTWOOD LUMBER STANDARD

The American Softwood Lumber Standard (PS 20-70), promulgated by the U.S. Department of Commerce, relates lumber size to moisture content. Separate size schedules have been established for green and dry lumber to assure that both products will approximate the same size in service. This applies on a uniform national basis a principle long recognized in the manufacture of Southern Pine, wherein grading rules continue to limit moisture content of house framing lumber to a maximum of 19%. PS 20-70 provides for a National Grading Rule with simplified grade names and sizes designed to assure greater uniformity, efficiency and economy in the use of dimension lumber. The NGR was incorporated in 1977 grading rules published by the Southern Pine Inspection Bureau.

In conformity with the national standard, strength and stiffness values for Southern Pine in current SPIB rules have been developed through advanced technology and stringent testing procedures in accordance with standards of the American Society for Testing and Materials, and approved by the National Bureau of Standards and the U.S. Forest Products Laboratory. As a result of the Southern Pine Density Survey, conducted by the U.S. Forest Service, new minimum design values were developed for Southern Pine Structural Grades.

To protect the consumer, the national standard requires further that all bills and invoices show actual net size of lumber so that the buyer knows exactly what he's getting and paying for.

Grade names and sizes provided by the National Grading Rule and incorporated in 1977 SPIB rules are as follows:

Structural Light Framing
2″ to 4″ thick, 2″ to 4″ wide
Select Structural
No. 1
No. 2
No. 3

Light Framing
2″ to 4″ thick, 2″ to 4″ wide
Construction
Standard
Utility

Studs
2″ to 4″ thick, 2″ to 6″ wide
10′ and shorter
Stud

Structural Joists & Planks
2″ to 4″ thick, 5″ & wider
Select Structural
No. 1
No. 2
No. 3

Appearance Framing
2″ to 4″ thick, 2″ and wider
Appearance

NGR applies to dimension lumber and excludes items such as crossarms, factory and shop lumber, finish (select), foundation lumber, industrial clears, ladder stock, laminating stock, railroad stock, rough lumber, scaffold planks, ship decking and plank stock, stadium seats and worked lumber.

Southern Pine Seasoning Requirements

Southern Pine grading rules restrict moisture content of lumber 2″ and less in thickness to a maximum of 19%. If specified as "KD" (kiln-dried) or "MC15" the maximum is 15%. Appearance of a grade mark is evidence that Southern Pine has been properly seasoned. Lumber grade-marked "KD" or "MC15" is entitled to higher design values as shown in Table 2.

Grade mark MC15 applies to material which has been air-dried, kiln-dried, or both to 15% maximum moisture content.

Moisture content restrictions apply at time of shipment and delivery to buyer as well as time of dressing, if dressed lumber is involved.

SEASONING REQUIREMENTS*

ITEMS (Nominal)	MAXIMUM (DRY)	KILN-DRIED (KD or MC15)
D&Btr Grades 1″ & 1¼″	15%	12% on 90% of pieces 15% on remainder
1½″, 1¾″ & 2″	18%	15%
Over 2″ not over 4″	19%	15%
Over 4″	20%	18%
Paneling[1] 1″		12%
Boards 2″ and less & Dimension 2″ to 4″	19%	15%
Decking[2] 2″ thick	19%	15%
3″ and 4″ thick		15% on 90% of pieces 18% on remainder
Heavy Dimension[3] Over 2″ not over 4″	19%	15%
Timbers[3] 5″ and thicker	23%	20%

[1] Required to be kiln-dried to 12% maximum moisture content.
[2] All thickness of Decking should be specified at 15% maximum moisture content.
[3] Moisture content provisions must be specified as seasoning is not mandatory in these sizes.
* Paragraph 168 of the 1977 SPIB Grading Rules states: "Lumber dressed at a moisture content within the limits of these rules is sufficiently stabilized for most uses, but limited size changes will occur from shrinkage or expansion if the moisture content is further reduced or increased after dressing. The normal shrinkage allowance is 1% reduction in size for each 4-point reduction in percentage of moisture content and same tolerance for any expansion."

3

TABLE 1 / SOUTHERN PINE GRADE DESCRIPTIONS

PRODUCT	GRADE	CHARACTER OF GRADE AND TYPICAL USES
FINISH	*B&B	Highest recognized grade of finish. Generally clear although a limited number of pin knots permitted. Finest quality for natural or stain finish.
	C	Excellent for painted or natural finish where requirements are less exacting. Reasonably clear but permits limited number of surface checks, and small tight knots.
	C&Btr	Combination of "B&B" and "C" grades, satisfies requirements for high quality finish.
	D	Economical, serviceable grade for natural or painted finish.
*PANELING INCLUDING FILLETS	B&B C C&Btr	Similar to above grades with additional restrictions on stain and wane.
	D	Top quality knotty pine paneling for natural or stained finish. Knots are smooth and even with surrounding surface.
	No. 1	Not contained in current SPIB Grading Rules; however, if specified, will be designated and graded as "D" grade.
	No. 2	Knotty pine grade somewhat less exacting than "D" but suitable for natural or stained finish. Tight-knotted, with knots generally smooth across surface. Minor surface pits and cavities permitted. Wane not permitted on face.
	No. 3	More manufacturing imperfections allowed than in No. 2 but suitable for economical use.
*FLOORING CEILING PARTITION DROP SIDING BEVEL SIDING	B&B C C&Btr D	See Finish grades.
	No. 1	No. 1 Flooring not provided under SPIB Grading Rules as separate grade, but if specified, will be designated and graded as "D." No. 1 drop siding is graded as No. 1 boards.
	No. 2	Slightly better than No. 2 boards. High utility value where appearance is not factor.
	No. 3	More manufacturing imperfections allowed than in No. 2 but suitable for economical use.
BOARDS S4S SHIPLAP S2S&CM	No. 1	High quality with good appearance characteristics. Generally sound and tight-knotted. Largest hole permitted is 1/16″. A superior product suitable for wide range of uses including shelving, form and crating lumber.
	No. 2	High quality sheathing material, characterized by tight knots. Generally free of holes.
	No. 3	Good, serviceable sheathing, usable for many applications without waste.
	No. 4	Admit pieces below No. 3 which can be used without waste or contain usable portions at least 24″ in length.
STRUCTURAL LUMBER	*Dense Str. 86 *Dense Str. 72 *Dense Str. 65	Number at end of grade names indicates the percentage stress of clear wood value. (All grades identified as "Structural" contain only sound wood free from any form of decay.)

*See page 6 for footnote.   **(cont'd)**

TABLE 1 / SOUTHERN PINE GRADE DESCRIPTIONS (cont'd)

PRODUCT	GRADE	CHARACTER OF GRADE AND TYPICAL USES
DIMENSION **Structural Light** **Framing** 2'' to 4'' thick 2'' to 4'' wide	*Select Structural *Dense Select Structural	High quality, relatively free of characteristics which impair strength or stiffness. Recommended for uses where high strength, stiffness and good appearance are required.
	No. 1 **No. 1 Dense**	Provide high strength, recommended for general utility and construction purposes. Good appearance, especially suitable where exposed because of the knot limitations.
	No. 2 **No. 2 Dense**	Although less restricted than No. 1, suitable for all types of construction. Tight knots.
	No. 3 **No. 3 Dense**	Assigned design values meet wide range of design requirements. Recommended for general construction purposes where appearance is not a controlling factor. Many pieces included in this grade would qualify as No. 2 except for single limiting characteristic. Provides high quality and low cost construction.
STUDS 2'' to 4'' thick 2'' to 6'' wide 10' and Shorter	**Stud**	Stringent requirements as to straightness, strength and stiffness adapt this grade to all stud uses, including load-bearing walls. Crook restricted in 2'' x 4'' — 8' to ¼'', with wane restricted to 1/3 of thickness.
Structural **Joists & Planks** 2'' to 4'' thick 5'' and wider	*Select Structural Dense Select *Structural	High quality, relatively free of characteristics which impair strength or stiffness. Recommended for uses where high strength, stiffness and good appearance are required.
	No. 1 **No. 1 Dense**	Provide high strength, recommended for general utility and construction purposes. Good appearance, especially suitable where exposed because of the knot limitations.
	No. 2 **No. 2 Dense**	Although less restricted than No. 1, suitable for all types of construction. Tight knots.
	No. 3 **No. 3 Dense**	Assigned stress values meet wide range of design requirements. Recommended for general construction purposes where appearance is not a controlling factor. Many pieces included in this grade would qualify as No. 2 except for single limiting characteristic. Provides high quality and low cost construction.
**Light Framing 2'' to 4'' thick 2'' to 4'' wide	*Construction	Recommended for general framing purposes. Good appearance, strong and serviceable.
	*Standard	Recommended for same uses as Construction grade, but allows larger defects.
	*Utility	Recommended where combination of strength and economy is desired. Excellent for blocking, plates and bracing.
	*Economy	Usable lengths suitable for bracing, blocking, bulkheading and other utility purposes where strength and appearance not controlling factors.
Appearance **Framing** 2'' to 4'' thick 2'' and wider	*Appearance	Designed for uses such as exposed-beam roof systems. Combines strength characteristics of No. 1 with appearance of "C&Btr."

TABLE 1 / SOUTHERN PINE GRADE DESCRIPTIONS (cont'd)

PRODUCT	GRADE	CHARACTER OF GRADE AND TYPICAL USES
TIMBERS 5″ x 5″ & larger	**No. 1 SR** **No. 1** **Dense SR** **No. 2 SR** **No. 2** **Dense SR**	No. 1 and No. 2 are similar in appearance to corresponding grades of 2″ dimension. Recommended for general construction uses. SR in grade name STRESS RATED.
	Square Edge and Sound No. 1, No. 2, No. 3	Not stress-rated but economical for general construction purposes.
INDUSTRIAL LUMBER	***Dense Industrial 86** ***Industrial 86** ***Dense Industrial 72** ***Industrial 72** ***Dense Industrial 65** ***Industrial 65**	These classifications cover a variety of industrial grades where resistance to abrasive action, mechanical wear, or ability to absorb shock is desirable on specific use conditions.
***FACTORY FLOORING AND DECKING**	**Dense Standard**	High quality product, suitable for plank floor where face serves as finish floor. Has a better appearance than No. 1 Dense because of additional restrictions on pitch, knots, pith and wane.
	Select Dense Select	Slightly less restrictive than Dense Standard but more restrictive than No. 1 dimension. Sound, solid appearance.
	Commercial Dense Commercial	Same requirements as corresponding grades of No. 2 dimension.
SCAFFOLD PLANK	***Dense Industrial 72 Scaffold Plank**	Extra high quality. Available in dimensions 2″ and thicker and all widths. (For design values see Table 2.)
	Dense Industrial 65 Scaffold Plank	High quality. Available in dimensions 2″ and thicker and all widths. (For design values see Table 2.)
STADIUM SEATS	***No. 1 Dense Stadium Grade**	Superior material with one face free of pitch and otherwise complying with No. 1 Dense dimension.
	***No. 1 Stadium Grade**	Similar to No. 1 Dense Stadium Grade, except density not required.

***Caution!** Most mills do not manufacture all products and make all grade separations. Those products and grades manufactured by a relatively few mills are noted with an asterisk.

STANDARD SIZES OF SOUTHERN PINE

Rough structural lumber

THICKNESS[1] (Inches)			WIDTH (Inches)		
Rough			Rough		
Nominal	Dry	Green	Nominal	Dry	Green
2	1-5/8[4]		2	1-5/8	
3	2-5/8[4]	2-11/16	3	2-5/8	2-11/16[2]
4	3-5/8[4]	3-11/16	4	3-5/8	3-11/16[2]
			5	4-5/8	4-3/4[2]
			6	5-5/8	5-3/4[2]
			8	7-3/8[2]	7-5/8
			10	9-3/8[2]	9-5/8
			12	11-3/8[2]	11-5/8
			14	13-3/8[2]	13-5/8
			16	15-3/8[2]	15-5/8
			18	17-3/8[2]	17-5/8
			20	19-3/8[2]	19-5/8
5" & thicker	3/8" off nominal[4]	3/8" off nominal	5" & wider	3/8" off nominal[3]	3/8" off nominal[3]

[1]Thicknesses apply to their corresponding widths as squares and wider, except 2" green thickness of 1-11/16 applies to widths of 14" and over.
[2]These widths apply only to thicknesses of less than 5".
[3]These widths apply only to thicknesses of 5" and over.
[4]These minimum thicknesses apply to 80% of the pieces of an item or shipment and the remainder (20%) may be 1/32" thinner.

Dimension and structural lumber, Dressed

THICKNESS[1] (Inches)			WIDTH (Inches)		
Nominal	Standard ALS Minimum Dressed		Nominal	Standard ALS Minimum Dressed	
	DRY	GREEN		DRY	GREEN
2	1-1/2		2	1-1/2	
2-1/2	2[3]	2-1/16	3	2-1/2	2-9/16[2]
3	2-1/2[3]	2-9/16	4	3-1/2	3-9/16[2]
3-1/2	3[3]	3-1/16	5	4-1/2	4-5/8[2]
4	3-1/2[3]	3-9/16	6	5-1/2	5-5/8[2]
			8	7-1/4	7-1/2
			10	9-1/4	9-1/2
			12	11-1/4	11-1/2
			14	13-1/4	13-1/2
			16	15-1/4	15-1/2
			18	17-1/4	17-1/2
			20	19-1/4	19-1/2
5" & thicker	1/2" off nominal[4]	1/2" off nominal	5" & wider	1/2" off nominal	1/2" off nominal

[1]2" dressed green thickness of 1-9/16 applies to widths of 14" and over.
[2]These green widths apply to thicknesses of 3" and 4" only, except as provided in Footnote (1).
[3]Not required to be dry unless specified.

	THICKNESS (Inches)		WIDTH (Inches)	
	Nominal	Dressed	Nominal	Dressed
Finish	3/8	5/16	2	1-1/2
	1/2	7/16	3	2-1/2
	5/8	9/16	4	3-1/2
	3/4	5/8	5	4-1/2
	1	3/4	6	5-1/2
	1-1/4	1	7	6-1/2
	1-1/2	1-1/4	8	7-1/4
	1-3/4	1-3/8	9	8-1/4
	2	1-1/2	10	9-1/4
	2-1/2	2	11	10-1/4
	3	2-1/2	12	11-1/4
	3-1/2	3	14	13-1/4
	4	3-1/2	16	15-1/4
Boards	1	3/4[1]	2	1-1/2
	1-1/4	1	3	2-1/2
	1-1/2	1-1/4	4	3-1/2
			5	4-1/2
			6	5-1/2
			7	6-1/2
			8	7-1/4
			9	8-1/4
			10	9-1/4
			11	10-1/4
			12	11-1/4
			over 12	off 3/4

[1]Boards less than the minimum dressed thickness for 1" nominal but which are 5/8" or greater thickness dry may be regarded as American Standard Lumber, but such boards shall be marked to show the size and condition of seasoning at the time of dressing. They shall also be distinguished from 1" boards on invoices and certificates.

	THICKNESS (Inches)		WIDTH (Inches)		
	Nominal	Worked	Nominal	Face	Over-all
Bevel Siding	1/2	3/16x7/16	4	3-1/2	3-1/2
	5/8	3/16x9/16	5	4-1/2	4-1/2
	3/4	3/16x11/16	6	5-1/2	5-1/2
	1	3/16x3/4	8	7-1/4	7-1/4
Drop Siding Rustic and Drop Siding (dressed and matched)	5/8	9/16	4	3-1/8	3-3/8*
	1	23/32	5	4-1/8	4-3/8*
			6	5-1/8	5-3/8*
			8	6-7/8	7-1/8*
			10	8-7/8	9-1/8*
Rustic and Drop Siding (shiplapped)	5/8	9/16	4	3	3-3/8*
	1	23/32	5	4	4-3/8*
			6	5	5-3/8*
			8	6-5/8	7-1/8*
			10	8-5/8	9-1/8*
			12	10-5/8	11-1/8*
Flooring	3/8	5/16	2	1-1/8	1-3/8**
	1/2	7/16	3	2-1/8	2-3/8**
	5/8	9/16	4	3-1/8	3-3/8**
	1	3/4	5	4-1/8	4-3/8**
	1-1/4	1	6	5-1/8	5-3/8**
	1-1/2	1-1/4			
Ceiling	3/8	5/16	3	2-1/8	2-3/8**
	1/2	7/16	4	3-1/8	3-3/8**
	5/8	9/16	5	4-1/8	4-3/8**
	3/4	11/16	6	5-1/8	5-3/8**
Partition	1	23/32	3	2-1/8	2-3/8
			4	3-1/8	3-3/8
			5	4-1/8	4-3/8
			6	5-1/8	5-3/8
Paneling	1	23/32	3	2-1/8	2-3/8
			4	3-1/8	3-3/8
			5	4-1/8	4-3/8
			6	5-1/8	5-3/8
			8	6-7/8	7-1/8
			10	8-7/8	9-1/8
			12	10-7/8	11-1/8
Shiplap	1	3/4	4	3-1/8	3-1/2
			6	5-1/8	5-1/2
			8	6-7/8	7-1/4
			10	8-7/8	9-1/4
			12	10-7/8	11-1/4
Dressed and Matched	1	3/4	4	3-1/8	3-3/8
	1-1/4	1	5	4-1/8	4-3/8
	1-1/2	1-1/4	6	5-1/8	5-3/8
			8	6-7/8	7-1/8
			10	8-7/8	9-1/8
			12	10-7/8	11-1/8

*Over-all widths for 5/8" thickness are 1/16" less.
**Over-all widths for 3/8", 1/2" and 5/8" thicknesses are 1/16" less.

Factory Flooring and Decking Heavy Roofing and Shiplap

THICKNESS (Inches)		WIDTH (Inches)			
			Dressed		
Nominal	Dressed	Nominal	D & M	Ship-lapped	For Splines
2	1-1/2	4	3	3	3-1/2
2-1/2	2	6	5	5	5-1/2
3	2-1/2	8	6-3/4	6-3/4	7-1/4
4	3-1/2	10	8-3/4	8-3/4	9-1/4
5	4-1/2	12	10-3/4	10-3/4	11-1/4

TABLE 2 / RECOMMENDED GRADES OF SOUTHERN PINE[1]

Use-Item	MINIMUM GRADES RECOMMENDED
FRAMING	
Sills on Foundation Walls or Slab on Ground*......	Utility
Sills on Piers*—Built-up...........	No. 2
Joists, Rafters, Headers.............	No. 3
Plates, Caps, Bucks..............	Utility
Studs......	Stud Grade
Ribbon Boards, Bracing, Ridge Boards (1″ nominal thickness).......	No. 2
Collar Beams....................	No. 2
Furring Grounds 1″ nominal thickness............	No. 3
Subflooring.....................	No. 3
Wall Sheathing..................	No. 3
Roof Sheathing, Pitched...........	No. 3
Roof Decking, Flat	
1″ thick.......................	No. 2 KD
2″ thick.......................	No. 2 KD
Exposed Decking—where appearance is of prime concern	
3″ & 4″ thick....................	Dense Standard DT&G Deck
Industrial—appearance not prime concern	
3″ & 4″ thick.....................	Commercial DT&G
Stair Stringers or Carriages........	No. 1
Cellar and Attic Stair Treads and Risers......................	No. 1 Dense
Roof Truss Members	
2″ to 4″ thick	
Upper and Lower Chords.......	No. 2
Other......................	No. 3
5″ & thicker....................	No. 2 SR
Heavy Timber Construction	
Beams	
Built-up—2″ to 4″ thick........	No. 2
Solid—over 5″ thick...........	No. 2 SR
Posts and Columns	
2″ to 4″ thick.................	No. 2
over 5″ thick.................	No. 2 SR
SIDING, PANELING, FINISH AND MILLWORK	
Siding	
Bevel, Drop, Rough Sawn	
For rustic applications.........	No. 2
For appearance applications....	C&Btr
Exterior Trim	
Cornice......................	C Finish or C Ceiling
Mouldings, Drip Cap, Water Table...	C Mouldings
Trim, Facia, Corner Boards, Soffits...	No. 1
Window and Door	
Frames, Sash, Shutters, Screens....	C
Doors, Garage and Warehouse.....	No. 1

Use-Item	MINIMUM GRADES RECOMMENDED
SIDING, PANELING, FINISH AND MILLWORK (cont'd)	
Porch	
Ceiling.....................	No. 2 Ceiling
Flooring**††	No. 2
Stair Treads...................	No. 1 Dense
Stair Stringers or Carriages & Risers††	No. 1
Columns, Built-up† †.	No. 2
Newel Posts, Railings, Balustrades††	No. 1
Finished or Top Flooring**††	
Uncovered Floors, Natural, Stained.....................	C Flooring
Covered Floors..................	No. 2 Flooring
Industrial or Workroom Floors......	No. 2 Flooring or End Grain Block Flooring
Interior Finish and Trim	
Stair Treads or Stepping..........	C
Trim...........................	C
Mouldings......................	C
Ceiling........................	C
Partition.......................	C
Closet Lining...................	No. 2 Ceiling
Shelving.......................	No. 1
Paneling	
For rustic application..........	No. 2 KD
For appearance application.....	C
FENCING AND ACCESSORIES††	
Fencing	
Framing, Posts, Boards..........	No. 3
Pickets........................	No. 2
Gates, 1-inch thick..............	No. 2
Gates, 2-inch thick..............	No. 3
BALCONY, DECKS, PATIOS AND BOARDWALKS††	
Posts and Caps	
2″ to 4″ thick..................	No. 1 Dense
5″ & thicker...................	No. 1 SR
Sills	
2″ to 4″ thick..................	No. 1
5″ & thicker...................	No. 1 SR
Beams, Stringers	
2″ to 4″ thick..................	No. 1
5″ & thicker...................	No. 1 SR
Railings, Rail Posts..............	No. 1
Steps and Ramps................	No. 2
Decking........................	No. 2 (Specify "Bark side up")
Decking, Laminated, on Edge.......	No. 2

(cont'd)

TABLE 2 / RECOMMENDED GRADES OF SOUTHERN PINE[1] (cont'd)

Use-Item	MINIMUM GRADES RECOMMENDED
HEAVY FALSEWORK, HEAVY FORMS AND CAISSONS	
Sills, Mud Sills, Posts and Caps......	No. 1 SR
Stringers......................	No. 1 SR
Truss Members	
Compression and Tension Members	
2″ to 4″ thick...............	No. 2
5″ and thicker...............	No. 2 SR
Centering, Lagging and Wedges.....	No. 1 SR
Bracing......................	No. 1
SCAFFOLDING	
Uprights and Bracing	
2″ to 4″ thick (19% MC).........	No. 1
2½″ and thicker (over 19%MC)....	Dense Select Structural
Planking.....................	Dense Industrial 65 Scaffold Plank
CONCRETE FORMS	
Shoring and Plates.............	No. 1
Joists and Beam Forms..........	No. 2
Bracing......................	No. 2
Boarding.....................	No. 2
STADIUM SEATS††	
Seats........................	No. 1 Stadium Grade
(Specify "Bark side up")	
HIGHWAY STRUCTURES/BRIDGES ††	
Sills, Posts, Caps..............	No. 1 SR
Bracing, Sway.................	No. 1 SR
Truss Members	
Compression and Tension........	No. 1 SR
Floor Beams, Stringers..........	No. 1 SR
Nailing Strips.................	No. 1
Sub Decking, Plank or Laminated Decking, Top	
2″ to 4″ thick...............	No. 1 Dense Select
5″ and thicker...............	No. 1 Dense SR
Bulkhead and Plank	
2″ to 4″ thick...............	No. 1
5″ and thicker...............	No. 1 SR
Sidewalk Plank................	No. 1 Dense
Cleats and Scupper Blocks	
2″ to 4″ thick...............	No. 2
5″ and thicker...............	No. 2 SR
Railings and Rail Posts	
2″ to 4″ thick...............	No. 1 Dense
5″ and thicker...............	No. 1 SR
Wheel and Fellow Guards.........	No. 1 Dense
Fire Stops....................	No. 2

Use-Item	MINIMUM GRADES RECOMMENDED
CULVERTS AND DRAINS††	
2″ to 4″ thick..................	No. 1
5″ and thicker..................	No. 1 SR
RIGHT OF WAY FENCING††	
Posts........................	No. 2
Framing......................	No. 2
Boards.......................	No. 2
Gates	
1″ thick...................	No. 2
2″ to 4″ thick...............	No. 3
Stakes.......................	Utility
GUARD RAIL††	
Railing & Rail Posts	
2″ to 4″ thick...............	No. 1 Dense
5″ and thicker...............	No. 1 SR
SIGNPOSTS††	
Posts	
2″ to 4″ thick...............	No. 2
5″ and thicker...............	No. 2 SR
PIERS AND WHARVES (OPEN CONSTRUCTION)††	
Timber Sheet Piling	
2″ to 4″ thick...............	No. 1
5″ and thicker...............	No. 1 SR
Timber in Cribs................	No. 1 SR
Caps.........................	No. 1 SR
Stringers.....................	No. 1 SR
Bracing	
2″ to 4″ thick...............	No. 1
5″ and thicker...............	No. 1 SR
Decking	No. 1 Dense Select
2″ to 4″ thick...............	
5″ and thicker...............	No. 1 Dense SR
Decking, Laminated, on Edge........	No. 1
Guard Timbers.................	No. 1 Dense SR
Mooring Posts.................	No. 1 Dense SR
Fenders and Wales..............	No. 1 Dense SR

Note: For Sheds or Houses over Piers and Wharves, see Framing Lumber.

[1]Grades should be selected on engineering requirements. Above grades are minimum grades for particular use. For other grades see Table 1. For design values see Table 2.

*For slab on ground where sill on foundation wall or piers is within 18″ of ground on inside or 12″ on outside, use pressure preservative treated sills. See SFPA Technical Bulletin No. 6 regarding preservative treatment.

** Flooring may be specified "end-matched" the grade being the same as if plain-end.

††See Technical Bulletin No. 6 regarding preservative treatments and Bulletin No. 14 regarding deck, patio and fence applications.

General

Spans in the following tables are given in feet and inches of horizontal projection of the member. The horizontal projection represents actual length of horizontal members such as floor joists and ceiling joists. On the other hand, the horizontal projected span for sloped members, such as roof rafters, must be converted into distance measured parallel to the member in order to ascertain the required length. For example, using the conversion diagram on page 29, a horizontal span distance of 20 on an 8 in 12 slope requires a 24 foot long rafter.

Spans are determined on the same basis as those given in the nationally recognized Span Tables for Joists and Rafters published by the National Forest Products Association. The primary purpose of this bulletin is to provide a convenient reference of the spans associated with specific grades of Southern Pine lumber.

In addition to the usual 12, 16, and 24 inch spacing of joists, 19.2 and 13.7 inch spacings have been introduced to accommodate division of 8 foot lengths of sheet material into 5 and 7 spaces respectively. This gives the designer greater flexibility and spacings which may result in more economical framing.

Design Criteria

Loads. Condition of loading is stated in the heading or caption to each table, the range of which accommodates those common to major portions of the country. The designer should exercise good judgment in the case of ceiling joists, particularly those forming a space that can readily be developed into a sleeping room or where a stairway provides space above a ceiling that can be used for unlimited storage. In such cases, spans for floor joists for 30 psf live load in Table No. 1 should be used. Table Nos. 7 and 8 cover situations where a stairway provides access to space suitable for limited storage only.

Roof loadings of 20-30-40 psf represent the usual minimum roof load up to a total of 40 psf which covers most areas except those subject to unusually heavy snow loads. See section on duration of loads for increases in span because of short time application of loads. For heavy snow loads, structures should be given detailed engineering considerations. The application of full roof live load on horizontal projection of the span of a sloped roof member equivalent to the resolution of the same load so that the resultant force acts perpendicular to the member on the sloped distance.

Lumber Sizes. The allowable spans in the tables are based on the following dressed American Softwood Lumber Standard (PS 20-70) sizes:

Nominal Size Inches	Dressed Size, Inches 19% Max. MC
2 x 4	1½ x 3½
2 x 5	1½ x 4½
2 x 6	1½ x 5½
2 x 8	1½ x 7¼
2 x 10	1½ x 9¼
2 x 12	1½ x 11¼

Deflection. Deflection limitations are stated in terms of the span, l, in inches divided by either the factor 360, 240 or 180. To provide a high level of stiffness, floor joists and ceiling joists supporting plaster ceilings are held to the low deflection of $l/360$. Where stiffness is of lesser importance, as for ceiling joists and low sloped rafters with sheet type ceiling material such as gypsum board, the deflection limitation is required to be not more than $l/240$. For high sloped roof rafters where no ceiling is involved and live loads are usually of short duration, the deflection limitation used in design is $l/180$.

Design Values. Joist and rafter spans were determined on the basis of the design values in the "1977 Standard Grading Rules for Southern Pine Lumber" promulgated by the Southern Pine Inspection Bureau. Design values therein were determined in accordance with ASTM D245-76, Establishing Structural Grades for Visually Graded Lumber, and are shown under the "F_b" and "E" columns of the following table. Also in accordance with ASTM D245 the extreme fiber stress in bending "F_b" values were increased 15% for repetitive member use and are shown in the "1.15 F_b" column. Where the fiber stress in bending became the controlling factor in design, the "1.15 F_b" was used. Repetitive member use is a condition where not less than 3 framing members, such as joists, rafters, studs, planks, decking and similar members are spaced not more than 24" on center and are joined by floor, roof or other load distributing members.

Span Increases for Short Duration of Loads. Spans in this bulletin are conservative since they do not reflect increase in design values for loads of short duration, such as snow and wind, permitted by established engineering design criteria and building code regulations. Architects, engineers and designers should exercise judgment in applying the allowable increases. The following table provides the percentage increase in design values and resulting percentage increase by which the tabulated spans can be multiplied, depending on load conditions:

	Color, bold face type Limited by "F_b"
15% for 2 months as for snow—	6.5%
25% for 7 days as for construction	11.0%
33⅓% for wind or earthquake—	15.0%

GRADE	2-4" THICK, 5" & WIDER			2-4" THICK, 2-4" WIDE	
	Extreme Fiber In Bending*		Modulus of Elasticity	Extreme Fiber In Bending*	
	"F_b" psi	"1.15F_b" psi	"E" psi	"F_b" psi	"1.15F_b" psi
Dense Sel Str KD	2200	2550	1,900,000	2500	2900
Dense Sel Str	2050	2350	1,800,000	2350	2700
Sel Str KD	1850	2150	1,800,000	2150	2450
Sel Str	1750	2000	1,700,000	2000	2300
No. 1 Dense KD	1850	2150	1,900,000	2150	2450
No. 1 Dense	1700	1950	1,800,000	2000	2300
No. 1 KD	1600	1850	1,800,000	1850	2150
No. 1	1450	1650	1,700,000	1700	1950
No. 2 Dense KD	1550	1800	1,700,000	1800	2050
No. 2 Dense	1400	1600	1,600,000	1650	1900
No. 2 KD	1300	1500	1,600,000	1550	1800
No. 2	1200	1400	1,600,000	1400	1600
No. 3 Dense KD	875	1000	1,500,000	1000	1150
No. 3 Dense	825	950	1,500,000	925	1075
No. 3 KD	750	850	1,500,000	850	975
No. 3	700	800	1,400,000	775	900
Construction KD			1,500,000	1100	1150
Construction			1,400,000	1000	1050
Standard KD			1,500,000	625	725
Standard			1,400,000	575	650
Utility KD			1,500,000	275	325
Utility			1,400,000	275	325
Stud KD	800**	925	1,500,000	850	975
Stud	725**	900	1,400,000	775	900

*See section entitled "Design Values"
**Applies to 5" and 6" widths only.

Terms and abbreviations: Sel. Str. means select structural; KD means kiln dried to a moisture content of 15% or less; and where KD is not shown the material is dried to a moisture content of 19% or less.

Because it readily accepts preservative chemicals, Southern Pine is favored where pressure treatment is specified. And it excels in such engineering systems as the All-Weather Wood Foundation (over 10,000 built), glue-laminated structures, and all-important energy-conserving systems like Engineered 24 framing and the Plenwood.

From the Harvest

to the Homesite

Production figures tell it: In 1960 — 5.6 billion board feet of Southern Pine lumber. In 1976 this total reached 7.89 billion. And in 1977 8.92 billion. Ninety percent of production by SFPA members is kiln dried, and 10 percent of it is pressure treated. No wonder that grademarked Southern Pine lumber is called the supreme structural wood of the world.

TABLE NO. 3. FLOOR JOISTS—30 psf live load. Sleeping rooms and attic floors. (Spans shown in light face type are based on a deflection limitation of l/360. Spans shown in color, bold face type are limited by the recommended extreme fiber stress in bending value of the grade and includes a 10 psf dead load.)

Size and Spacing in.	Grade in. o.c.	Dense Sel Str KD and No. 1 Dense KD	Dense Sel Str, Sel Str KD, No. 1 Dense and No. 1 KD	Sel Str, No. 1 and No. 2 Dense KD	No. 2 Dense, No. 2 KD and No. 2	No. 3 Dense KD	No. 3 Dense	No. 3 KD	No. 3
	12.0	10-3	10-0	9-10	9-8	9-3	8-11	8-6	8-3
	13.7	9-9	9-7	9-5	9-3	8-7	8-4	8-0	7-9
2 x 5	16.0	9-3	9-1	8-11	8-9	8-0	7-9	7-5	7-2
	19.2	8-9	8-7	8-5	8-3	7-3	7-1	6-9	6-6
	24.0	8-1	8-0	7-10	7-8	6-6	6-4	6-0	5-10
	12.0	12-6	12-3	12-0	11-10	11-3	10-11	10-5	10-1
	13.7	11-11	11-9	11-6	11-3	10-6	10-3	9-9	9-5
2 x 6	16.0	11-4	11-2	10-11	10-9	9-9	9-6	9-0	8-9
	19.2	10-8	10-6	10-4	10-1	8-11	8-8	8-3	8-0
	24.0	9-11	9-9	9-7	9-4	8-0	7-9	7-4	7-1
	12.0	16-6	16-2	15-10	15-7	14-10	14-5	13-9	13-3
	13.7	15-9	15-6	15-2	14-11	13-11	13-6	12-10	12-5
2 x 8	16.0	15-0	14-8	14-5	14-2	12-10	12-6	11-11	11-6
	19.2	14-1	13-10	13-7	13-4	11-9	11-5	10-10	10-6
	24.0	13-1	12-10	12-7	12-4	10-6	10-2	9-9	9-5
	12.0	21-0	20-8	20-3	19-10	18-11	18-5	17-6	16-11
	13.7	20-1	19-9	19-4	19-0	17-9	17-2	16-5	15-10
2 x 10	16.0	19-1	18-9	18-5	18-0	16-5	15-11	15-2	14-8
	19.2	18-0	17-8	17-4	17-0	15-0	14-6	13-10	13-5
	24.0	16-8	16-5	16-1	15-9[1]	13-5	13-0	12-5	12-0
	12.0	25-7	25-1	24-8	24-2	23-0	22-4	21-4	20-7
	13.7	24-5	24-0	23-7	23-1	21-7	20-11	19-11	19-3
2 x 12	16.0	23-3	22-10	22-5	21-11	19-11	19-4	18-6	17-10
	19.2	21-10	21-6	21-1	20-8	18-3	17-8	16-10	16-3
	24.0	20-3	19-11	19-7	19-2[1]	16-3	15-10	15-1	14-7

1. The span for No. 2 grade, 24 inches o.c. spacing is: 2x10, 15-8; 2x12, 19-1.

TABLE NO. 4. FLOOR JOISTS—40 psf live load. All rooms except sleeping rooms and attic floors. (Spans shown in light face type are based on a deflection limitation of $l/360$. Spans shown in color, bold face type are limited by the recommended extreme fiber stress in bending value of the grade and includes a 10 psf dead load.)

Size and Spacing in	Grade in. o.c.	Dense Sel Str KD and No. 1 Dense KD	Dense Sel Str, Sel Str KD, No. 1 Dense and No. 1 KD	Sel Str, No. 1 and No. 2 Dense KD	No. 2 Dense, No. 2 KD and No. 2	No. 3 Dense KD	No. 3 Dense	No. 3 KD	No. 3
2 x 5	12.0	9-3	9-1	8-11	8-9	8-3	8-0	7-8	7-4
	13.7	8-11	8-9	8-7	8-5	7-9	7-6	7-2	6-11
	16.0	8-5	8-3	8-2	8-0	7-2	6-11	6-7	6-5
	19.2	7-11	7-10	7-8	7-6	6-6	6-4	6-0	5-10
	24.0	7-4	7-3	7-1	7-0[1]	5-10	5-8	5-5	5-3
2 x 6	12.0	11-4	11-2	10-11	10-9	10-1	9-9	9-4	9-0
	13.7	10-10	10-8	10-6	10-3	9-5	9-2	8-9	8-5
	16.0	10-4	10-2	9-11	9-9	8-9	8-6	8-1	7-10
	19.2	9-8	9-6	9-4	9-2	8-0	7-9	7-4	7-1
	24.0	9-0	8-10	8-8	8-6[1]	7-1	6-11	6-7	6-4
2 x 8	12.0	15-0	14-8	14-5	14-2	13-3	12-11	12-4	11-11
	13.7	14-4	14-1	13-10	13-6	12-5	12-1	11-6	11-1
	16.0	13-7	13-4	13-1	12-10	11-6	11-2	10-8	10-3
	19.2	12-10	12-7	12-4	12-1	10-6	10-2	9-9	9-5
	24.0	11-11	11-8	11-5	11-3[1]	9-5	9-1	8-8	8-5
2 x 10	12.0	19-1	18-9	18-5	18-0	16-11	16-5	15-8	15-2
	13.7	18-3	17-11	17-7	17-3	15-10	15-5	14-8	14-2
	16.0	17-4	17-0	16-9	16-5	14-8	14-3	13-7	13-1
	19.2	16-4	16-0	15-9	15-5	13-5	13-0	12-5	12-0
	24.0	15-2	14-11	14-7	14-4[1]	12-0	11-8	11-1	10-9
2 x 12	12.0	23-3	22-10	22-5	21-11	20-7	20-0	19-1	18-5
	13.7	22-3	21-10	21-5	21-0	19-3	18-9	17-10	17-3
	16.0	21-1	20-9	20-4	19-11	17-10	17-4	16-6	16-0
	19.2	19-10	19-6	19-2	18-9	16-3	15-10	15-1	14-7
	24.0	18-5	18-1	17-9	17-5[1]	14-7	14-2	13-6	13-0

1. The span for No. 2 grade, 24 inches o.c. spacing is: 2x5, 6-10; 2x6, 8-4; 2x8, 11-0; 2x10, 14-0; 2x12, 17-1.

TABLE NO. 5. FLOOR JOISTS, CONCRETE SUBFLOOR—30 psf live load. Sleeping rooms. (Spans shown in light face type are based on a deflection limitation of $l/360$. Spans shown in color, bold face type are limited by recommended extreme fiber stress in bending value of the grade and includes a 27 psf dead load consisting of 17 psf for 2" of lightweight concrete and 10 psf for framing.)

Size	Grade and Spacing in. o.c.	Dense Sel Str KD and No. 1 Dense KD	Dense Sel Str and Sel Str KD	Sel Str	No. 1 Dense	No. 1 KD	No. 2 Dense KD	No. 1	No. 2 Dense	No. 2 KD	No. 2	No. 3 Dense KD	No. 3 Dense	No. 3 KD	No. 3
2 x 5	12.0	10-3	10-0	9-10	10-0	10-0	9-10	9-10	9-8	9-5	9-0	7-9	7-6	7-2	6-11
	13.7	9-9	9-7	9-5	9-7	9-7	9-5	9-4	9-2	8-10	8-5	7-3	7-0	6-8	6-6
	16.0	9-3	9-1	8-11	9-1	9-0	8-11	8-7	8-5	8-2	7-10	6-8	6-6	6-2	6-0
	19.2	8-9	8-7	8-5	8-6	8-3	8-1	7-10	7-9	7-5	7-2	6-1	5-11	5-8	5-5
	24.0	8-1¹	8-0¹	7-9	7-7	7-5	7-3	7-0	6-11	6-8	6-5	5-5	5-4	5-1	4-11
2 x 6	12.0	12-6	12-3	12-0	12-3	12-3	12-0	12-0	11-10	11-6	11-1	9-5	9-2	8-9	8-5
	13.7	11-11	11-9	11-6	11-9	11-9	11-6	11-4	11-2	10-9	10-4	8-10	8-7	8-2	7-11
	16.0	11-4	11-2	10-11	11-2	11-1	10-10	10-6	10-4	10-0	9-7	8-2	7-11	7-7	7-4
	19.2	10-8	10-6	10-4	10-5	10-1	9-11	9-7	9-5	9-1	8-9	7-6	7-3	6-11	6-8
	24.0	9-11¹	9-9¹	9-5	9-4	9-0	8-11	8-7	8-5	8-2	7-10	6-8	6-6	6-2	6-0
2 x 8	12.0	16-6	16-2	15-10	16-2	16-2	15-10	15-10	15-7	15-2	14-7	12-5	12-1	11-6	11-1
	13.7	15-9	15-6	15-2	15-6	15-6	15-2	15-0	14-9	14-2	13-7	11-8	11-4	10-9	10-5
	16.0	15-0	14-8	14-5	14-8	14-7	14-4	13-10	13-7	13-2	12-7	10-9	10-5	10-0	9-8
	19.2	14-1	13-10	13-7	13-8	13-4	13-1	12-8	12-5	12-0	11-6	9-10	9-7	9-1	8-10
	24.0	13-1¹	12-10¹	12-5	12-3	11-11	11-8	11-4	11-1	10-9	10-4	8-10	8-6	8-2	7-10
2 x 10	12.0	21-0	20-8	20-3	20-8	20-8	20-3	20-3	19-10	19-4	18-7	15-10	15-5	14-8	14-2
	13.7	20-1	19-9	19-4	19-9	19-9	19-4	19-1	18-9	18-1	17-5	14-10	14-5	13-9	13-3
	16.0	19-1	18-9	18-5	18-9	18-7	18-3	17-8	17-5	16-9	16-1	13-9	13-4	12-9	12-3
	19.2	18-0	17-8	17-4	17-6	17-0	16-8	16-2	15-10	15-3	14-8	12-7	12-2	11-7	11-3
	24.0	16-8¹	16-5¹	15-10	15-8	15-2	14-11	14-5	14-2	13-8	13-2	11-3	10-11	10-5	10-0
2 x 12	12.0	25-7	25-1	24-8	25-1	25-1	24-8	24-8	24-2	23-6	22-7	19-4	18-9	17-10	17-3
	13.7	24-5	24-0	23-7	24-0	24-0	23-7	23-3	22-10	22-0	21-2	18-1	17-6	16-9	16-2
	16.0	23-3	22-10	22-5	22-10	22-7	22-3	21-6	21-2	20-4	19-7	16-9	16-3	15-6	14-11
	19.2	21-10	21-6	21-1	21-3	20-8	20-4	19-8	19-4	18-7	17-10	15-3	14-10	14-1	13-8
	24.0	20-3¹	19-11¹	19-4	19-0	18-5	18-2	17-7	17-3	16-8	16-0	13-8	13-3	12-8	12-2

1. The spans for No. 1 Dense KD and Select Structural KD, 24 inches o.c. spacing is: 2x5, 7-11; 2x6, 9-8; 2x8, 12-9; 2x10, 16-4; 2x12, 19-10.

ts | technical support

TABLE NO. 6.   CONCRETE SUBFLOOR—40 psf live load. All rooms except sleeping rooms. (Spans shown in light face type are based on a deflection limitation of $l/360$, bold face type are limited by recommended extreme fiber stress in bending value of the grade and includes a 27 psf dead load consisting of 17 psf for 2″ lightweight concrete and 10 psf for framing.)

Size and Spacing	Grade in. o.c.	Dense Sel Str KD and No. 1 Dense KD	Dense Sel Str and Sel Str KD	Sel Str	No. 1 Dense	No. 1 KD	No. 2 Dense KD	No. 1	No. 2 Dense	No. 2 KD	No. 2	No. 3 Dense KD	No. 3 Dense	No. 3 KD	No. 3
	12.0	9-3	9-1	8-11	9-1	9-1	8-11	8-11	8-9	8-8	8-4	7-1	6-11	6-7	6-4
	13.7	8-11	8-9	8-7	8-9	8-9	8-7	8-7	8-5	8-1	7-10	6-8	6-6	6-2	5-11
2 x 5	16.0	8-5	8-3	8-2	8-3	8-3	8-2	7-11	7-10	7-6	7-3	6-2	6-0	5-9	5-6
	19.2	7-11	7-10	7-8	7-10	7-7	7-6	7-3	7-1	6-10	6-7	5-8	5-6	5-3	5-0
	24.0	7-4[1]	7-3	7-1	7-0	6-10	6-8	6-6	6-4	6-2	5-11	5-0	4-11	4-8	4-6
	12.0	11-4	11-2	10-11	11-2	11-2	10-11	10-11	10-9	10-7	10-2	8-8	8-5	8-1	7-9
	13.7	10-10	10-8	10-6	10-8	10-8	10-6	10-6	10-3	9-11	9-6	8-2	7-11	7-6	7-3
2 x 6	16.0	10-4	10-2	9-11	10-2	10-2	9-11	9-8	9-6	9-2	8-10	7-6	7-4	7-0	6-9
	19.2	9-8	9-6	9-4	9-6	9-4	9-2	8-10	8-8	8-5	8-1	6-11	6-8	6-4	6-2
	24.0	9-0[1]	8-10	8-8	8-7	8-4	8-2	7-11	7-9	7-6	7-2	6-2	6-0	5-8	5-6
	12.0	15-0	14-8	14-5	14-8	14-8	14-5	14-5	14-2	14-0	13-5	11-6	11-2	10-7	10-3
	13.7	14-4	14-1	13-10	14-1	14-1	13-10	13-10	13-6	13-1	12-7	10-9	10-5	9-11	9-7
2 x 8	16.0	13-7	13-4	13-1	13-4	13-4	13-1	12-9	12-7	12-1	11-8	9-11	9-8	9-2	8-11
	19.2	12-10	12-7	12-4	12-7	12-3	12-1	11-8	11-6	11-1	10-7	9-1	8-10	8-5	8-1
	24.0	11-11[1]	11-8	11-5	11-4	11-0	10-10	10-5	10-3	9-11	9-6	8-1	7-11	7-6	7-3
	12.0	19-1	18-9	18-5	18-9	18-9	18-5	18-5	18-0	17-10	17-2	14-8	14-3	13-7	13-1
	13.7	18-3	17-11	17-7	17-11	17-11	17-7	17-7	17-3	16-8	16-0	13-8	13-4	12-8	12-3
2 x 10	16.0	17-4	17-0	16-9	17-0	17-0	16-9	16-4	16-0	15-5	14-10	12-8	12-4	11-9	11-4
	19.2	16-4	16-0	15-9	16-0	15-8	15-5	14-11	14-8	14-1	13-7	11-7	11-3	10-9	10-4
	24.0	15-2[1]	14-11	14-7	14-5	14-0	13-9	13-4	13-1	12-7	12-1	10-4	10-1	9-7	9-3
	12.0	23-3	22-10	22-5	22-10	22-10	22-5	22-5	21-11	21-8	20-10	17-10	17-3	16-6	15-11
	13.7	22-3	21-10	21-5	21-10	21-10	21-5	21-5	21-0	20-4	19-6	16-8	16-2	15-5	14-11
2 x 12	16.0	21-1	20-9	20-4	20-9	20-9	20-4	19-10	19-6	18-9	18-1	15-5	15-0	14-3	13-9
	19.2	19-10	19-6	19-2	19-6	19-0	18-9	18-1	17-10	17-2	16-6	14-1	13-8	13-0	12-7
	24.0	18-5[1]	18-1	17-9	17-7	17-0	16-9	16-2	15-11	15-4	14-9	12-7	12-3	11-8	11-3

1. The span for No. 1 Dense KD, 24 inches o.c. is: 2x5, 7-4; 2x6, 8-11; 2x8, 11-10; 2x10, 15-1; 2x12, 18-4.

17

ts technical support

TABLE NO. 7. CEILING JOISTS—Drywall Ceiling—10 psf live load. No future sleeping rooms and no attic storage, roof slopes 3 in 12 or less. (Spans shown in light face type are based on a deflection limitation of $l/240$. Spans shown in color, bold face type are limited by the recommended extreme fiber stress in bending value of the grade and includes a 5 psf dead load.)

Size and Spacing in.	Grade in. o.c.	Dense Sel Str KD and No. 1 Dense KD	Dense Sel Str, Sel Str KD, No. 1 Dense and No. 1 KD	Sel Str, No. 1 and No. 2 Dense KD	No. 2 Dense, No. 2 KD and No. 2	No. 3 Dense KD	No. 3 Dense	No. 3 KD	No. 3	Construction KD	Construction	Standard KD	Standard
2 x 4	12.0	13-2	12-11	12-8	12-5	12-2	12-0	11-6	11-0	12-2	11-10	9-11	9-6
	13.7	12-7	12-4	12-1	11-10	11-7	11-3	10-9	10-4	11-7	11-4	9-3	8-11
	16.0	11-11	11-9	11-6	11-3	10-10	10-5	10-0	9-6	11-0	10-9	8-7	8-3
	19.2	11-3	11-0	10-10	10-7	9-11	9-6	9-1	8-8	10-4	9-11	7-10	7-6
	24.0	10-5	10-3	10-0	9-10	8-10	8-6	8-2	7-9	9-3	8-10	7-0	6-9
2 x 5	12.0	16-11	16-7	16-3	15-11	15-1	14-7	13-11	13-5				
	13.7	16-2	15-10	15-7	15-3	14-1	13-8	13-0	12-7				
	16.0	15-4	15-1	14-9	14-6	13-0	12-8	12-1	11-8				
	19.2	14-5	14-2	13-11	13-8	11-11	11-7	11-0	10-8				
	24.0	13-5	13-2	12-11	12-8[1]	10-8	10-4	9-10	9-6				
2 x 6	12.0	20-8	20-3	19-11	19-6	18-5	17-10	17-0	16-5				
	13.7	19-9	19-5	19-0	18-8	17-2	16-8	15-11	15-5				
	16.0	18-9	18-5	18-1	17-8	15-11	15-6	14-9	14-3				
	19.2	17-8	17-4	17-0	16-8	14-6	14-1	13-6	13-0				
	24.0	16-4	16-1	15-9	15-6[1]	13-0	12-8	12-0	11-8				
2 x 8	12.0	27-2	26-9	26-2	25-8	24-3	23-6	22-5	21-8				
	13.7	26-0	25-7	25-1	24-7	22-8	22-0	21-0	20-3				
	16.0	24-8	24-3	23-10	23-4	21-0	20-5	19-5	18-9				
	19.2	23-3	22-10	22-5	21-11	19-2	18-7	17-9	17-2				
	24.0	21-7	21-2	20-10	20-5[1]	17-2	16-8	15-10	15-4				
2 x 10	12.0	34-8	34-1	33-5	32-9	30-11	30-0	28-8	27-8				
	13.7	33-2	32-7	32-0	31-4	28-11	28-1	26-9	25-11				
	16.0	31-6	31-0	30-5	29-9	26-9	26-0	24-10	23-11				
	19.2	29-8	29-2	28-7	28-0	24-5	23-9	22-8	21-10				
	24.0	27-6	27-1	26-6	26-0[1]	21-10	21-3	20-3	19-7				

1. The span for No. 2 grade, 24 inches o.c. spacing is: 2x5, 12-6; 2x6, 15-3; 2x8, 20-1; 2x10, 25-7.

TABLE NO. 8. CEILING JOISTS—Drywall Ceiling—20 psf live load. No future sleeping rooms but limited storage available. (Spans shown in light face type are based on a deflection limitation of l/240. Spans shown in a color, bold face type are limited by the recommended extreme fiber stress in bending value of the grade and includes a 10 psf dead load.)

Size and Spacing in.	Grade in. o.c.	Dense Sel Str KD and No. 1 Dense KD	Dense Sel Str, Sel Str KD, No. 1 Dense and No. 1 KD	Sel Str, No. 1 and No. 2 Dense KD	No. 2 Dense	No. 2 KD	No. 2	No. 3 Dense KD	No. 3 Dense	No. 3 KD	No. 3	Construction KD	Construction	Standard KD	Standard
2 x 4	12.0	10-5	10-3	10-0	9-10	9-10	9-10	8-10	8-6	8-2	7-9	9-3	8-10	7-0	6-9
	13.7	10-0	9-9	9-7	9-5	9-5	9-5	8-3	8-0	7-8	7-3	8-8	8-3	6-7	6-3
	16.0	9-6	9-4	9-1	8-11	8-11	8-11	7-8	7-4	7-1	6-9	8-0	7-8	6-1	5-10
	19.2	8-11	8-9	8-7	8-5	8-5	8-3	7-0	6-9	6-5	6-2	7-4	7-0	5-6	5-4
	24.0	8-3	8-1	8-0	7-10	7-9	7-5	6-3	6-0	5-9	5-6	6-7	6-3	4-11	4-9
2 x 5	12.0	13-5	13-2	12-11	12-8	12-8	12-6	10-8	10-4	9-10	9-6				
	13.7	12-10	12-7	12-4	12-1	12-1	11-8	9-11	9-8	9-3	8-11				
	16.0	12-2	11-11	11-9	11-6	11-3	10-9	9-3	8-11	8-6	8-3				
	19.2	11-5	11-3	11-0[2]	10-8	10-3	9-10	8-5	8-2	7-9	7-6				
	24.0	10-8	10-5[1]	10-3[2,3]	9-6	9-2	8-10	7-6	7-4	7-0	6-9				
2 x 6	12.0	16-4	16-1	15-9	15-6	15-6	15-3	13-0	12-8	12-0	11-8				
	13.7	15-8	15-5	15-1	14-9	14-9	14-3	12-2	11-10	11-3	10-11				
	16.0	14-11	14-7	14-4	14-1	13-9	13-2	11-3	10-11	10-5	10-1				
	19.2	14-0	13-9	13-6[2]	13-0	12-6	12-0	10-3	10-0	9-6	9-2				
	24.0	13-0	12-9[1]	12-6[2,3]	11-8	11-2	10-9	9-2	8-11	8-6	8-3				
2 x 8	12.0	21-7	21-2	20-10	20-5	20-5	20-1	17-2	16-8	15-10	15-4				
	13.7	20-8	20-3	19-11	19-6	19-6	18-9	16-0	15-7	14-10	14-4				
	16.0	19-7	19-3	18-11	18-6	18-1	17-5	14-10	14-5	13-9	13-3				
	19.2	18-5	18-2	17-9[2]	17-2	16-6	15-10	13-7	13-2	12-7	12-1				
	24.0	17-2	16-10[1]	16-6[2,3]	15-4	14-9	14-2	12-1	11-9	11-3	10-10				
2 x 10	12.0	27-6	27-1	26-6	26-0	26-0	25-7	21-10	21-3	20-3	19-7				
	13.7	26-4	25-10	25-5	24-11	24-11	24-0	20-6	19-10	18-11	18-4				
	16.0	25-0	24-7	24-1	23-8	23-1	22-2	18-11	18-5	17-6	16-11				
	19.2	23-7	23-2	22-8[2]	21-10	21-1	20-3	17-3	16-9	16-0	15-6				
	24.0	21-10	21-6[1]	21-11[2,3]	19-7	18-11	18-1	15-6	15-0	14-4	13-10				

1. The span for No. 1 KD grade, 24 inches o.c. is:
2x5, 10-2; 2x6, 12-5; 2x8, 16-5; 2x10, 20-11.

2. The span for No. 1 grade is:
2x5, 19.2 o.c., 10-10; 24 o.c., 9-8; 2x6, 19.2 o.c., 13-3; 24 o.c., 11-10;
2x8, 19.2 o.c., 17-5; 2x10, 19.2 o.c., 22-3; 24 o.c., 19-11.

3. The span for No. 2 Dense KD grade, 24 inches o.c. is:
2x5, 10-0; 2x6, 12-3; 2x8, 16-2; 2x10, 20-7.

TABLE NO. 9. RAFTERS—Any Slope—With Drywall Ceiling—20 psf live load. (Spans shown in light face type are based on a deflection limitation of l/240. Spans shown in color, bold face type are limited by the recommended extreme fiber stress in bending value of the grade and includes 15 psf dead load.)

Size and Spacing in in. o.c.		Dense Sel Str KD	No. 1 Dense KD	Dense Sel Str and Sel Str KD	No. 1 Dense	Sel Str	No. 1 KD	No. 2 Dense KD	No. 1	No. 2 Dense	No. 2 KD	No. 2	No. 3 Dense KD	No. 3 Dense	No. 3 KD	No. 3
2 x 5	12.0	13-5	13-15	13-2	13-2	12-11	13-2	12-11	12-8	12-6	12-0	11-6	9-10	9-7	9-1	8-10
	13.7	12-10	12-10	12-7	12-7	12-4	12-6	12-3	11-10	11-8	11-3	10-10	9-3	8-11	8-6	8-3
	16.0	12-2	12-2	11-11	11-11	11-9	11-6	11-4	11-0	10-9	10-5	10-0	8-6	8-3	7-11	7-8
	19.2	11-5	11-4	11-3	11-3	11-0	10-6	10-4	10-0	9-10	9-6	9-1	7-9	7-7	7-3	7-0
	24.0	10-8	10-2	10-5¹	9-9	9-10	9-5	9-3	9-0	8-10	8-6	8-2	7-0	6-9	6-5	6-3
2 x 6	12.0	16-4	16-4	16-1	16-1	15-9	16-1	15-9	15-6	15-3	14-8	14-1	12-0	11-8	11-2	10-9
	13.7	15-8	15-8	15-5	15-5	15-1	15-3	15-0	14-6	14-3	13-9	13-2	11-3	10-11	10-5	10-1
	16.0	14-11	14-11	14-7	14-6	14-4	14-1	13-11	13-5	13-2	12-9	12-3	10-5	10-1	9-8	9-4
	19.2	14-0	13-10	13-9	13-3	13-6	12-10	12-8	12-3	12-0	11-7	11-2	9-6	9-3	8-10	8-6
	24.0	13-0	12-5	12-9¹	11-10	12-0	11-6	11-4	11-0	10-9	10-5	10-0	8-6	8-3	7-11	7-7
2 x 8	12.0	21-7	21-7	21-2	21-2	20-10	21-2	20-10	20-5	20-1	19-4	18-7	15-10	15-5	14-8	14-2
	13.7	20-8	20-8	20-3	20-3	19-11	20-1	19-9	19-1	18-9	18-1	17-5	14-10	14-5	13-9	13-3
	16.0	19-7	19-7	19-3	19-2	18-11	18-7	18-4	17-8	17-5	16-9	16-1	13-9	13-4	12-9	12-4
	19.2	18-5	18-3	18-2	17-6	17-9	17-0	16-8	16-2	15-10	15-4	14-8	12-7	12-2	11-7	11-3
	24.0	17-2	16-4	16-10¹	15-8	15-10	15-2	14-11	14-5	14-2	13-8	13-2	11-3	10-11	10-5	10-0
2 x 10	12.0	27-6	27-6	27-1	27-1	26-6	27-1	26-6	26-1	25-7	24-8	23-9	20-3	19-8	18-9	18-1
	13.7	26-4	26-4	25-10	25-10	25-5	25-7	25-3	24-5	24-0	23-1	22-2	18-11	18-5	17-6	16-11
	16.0	25-0	25-0	24-7	24-5	24-1	23-9	23-4	22-7	22-2	21-4	20-6	17-6	17-0	16-3	15-8
	19.2	23-7	23-3	23-2	22-4	22-8	21-8	21-4	20-7	20-3	19-6	18-9	16-0	15-7	14-10	14-4
	24.0	21-10	20-10	21-6¹	19-11	20-3	19-4	19-1	18-5	18-1	17-5	16-9	14-4	13-11	13-3	12-10
2 x 12	12.0	33-6	33-6	32-11	32-11	32-3	32-11	32-3	31-8	31-2	30-0	28-10	24-8	23-11	22-10	22-0
	13.7	32-0	32-0	31-6	31-6	30-10	31-2	30-8	29-8	29-2	28-1	27-0	23-0	22-4	21-4	20-7
	16.0	30-5	30-5	29-11	29-9	29-4	28-10	28-5	27-5	27-0	26-0	25-0	21-4	20-9	19-9	19-1
	19.2	28-8	28-4	28-2	27-2	27-6	26-4	25-11	25-1	24-8	23-9	22-10	19-6	18-11	18-0	17-5
	24.0	26-7	25-4	26-1¹	24-3	24-8	23-7	23-2	22-5	22-0	21-3	20-5	17-5	16-11	16-1	15-7

1. The span for Select Structural KD, 24 inches o.c. spacing is: 2x5, 10-2; 2x6, 12-5; 2x8, 16-4; 2x10, 20-10; 2x12, 25-4.

ts technical support

TABLE NO. 10. RAFTERS—Any Slope—With Drywall Ceiling—30 psf live load. (Spans shown in light face type are based on a deflection limitation of $l/240$. Spans shown in color, bold face type are limited by the recommended fiber stress in bending value of the grade and includes a 15 psf dead load.)

Size and Spacing / Grade (in. o.c.)	Dense Sel Str KD	No. 1 Dense KD	Dense Sel Str and Sel Str KD	No. 1 Dense	Sel Str	No. 1 KD	No. 2 Dense KD	No. 1	No. 2 Dense	No. 2 KD	No. 2	No. 3 Dense KD	No. 3 Dense	No. 3 KD	No. 3
2 x 5 12.0	11-8	11-8	11-6	11-6	11-3	11-6	11-3	11-2	11-0	10-7	10-2	8-8	8-5	8-1	7-9
13.7	11-2	11-2	11-0	11-0	10-9	11-0	10-9	10-6	10-3	9-11	9-6	8-2	7-11	7-6	7-3
16.0	10-8	10-8	10-5	10-5	10-3	10-2	10-0	9-8	9-6	9-2	8-10	7-6	7-4	7-0	6-9
19.2	10-0	10-0	9-10	9-7	9-8	9-3	9-2	8-10	8-8	8-4	8-1	6-10	6-8	6-4	6-2
24.0	9-3	8-11	9-1¹	8-7	8-8	8-4	8-2	7-11	7-9	7-6	7-2	6-2	6-0	5-8	5-6
2 x 6 12.0	14-4	14-4	14-1	14-1	13-9	14-1	13-9	13-8	13-5	12-11	12-5	10-7	10-4	9-10	9-6
13.7	13-8	13-8	13-5	13-5	13-2	13-5	13-2	12-9	12-7	12-1	11-8	9-11	9-8	9-2	8-11
16.0	13-0	13-0	12-9	12-9	12-6	12-5	12-3	11-10	11-8	11-2	10-9	9-2	8-11	8-6	8-3
19.2	12-3	12-2	12-0	11-8	11-9	11-4	11-2	10-10	10-7	10-3	9-10	8-5	8-2	7-9	7-6
24.0	11-4	10-11	11-2¹	10-6	10-7	10-2	10-0	9-8	9-6	9-2	8-10	7-6	7-3	6-11	6-9
2 x 8 12.0	18-10	18-10	18-6	18-6	18-2	18-6	18-2	18-0	17-8	17-1	16-5	14-0	13-7	12-11	12-6
13.7	18-0	18-0	17-9	17-9	17-5	17-8	17-5	16-10	16-7	16-0	15-4	13-1	12-9	12-1	11-9
16.0	17-2	17-2	16-10	16-10	16-6	16-5	16-2	15-7	15-4	14-9	14-2	12-1	11-9	11-3	10-10
19.2	16-1	16-1	15-10	15-5	15-6	15-0	14-9	14-3	14-0	13-6	12-11	11-1	10-9	10-3	9-11
24.0	15-0	14-5	14-8¹	13-10	14-0	13-5	13-2	12-9	12-6	12-1	11-7	9-11	9-7	9-2	8-10
2 x 10 12.0	24-1	24-1	23-8	23-8	23-2	23-8	23-2	23-0	22-7	21-9	20-11	17-10	17-4	16-6	16-0
13.7	23-0	23-0	22-7	22-7	22-2	22-7	22-2	21-6	21-2	20-4	19-7	16-8	16-3	15-6	14-11
16.0	21-10	21-10	21-6	21-6	21-1	20-11	20-7	19-11	19-7	18-10	18-1	15-6	15-0	14-4	13-10
19.2	20-7	20-6	20-2	19-8	19-10	19-1	18-9	18-2	17-10	17-2	16-6	14-1	13-8	13-1	12-8
24.0	19-1	18-4	18-9¹	17-7	17-10	17-1	16-10	16-3	16-0	15-5	14-9	12-8	12-3	11-8	11-4
2 x 12 12.0	29-3	29-3	28-9	28-9	28-2	28-9	28-2	27-11	27-6	26-6	25-5	21-9	21-1	20-1	19-5
13.7	28-0	28-0	27-6	27-6	27-0	27-6	27-0	26-2	25-8	24-9	23-10	20-4	19-9	18-10	18-2
16.0	26-7	26-7	26-1	26-1	25-7	25-5	25-0	24-3	23-9	22-11	22-0	18-10	18-3	17-5	16-10
19.2	25-0	25-0	24-7	23-11	24-1	23-3	22-10	22-1	21-9	20-11	20-1	17-2	16-8	15-11	15-4
24.0	23-3	22-4	22-10¹	21-5	21-9	20-9	20-5	19-9	19-5	18-9	18-0	15-4	14-11	14-3	13-9

1. The span for Select Structural KD, 24 inches .o.c. spacing is: 2x5, 8-11; 2x6, 10-11; 2x8, 14-5; 2x10, 18-4; 2x12, 22-4.

21

TABLE NO. 11. RAFTERS—Any Slope—With Drywall Ceiling—40 psf live load. (Spans shown in light face type are based on a deflection limitation of l/240. Spans shown in color, bold face type are limited by the recommended fiber stress in bending value of the grade and includes a 15 psf dead load.)

Size and Spacing in. in o.c.	Dense Sel Str KD	No. 1 Dense KD	Dense Sel Str and Sel Str KD	No. 1 Dense	Sel Str	No. 1 KD	No. 2 Dense KD	No. 1	No. 2 Dense	No. 2 KD	No. 2	No. 3 Dense KD	No. 3 Dense	No. 3 KD	No. 3
2 x 5 12.0	10-8	10-8	10-5	10-5	10-3	10-5	10-3	10-1	9-11	9-7	9-2	7-10	7-8	7-3	7-0
13.7	10-2	10-2	10-0	10-0	9-10	9-11	9-9	9-6	9-4	9-0	8-7	7-4	7-2	6-10	6-7
16.0	9-8	9-8	9-6	9-6	9-4	9-2	9-1	8-9	8-7	8-4	8-0	6-10	6-7	6-4	6-1
19.2	9-1	9-0	8-11	8-8	8-9	8-5	8-3	8-0	7-10	7-7	7-3	6-3	6-0	5-9	5-7
24.0	8-5	8-1	8-3¹	7-9	7-10	7-6	7-5	7-2	7-0	6-9	6-6	5-7	5-5	5-2	5-0
2 x 6 12.0	13-0	13-0	12-9	12-9	12-6	12-9	12-6	12-4	12-2	11-8	11-3	9-7	9-4	8-11	8-7
13.7	12-5	12-5	12-3	12-3	12-0	12-2	12-0	11-7	11-4	10-11	10-6	9-0	8-9	8-4	8-0
16.0	11-10	11-10	11-7	11-7	11-5	11-3	11-1	10-8	10-6	10-2	9-9	8-4	8-1	7-8	7-5
19.2	11-1	11-0	10-11	10-7	10-8	10-3	10-1	9-9	9-7	9-3	8-11	7-7	7-4	7-0	6-9
24.0	10-4	9-10	10-2¹	9-6	9-7	9-2	9-0	8-9	8-7	8-3	7-11	6-9	6-7	6-3	6-1
2 x 8 12.0	17-2	17-2	16-10	16-10	16-6	16-10	16-6	16-4	16-0	15-5	14-10	12-8	12-4	11-9	11-4
13.7	16-5	16-5	16-1	16-1	15-9	16-0	15-9	15-3	15-0	14-5	13-10	11-10	11-6	11-0	10-7
16.0	15-7	15-7	15-3	15-3	15-0	14-10	14-7	14-1	13-10	13-4	12-10	11-0	10-8	10-2	9-10
19.2	14-8	14-7	14-5	13-11	14-1	13-6	13-4	12-11	12-8	12-2	11-9	10-0	9-9	9-3	8-11
24.0	13-7	13-0	13-4¹	12-6	12-8	12-1	11-11	11-6	11-4	10-11	10-6	8-11	8-8	8-3	8-0
2 x 10 12.0	21-10	21-10	21-6	21-6	21-1	21-6	21-1	20-10	20-5	19-8	18-11	16-2	15-8	14-11	14-5
13.7	20-11	20-11	20-6	20-6	20-2	20-5	20-1	19-5	19-1	18-5	17-8	15-1	14-8	14-0	13-6
16.0	19-10	19-10	19-6	19-6	19-2	18-11	18-7	18-0	17-8	17-1	16-5	14-0	13-7	12-11	12-6
19.2	18-8	18-7	18-4	17-10	18-0	17-3	17-0	16-5	16-2	15-7	14-11	12-9	12-5	11-10	11-5
24.0	17-4	16-7	16-7¹	15-11	16-2	15-5	15-2	14-8	14-5	13-11	13-5	11-5	11-1	10-7	10-3
2 x 12 12.0	26-7	26-7	26-1	26-1	25-7	26-1	25-7	25-3	24-10	23-11	23-0	19-8	19-1	18-2	17-7
13.7	25-5	25-5	25-0	25-0	24-6	24-10	24-6	23-8	23-3	22-5	21-6	18-5	17-10	17-0	16-5
16.0	24-2	24-2	23-9	23-9	23-3	23-0	22-8	21-11	21-6	20-9	19-11	17-0	16-6	15-9	15-3
19.2	22-9	22-7	22-4	21-8	21-11	21-0	20-8	20-0	19-8	18-11	18-2	15-6	15-1	14-5	13-11
24.0	21-1	20-2	20-9¹	19-4	19-8	18-9	18-6	17-11	17-7	16-11	16-3	13-11	13-6	12-10	12-5

1. The span for Select Structural KD, 24 inches o.c. spacing is: 2x5, 8-1; 2x6, 9-10; 2x8, 13-0; 2x10, 16-2; 2x12, 20-2.

TABLE NO. 12. RAFTERS—Low Slope (3 in 12 or less)—With No Finished Ceiling—20 psf live load. (Spans shown in light face type are based on a deflection limitation of _l_/240. Spans shown in color, bold face type are limited by the recommended extreme fiber stress in bending value of the grade and includes a 10 psf dead load.)

Size and Spacing in.	Grade in. o.c.	Dense Sel Str KD and No. 1 Dense KD	Dense Sel Str, Sel Str KD, No. 1 Dense and No. 1 KD	Sel Str, No. 2 Dense KD	No. 1	No. 2 Dense	No. 2 KD	No. 2	No. 3 Dense KD	No. 3 Dense	No. 3 KD	No. 3
2 x 5	12.0	13-5	13-2	12-11	12-11	12-8	12-8	12-6	10-8	10-4	9-10	9-6
	13.7	12-10	12-7	12-4	12-4	12-1	12-1	11-8	9-11	9-8	9-3	8-11
	16.0	12-2	11-11	11-9	11-9	11-6	11-3	10-9	9-3	8-11	8-6	8-3
	19.2	11-5	11-3	11-0	10-10	10-8	10-3	9-10	8-5	8-2	7-9	7-6
	24.0	10-8	10-5[1]	10-3[2]	9-8	9-6	9-2	8-10	7-6	7-4	7-0	6-9
2 x 6	12.0	16-4	16-1	15-9	15-9	15-6	15-6	15-3	13-0	12-8	12-0	11-8
	13.7	15-8	15-5	15-1	15-1	14-9	14-9	14-3	12-2	11-10	11-3	10-11
	16.0	14-11	14-7	14-4	14-4	14-1	13-9	13-2	11-3	10-11	10-5	10-1
	19.2	14-0	13-9	13-6	13-3	13-0	12-6	12-0	10-3	10-0	9-6	9-2
	24.0	13-0	12-9[1]	12-6[2]	11-10	11-8	11-2	10-9	9-2	8-11	8-6	8-3
2 x 8	12.0	21-7	21-2	20-10	20-10	20-5	20-5	20-1	17-2	16-8	15-10	15-4
	13.7	20-8	20-3	19-11	19-11	19-6	19-6	18-9	16-0	15-7	14-10	14-4
	16.0	19-7	19-3	18-11	18-11	18-6	18-1	17-5	14-10	14-5	13-9	13-3
	19.2	18-5	18-2	17-9	17-5	17-2	16-6	15-10	13-7	13-2	12-7	12-1
	24.0	17-2	16-10[1]	16-6[2]	15-7	15-4	14-9	14-2	12-1	11-9	11-3	10-10
2 x 10	12.0	27-6	27-1	26-6	26-6	26-0	26-0	25-7	21-10	21-3	20-3	19-7
	13.7	26-4	25-10	25-5	25-5	24-11	24-11	24-0	20-6	19-10	18-11	18-4
	16.0	25-0	24-7	24-1	24-1	23-8	23-1	22-2	18-11	18-5	17-6	16-11
	19.2	23-7	23-2	22-8	22-3	21-10	21-1	20-3	17-3	16-9	16-0	15-6
	24.0	21-10	21-6[1]	21-1[2]	19-11	19-7	18-10	18-1	15-6	15-0	14-4	13-10
2 x 12	12.0	33-6	32-11	32-3	32-3	31-8	31-8	31-2	26-7	25-10	24-8	23-9
	13.7	32-0	31-6	30-10	30-10	30-3	30-3	29-2	24-11	24-2	23-0	22-3
	16.0	30-5	29-11	29-4	29-4	28-9	28-1	27-0	23-0	22-4	21-4	20-7
	19.2	28-8	28-2	27-7	27-1	26-7	25-8	24-8	21-0	20-5	19-6	18-10
	24.0	26-7	26-1[1]	25-7[2]	24-3	23-9	22-11	22-0	18-10	18-3	17-5	16-10

1. The span for No. 1 KD, 24 inches o.c. is:
2x5, 10-2; 2x6, 12-5; 2x8, 16-5; 2x10, 20-11; 2x12, 25-5.

2. The span for No. 2 Dense KD, 24 inches o.c. is:
2x5, 10-0; 2x6, 12-3; 2x8, 16-2; 2x10, 20-7; 2x12, 25-0.

23

TABLE NO. 13. RAFTERS—Low Slope (3 in 12 or less)—With No Finished Ceiling—30 psf live load. (Spans shown in light face type are based on a deflection limitation of $l/240$. Spans shown in color, bold face type are limited by the recommended extreme fiber stress in bending value of the grade and includes a 10 psf dead load.)

Size and Spacing in.	Grade in. o.c.	Dense Sel Str KD and No. 1 Dense KD	Dense Sel Str and Sel Str KD	No. 1 Dense and No. 1 KD	Sel Str	No. 2 Dense KD	No. 1	No. 2 Dense	No. 2 KD	No. 2	No. 3 Dense KD	No. 3 Dense	No. 3 KD	No. 3
2 x 5	12.0	11-8	11-6	11-6	11-13	11-3	11-3	11-1	11-1	10-9	9-3	8-11	8-6	8-3
	13.7	11-2	11-0	11-0	10-9	10-9	10-9	10-7	10-6	10-1	8-7	8-4	8-0	7-9
	16.0	10-8	10-5	10-5	10-3	10-3	10-3	10-0	9-9	9-4	8-0	7-9	7-5	7-2
	19.2	10-0	9-10	9-10	9-8	9-8	9-5	9-3	8-11	8-6	7-3	7-1	6-9	6-6
	24.0	9-3	9-1	9-1¹	8-11	8-8	8-5	8-3	7-11	7-8	6-6	6-4	6-0	5-10
2 x 6	12.0	14-4	14-1	14-1	13-9	13-9	13-9	13-6	13-6	13-2	11-3	10-11	10-5	10-1
	13.7	13-8	13-5	13-5	13-2	13-2	13-2	12-11	12-10	12-4	10-6	10-3	9-9	9-5
	16.0	13-0	12-9	12-9	12-6	12-6	12-6	12-3	11-11	11-5	9-9	9-6	9-0	8-9
	19.2	12-3	12-0	12-0	11-9	11-9	11-6	11-3	10-10	10-5	8-11	8-8	8-3	8-0
	24.0	11-4	11-2	11-1¹	10-11	10-7	10-3	10-1	9-8	9-4	8-0	7-9	7-4	7-1
2 x 8	12.0	18-10	18-6	18-6	18-2	18-2	18-2	17-10	17-10	17-5	14-10	14-5	13-9	13-3
	13.7	18-0	17-9	17-9	17-5	17-5	17-5	17-0	16-11	16-3	13-11	13-6	12-10	12-5
	16.0	17-2	16-10	16-10	16-6	16-6	16-6	16-2	15-8	15-1	12-10	12-6	11-11	11-6
	19.2	16-1	15-10	15-10	15-6	15-6	15-1	14-10	14-4	13-9	11-9	11-5	10-10	10-6
	24.0	15-0	14-8	14-8¹	14-5	14-0	13-6	13-3	12-10	12-4	10-6	10-2	9-9	9-5
2 x 10	12.0	24-1	23-8	23-8	23-2	23-2	23-2	22-9	22-9	22-2	18-11	18-5	17-6	16-11
	13.7	23-0	22-7	22-7	22-2	22-2	22-2	21-9	21-7	20-9	17-9	17-2	16-5	15-10
	16.0	21-10	21-6	21-6	21-1	21-1	21-1	20-8	20-0	19-3	16-5	15-11	15-2	14-8
	19.2	20-7	20-2	20-2	19-10	19-10	19-3	18-11	18-3	17-6	15-0	14-6	13-10	13-5
	24.0	19-1	18-9	18-8¹	18-5	17-10	17-3	16-11	16-4	15-8	13-5	13-0	12-5	12-0
2 x 12	12.0	29-3	28-9	28-9	28-2	28-2	28-2	27-8	27-8	27-0	23-0	22-4	21-4	20-7
	13.7	28-0	27-6	27-6	27-0	27-0	27-0	26-5	26-3	25-3	21-7	20-11	19-11	19-3
	16.0	26-7	26-1	26-1	25-7	25-7	25-7	25-1	24-4	23-4	19-11	19-4	18-6	17-10
	19.2	25-0	24-7	24-7	24-1	24-1	23-5	23-0	22-2	21-4	18-3	17-8	16-10	16-3
	24.0	23-3	22-10	22-8¹	22-5	21-8	21-0	20-7	19-10	19-1	16-3	15-10	15-1	14-7

1. The span for No. 1 KD, 24 inches o.c. is:
2x5, 8-10; 2x6, 10-9; 2x8, 14-2; 2x10, 18-1; 2x12, 22-0.

TABLE NO. 14. RAFTERS—Low Slope (3 in 12 or less)—With No Finished Ceiling—40 psf live load. (Spans shown in light face type are based on a deflection limitation of l/240. Spans shown in color, bold face type are limited by the recommended extreme fiber stress in bending value of the grade and includes a 10 psf dead load.)

Size and Spacing in.	Grade Spacing in. o.c.	Dense Sel Str KD and No. 1 Dense KD	Dense Sel Str and Sel Str KD	No. 1 Dense	No. 1 KD	Sel Str	No. 2 Dense KD	No. 1	No. 2 Dense	No. 2 KD	No. 2	No. 3 Dense KD	No. 3 Dense	No. 3 KD	No. 3
2 x 5	12.0	10-8	10-5	10-5	10-5	10-3	10-3	10-3	10-0	10-0	9-8	8-3	8-0	7-8	7-4
	13.7	10-2	10-0	10-0	10-0	9-10	9-10	9-10	9-7	9-5	9-0	7-9	7-6	7-2	6-11
	16.0	9-8	9-6	9-6	9-6	9-4	9-4	9-2	9-0	8-8	8-4	7-2	6-11	6-7	6-5
	19.2	9-1	8-11	8-11	8-10	8-9	8-8	8-5	8-3	7-11	7-8	6-6	6-4	6-0	5-10
	24.0	8-5	8-3	8-1	7-11	8-2	7-9	7-6	7-4	7-1	6-10	5-10	5-8	5-5	5-3
2 x 6	12.0	13-0	12-9	12-9	12-9	12-6	12-6	12-6	12-3	12-3	11-10	10-1	9-9	9-4	9-0
	13.7	12-5	12-3	12-3	12-3	12-0	12-0	12-0	11-9	11-6	11-0	9-5	9-2	8-9	8-5
	16.0	11-10	11-7	11-7	11-7	11-5	11-5	11-3	11-0	10-8	10-3	8-9	8-6	8-1	7-10
	19.2	11-1	10-11	10-11	10-9	10-8	10-7	10-3	10-1	9-8	9-4	8-0	7-9	7-4	7-1
	24.0	10-4	10-2	9-11	9-8	9-11	9-6	9-6	9-0	8-8	8-4	7-1	6-11	6-7	6-4
2 x 8	12.0	17-2	16-10	16-10	16-10	16-6	16-6	16-6	16-2	16-2	15-7	13-3	12-11	12-4	11-11
	13.7	16-5	16-1	16-1	16-1	15-9	15-9	15-9	15-6	15-2	14-7	12-5	12-1	11-6	11-1
	16.0	15-7	15-3	15-3	15-3	15-0	15-0	14-10	14-7	14-0	13-6	11-6	11-2	10-8	10-3
	19.2	14-8	14-5	14-5	14-2	14-1	14-0	13-6	13-3	12-10	12-4	10-6	10-2	9-9	9-5
	24.0	13-7	13-4	13-1	12-8	13-1	12-6	12-1	11-11	11-5	11-0	9-5	9-1	8-8	8-5
2 x 10	12.0	21-10	21-6	21-6	21-6	21-1	21-1	21-1	20-8	20-8	19-10	16-11	16-5	15-8	15-2
	13.7	20-11	20-6	20-6	20-6	20-2	20-2	20-2	19-9	19-4	18-7	15-10	15-5	14-8	14-2
	16.0	19-10	19-6	19-6	19-6	19-2	19-2	18-11	18-7	17-11	17-2	14-8	14-3	13-7	13-1
	19.2	18-8	18-4	18-4	18-1	18-0	17-10	17-3	16-11	16-4	15-8	13-5	13-0	12-5	12-0
	24.0	17-4	17-0	16-8	16-2	16-9	15-11	15-5	15-2	14-7	14-0	12-0	11-8	11-1	10-9
2 x 12	12.0	26-7	26-1	26-1	26-1	25-7	25-7	25-7	25-1	25-1	24-2	20-7	20-0	19-1	18-5
	13.7	25-5	25-0	25-0	25-0	24-6	24-6	24-6	24-0	23-6	22-7	19-3	18-9	17-10	17-3
	16.0	24-2	23-9	23-9	23-9	23-3	23-3	23-0	22-7	21-9	20-11	17-10	17-4	16-6	16-0
	19.2	22-9	22-4	22-4	22-0	21-11	21-8	21-0	20-7	19-10	19-1	16-3	15-10	15-1	14-7
	24.0	21-1	20-9	20-4	19-8	20-4	19-5	18-9	18-5	17-9	17-1	14-7	14-2	13-6	13-0

TABLE NO. 15. RAFTERS—High Slope (over 3 in 12)—With No Finished Ceiling. 20 psf live load + 15 psf dead load—heavy roofing. (Spans shown in light face type are based on a deflection limitation of $l/180$. Spans shown in color, bold face type are limited by the recommended extreme fiber stress in bending value of the grade and includes a 15 psf dead load.)

Size	Grade and Spacing in. o.c.	Dense Sel Str KD	Dense Sel Str	No. 1 Dense KD and Sel Str KD	Sel Str	No. 1 Dense	No. 1 KD	No. 2 Dense KD	No. 1	No. 2 Dense	No. 2 KD	No. 2	No. 3 Dense KD	No. 3 Dense	No. 3 KD	No. 3	Construction KD	Construction	Standard KD	Standard
2 x 4	12.0	11-6	11-3	11-6¹	11-1	11-3	11-2	11-0	10-8	10-6	10-2	9-8	8-2	7-11	7-7	7-3	8-7	8-2	6-6	6-3
	13.7	11-0	10-9	11-0¹	10-7	10-9	10-5	10-3	10-0	9-10	9-6	9-1	7-8	7-4	7-1	6-9	8-0	7-8	6-1	5-10
	16.0	10-5	10-3	10-5¹	10-0	10-0	9-8	9-6	9-3	9-1	8-10	8-5	7-1	6-10	6-6	6-3	7-5	7-1	5-7	5-5
	19.2	9-10	9-8	9-6	9-2	9-2	8-10	8-8	8-5	8-4	8-1	7-8	6-6	6-3	6-0	5-8	6-9	6-6	5-1	4-11
	24.0	9-1	8-11	8-6	8-2	8-2	7-11	7-9	7-7	7-5	7-3	6-10	5-9	5-7	5-4	5-1	6-1	5-9	4-7	4-5
2 x 5	12.0	14-9	14-6	14-4	13-11	13-9	13-4	13-1	12-8	12-6	12-0	11-6	9-10	9-7	9-1	8-10				
	13.7	14-1	13-10	13-5	13-0	12-10	12-6	12-3	11-10	11-8	11-3	10-10	9-3	8-11	8-6	8-3				
	16.0	13-5	13-1	12-5	12-1	11-11	11-6	11-4	11-0	10-9	10-5	10-0	8-6	8-3	7-11	7-8				
	19.2	12-4	11-11	11-4	11-0	10-10	10-6	10-4	10-0	9-10	9-6	9-1	7-9	7-7	7-3	7-0				
	24.0	11-1	10-8	10-2	9-10	9-9	9-5	9-3	9-0	8-10	8-6	8-2	7-0	6-9	6-5	6-3				
2 x 6	12.0	18-0	17-8	17-6	17-0	16-9	16-3	16-0	15-6	15-3	14-8	14-1	12-0	11-8	11-2	10-9				
	13.7	17-3	16-11	16-5	15-11	15-8	15-3	15-0	14-6	14-3	13-9	13-2	11-3	10-11	10-5	10-1				
	16.0	16-4	16-0	15-2	14-9	14-6	14-1	13-11	13-5	13-2	12-9	12-3	10-5	10-1	9-8	9-4				
	19.2	15-1	14-7	13-10	13-6	13-3	12-10	12-8	12-3	12-0	11-7	11-2	9-6	9-3	8-10	8-6				
	24.0	13-6	13-0	12-5	12-0	11-10	11-6	11-4	11-0	10-9	10-5	10-0	8-6	8-3	7-11	7-7				
2 x 8	12.0	23-9	23-4	23-1	22-5	22-1	21-6	21-1	20-5	20-1	19-4	18-7	15-10	15-5	14-8	14-2				
	13.7	22-9	22-4	21-7	21-0	20-8	20-1	19-9	19-1	18-9	18-1	17-5	14-10	14-5	13-9	13-3				
	16.0	21-7	21-0	20-0	19-5	19-2	18-7	18-4	17-8	17-5	16-9	16-1	13-9	13-4	12-9	12-4				
	19.2	19-11	19-2	18-3	17-9	17-6	17-0	16-8	16-2	15-10	15-4	14-8	12-7	12-2	11-7	11-3				
	24.0	17-10	17-2	16-4	15-10	15-8	15-2	14-11	14-5	14-2	13-8	13-2	11-3	10-11	10-5	10-0				
2 x 10	12.0	30-4	29-9	29-5	28-8	28-3	27-5	26-11	26-1	25-7	24-8	23-9	20-3	19-8	18-9	18-1				
	13.7	29-0	28-6	27-7	26-9	26-5	25-7	25-3	24-5	24-0	23-1	22-2	18-11	18-5	17-6	16-11				
	16.0	27-6	26-10	25-6	24-10	24-5	23-9	23-4	22-7	22-2	21-4	20-6	17-6	17-0	16-3	15-8				
	19.2	25-5	24-6	23-3	22-8	22-4	21-8	21-4	20-7	20-3	19-6	18-9	16-0	15-7	14-10	14-4				
	24.0	22-8	21-11	20-10	20-3	19-11	19-4	19-1	18-5	18-1	17-5	16-9	14-4	13-11	13-3	12-10				

1. The span for Select Structural KD, 2x4, 12 inches o.c. is 11-3; 13.7 inches o.c., 10-9, and 16 inches o.c., 10-3.

TABLE NO. 16. RAFTERS—High Slope (over 3 in 12)—With No Finished Ceiling. 30 psf live load + 15 psf dead load—heavy roofing. (Spans shown in light face type are based on a deflection limitation of $l/180$. Spans shown in color, bold face type are limited by the recommended extreme fiber stress in bending value of the grade and includes a 15 psf dead load.)

Size and Spacing in.	Grade in. o.c.	Dense Sel Str KD	Dense Sel Str	No. 1 Dense KD and Sel Str KD	Sel Str	No. 1 Dense	No. 1 KD	No. 2 Dense KD	No. 1	No. 2 Dense	No. 2 KD	No. 2	No. 3 Dense KD	No. 3 Dense	No. 3 KD	No. 3	Construction KD	Construction	Standard KD	Standard
2 x 4	12.0	10-0	9-10	10-0¹	9-8	9-10	9-10	9-8	9-5	9-3	9-0	8-7	7-3	6-11	6-8	6-4	7-7	7-3	5-9	5-6
	13.7	9-7	9-5	9-7¹	9-3	9-5	9-2	9-1	8-10	8-8	8-5	8-0	6-9	6-6	6-3	5-11	7-1	6-9	5-4	5-1
	16.0	9-1	8-11	9-1¹	8-9	8-10	8-6	8-5	8-2	8-0	7-9	7-5	6-3	6-0	5-9	5-6	6-7	6-3	4-11	4-9
	19.2	8-7	8-5	8-4	8-1	8-1	7-9	7-8	7-5	7-4	7-1	6-9	5-9	5-6	5-3	5-0	6-0	5-9	4-6	4-4
	24.0	7-11	7-10	7-6	7-3	7-3	6-11	6-10	6-8	6-7	6-4	6-1	5-1	4-11	4-9	4-6	5-4	5-1	4-0	3-10
2 x 5	12.0	12-11	12-8	12-8	12-3	12-1	11-9	11-7	11-2	11-0	10-7	10-2	8-8	8-5	8-1	7-9				
	13.7	12-4	12-1	11-10	11-6	11-4	11-0	10-10	10-6	10-3	9-11	9-6	8-2	7-11	7-6	7-3				
	16.0	11-8	11-6	10-11	10-8	10-6	10-2	10-0	9-8	9-6	9-2	8-10	7-6	7-4	7-0	6-9				
	19.2	10-11	10-6	10-0	9-9	9-7	9-3	9-2	8-10	8-8	8-4	8-1	6-10	6-8	6-4	6-2				
	24.0	9-9	9-5	8-11	8-8	8-7	8-4	8-2	7-11	7-9	7-6	7-2	6-2	6-0	5-8	5-6				
2 x 6	12.0	15-9	15-6	15-5	15-0	14-10	14-4	14-2	13-8	13-5	12-11	12-5	10-7	10-4	9-10	9-6				
	13.7	15-1	14-9	14-5	14-1	13-10	13-5	13-3	12-9	12-7	12-1	11-8	9-11	9-8	9-2	8-11				
	16.0	14-4	14-1	13-4	13-0	12-10	12-5	12-3	11-10	11-8	11-2	10-9	9-2	8-11	8-6	8-3				
	19.2	13-4	12-10	12-2	11-10	11-8	11-4	11-2	10-10	10-7	10-3	9-10	8-5	8-2	7-9	7-6				
	24.0	11-11	11-6	10-11	10-7	10-6	10-2	10-0	9-8	9-6	9-2	8-10	7-6	7-3	6-11	6-9				
2 x 8	12.0	20-9	20-5	20-4	19-10	19-6	18-11	18-8	18-0	17-8	17-1	16-5	14-0	13-7	12-11	12-6				
	13.7	19-10	19-6	19-0	18-6	18-3	17-8	17-5	16-10	16-7	16-0	15-4	13-1	12-9	12-1	11-9				
	16.0	18-10	18-6	17-7	17-2	16-11	16-5	16-2	15-7	15-4	14-9	14-2	12-1	11-9	11-3	10-10				
	19.2	17-7	16-11	16-1	15-8	15-5	15-0	14-9	14-3	14-0	13-6	12-11	11-1	10-9	10-3	9-11				
	24.0	15-8	15-2	14-5	14-0	13-10	13-5	13-2	12-9	12-6	12-1	11-7	9-11	9-7	9-2	8-10				
2 x 10	12.0	26-6	26-0	26-0	25-3	24-11	24-2	23-9	23-0	22-7	21-9	20-11	17-10	17-4	16-6	16-0				
	13.7	25-4	24-11	24-4	23-8	23-3	22-7	22-3	21-6	21-2	20-4	19-7	16-8	16-3	15-6	14-11				
	16.0	24-1	23-8	22-6	21-10	21-7	20-11	20-7	19-11	19-7	18-10	18-1	15-6	15-0	14-4	13-10				
	19.2	22-5	21-7	20-6	20-0	19-8	19-1	18-9	18-2	17-10	17-2	16-6	14-1	13-8	13-1	12-8				
	24.0	20-0	19-4	18-4	17-10	17-7	17-1	16-10	16-3	16-0	15-5	14-9	12-8	12-3	11-8	11-4				

1. The span for Select Structural KD, 2x4, 12 inches o.c. is 9-10; 13.7 inches o.c., 9-5, and 16 inches o.c., 8-11.

TABLE NO. 17. RAFTERS—High Slope (over 3 in 12)—With No Finished Ceiling. 40 psf live load + 15 psf dead load—heavy roofing. (Spans shown in light face type are based on a deflection limitation of l/180. Spans shown in color, bold face type are limited by the recommended extreme fiber stress in bending value of the grade and includes a 15 psf dead load.)

Size and Spacing in. o.c.		Dense Sel Str KD	Sel Str Dense	No. 1 Dense KD and Sel Str KD	Sel Str	No. 1 Dense	No. 1 KD	No. 2 Dense KD	No. 1	No. 2 Dense	No. 2 KD	No. 2	No. 3 Dense KD	No. 3 Dense	No. 3 KD	No. 3	Construction KD	Construction	Standard KD	Standard
2 x 4	12.0	9-1	8-11	9-11	8-9	8-11	8-11	8-9	8-6	8-5	8-2	7-9	6-6	6-3	6-0	5-9	6-10	6-6	5-2	4-11
	13.7	8-8	8-7	8-8¹	8-5	8-7	8-4	8-2	8-0	7-10	7-7	7-3	6-1	5-11	5-8	5-5	6-5	6-1	4-10	4-8
	16.0	8-3	8-1	8-3¹	8-0	8-0	7-8	7-7	7-5	7-3	7-1	6-8	5-8	5-5	5-3	5-0	5-11	5-8	4-6	4-3
	19.2	7-9	7-8	7-7	7-4	7-4	7-0	6-11	6-9	6-8	6-5	6-1	5-2	5-0	4-9	4-7	5-5	5-2	4-1	3-11
	24.0	7-3	7-1	6-9	6-6	6-6	6-3	6-2	6-0	5-11	5-9	5-6	4-7	4-5	4-3	4-1	4-10	4-7	3-8	3-6
2 x 5	12.0	11-8	11-6	11-5	11-1	10-11	10-8	10-6	10-1	9-11	9-7	9-2	7-10	7-8	7-4	7-0				
	13.7	11-2	11-0	10-8	10-5	10-3	9-11	9-9	9-6	9-4	9-0	8-7	7-4	7-2	6-10	6-7				
	16.0	10-8	10-5	9-11	9-7	9-6	9-2	9-1	8-9	8-7	8-4	8-0	6-10	6-7	6-4	6-1				
	19.2	9-10	9-6	9-0	8-9	8-8	8-5	8-3	8-0	7-10	7-7	7-3	6-3	6-0	5-9	5-7				
	24.0	8-10	8-6	8-1	7-10	7-9	7-6	7-5	7-2	7-0	6-9	6-6	5-7	5-5	5-2	5-0				
2 x 6	12.0	14-4	14-1	14-0	13-7	13-5	13-0	12-9	12-4	12-2	11-8	11-3	9-7	9-4	8-11	8-7				
	13.7	13-8	13-5	13-1	12-8	12-6	12-2	12-0	11-7	11-4	10-11	10-6	9-0	8-9	8-4	8-0				
	16.0	13-0	12-9	12-1	11-9	11-7	11-3	11-1	10-8	10-6	10-2	9-9	8-4	8-1	7-8	7-5				
	19.2	12-0	11-7	11-0	10-9	10-7	10-3	10-1	9-9	9-7	9-3	8-11	7-7	7-4	7-0	6-9				
	24.0	10-9	10-5	9-10	9-7	9-6	9-2	9-0	8-9	8-7	8-3	7-11	6-9	6-7	6-3	6-1				
2 x 8	12.0	18-10	18-6	18-5	17-11	17-8	17-1	16-10	16-4	16-0	15-5	14-10	12-8	12-4	11-9	11-4				
	13.7	18-0	17-9	17-3	16-9	16-6	16-0	15-9	15-3	15-0	14-5	13-10	11-10	11-6	11-0	10-7				
	16.0	17-2	16-9	15-11	15-6	15-3	14-10	14-7	14-1	13-10	13-4	12-10	11-0	10-8	10-2	9-10				
	19.2	15-10	15-4	14-7	14-2	13-11	13-6	13-4	12-11	12-8	12-2	11-9	10-0	9-9	9-3	8-11				
	24.0	14-2	13-8	13-0	12-8	12-6	12-1	11-11	11-6	11-4	10-11	10-6	8-11	8-8	8-3	8-0				
2 x 10	12.0	24-1	23-8	23-6	22-10	22-6	21-10	21-6	20-10	20-5	19-8	18-11	16-2	15-8	14-11	14-5				
	13.7	23-0	22-7	22-0	21-4	21-1	20-5	20-1	19-5	19-1	18-5	17-8	15-1	14-8	14-0	13-6				
	16.0	21-10	21-5	20-4	19-9	19-6	18-11	18-7	18-0	17-8	17-1	16-5	14-0	13-7	12-11	12-6				
	19.2	20-3	19-7	18-7	18-1	17-10	17-3	17-0	16-5	16-2	15-7	14-11	12-9	12-5	11-10	11-5				
	24.0	18-1	17-6	16-7	16-2	15-11	15-5	15-2	14-8	14-5	13-11	13-5	11-5	11-1	10-7	10-3				

1. The span for Select Structural KD, 2x4, 12 inches o.c. is 8-11; 13.7 inches o.c., 8-7, and 16 inches o.c., 8-1.

Specify Grade-Marked Southern Pine Bearing this Trademark

It meets the highest standards of the lumber industry

For the architect, designer or builder who selects Southern Pine, SFPA has some suggestions on how to reduce the cost of construction. These cost-saving ideas are covered in a series of six folders, and are available upon request. SFPA fieldstaff personnel are also in daily contact with architects, engineers, builders and other specifiers to assist with problems or information.

SOUTHERN FOREST PRODUCTS ASSOCIATION
P.O. Box 52468, New Orleans, Louisiana 70152

PRODUCT USE MANUAL

Lumber Design Values

The design values in this booklet are for lumber of species and combinations of species manufactured and shipped by mills in the 12 western states. The values are computed in accordance with the requirements of "Methods for Establishing Clear Wood Strength Values" ASTM D-2555 and "Methods for Establishing Structural Grades for Visually Graded Lumber" ASTM D-245 published by the **American Society for Testing and Materials.**

These design values are for use in all normal construction design. Higher or lower design values may be used to meet special structural requirements. The "National Design Specification," published by National Forest Products Association, 1619 Massachusetts Avenue, N.W., Washington, D.C., sets forth design methods for normal and most special structural uses.

Design values for visually graded lumber are assigned to six basic properties of wood. These are fiber stress in bending "Fb", tension parallel to grain "Ft", horizontal shear "Fv", compression parallel to grain "Fc", compression perpendicular to grain "Fc⊥", and modulus of elasticity "E".

Design Considerations

Single Member Design Values:

Single member fiber stress in bending "Fb" design values are for use where the strength of an individual piece, such as a beam, girder or post or may be responsible for carrying a specific design load. (See **Single Member Design Values,** bottom page 6.)

Repetitive Member Design Values:

In structures where 2" to 4" thick lumber is used repetitively such as joists, studs, rafters and decking, the pieces side by side share the load and the strength of the entire assembly is enhanced. Therefore where 3 or more members are adjacent or are not more than 24" apart and are joined by floor, roof or other load distributing elements, the repetitive member design values for fiber stress in bending "Fb" shown in Tables 1, 1a, 1b, 2, 3 and 6 are applicable.

Permanent Loads and Working Stresses:

Normal load duration contemplates stressing a member to the allowable stress by the application of the full maximum design load for a duration of approximately 10 years either continuously or cumulatively, without encroaching on the factor of safety.

When the duration of the full maximum load does not exceed the period indicated, increase the design values shown in the tables as follows:

15 percent for 2 months' duration, as for snow.

25 percent for 7 days' duration.

33⅓ percent for wind or earthquake.

100 percent for impact.

Where a member is fully stressed to the maximum allowable stress for more than 10 years, either continuously or cumula-

tively under the condition of maximum design load, use working stresses 90 percent of those in the tables.

Other Design Considerations:

For combinations of loads of different durations and other design considerations, see methods outlined in National Design Specification for Stress Grade Lumber and Its Fastenings available from National Forest Products Association, Washington, D.C. 20036.

Stress Rated Boards:

Stress rated boards with design values assigned provide for special uses such as light trusses, belt rails, horizontal bracing, rafters and box beams for mobile and factory built homes.

Stress rated boards are graded under the provisions of Light Framing and Studs, Structural Light Framing and Structural Joists and Planks. The design values shown in Tables 1, 1a, 1b, 2 and 3, apply to stress rated boards. In Table 1, Fb, Ft and Fc values apply only to 4" widths. Stress rated boards carry the symbol "SRB" in the grade stamp.

The WWPA Grading Rules

This publication incorporates the provisions from PS 20-70 (The American Lumber Standard), equating lumber size with moisture content. All dimension lumber under the new WWPA rules is graded so that working stresses can be applied.

Basic Selection Factors

Adherence to the following basic important factors makes the correct selection and specification of WWP lumber both easy and accurate.

PRODUCT CLASSIFICATION. Identify product names for clarity. Examples: paneling, structural decking, joists, rafters, studding, beams, siding, etc.

SPECIES. Include ALL species suited to the job. This broadens availability which can lower costs. Verify available species with your local supplier.

Where wood color, grain, durability or other special characteristics are important to the use intended, select and specify the proper species accordingly.

GRADE. Specify standard grades as described on page 3 or in the Official Western Wood Products Association Grading Rules Book. Consider all grades suitable for the intended use. For economy in construction, it is recommended that the lowest grade suited to a job be specified.

STRESS RATING. When strength is a controlling factor, specify the stress rating requirements WITHOUT reference to grades. There are two methods of assigning stress values—"visual" and "machine rated" (see page 15).

SIZE. For standard products such as boards and framing, specify the nominal size by thickness and width in full inches. Example: 1x6, 1x8, 2x4, 2x6.

SURFACE TEXTURE. Indicate whether lumber is to be smooth (surfaced), rough or saw textured.

PATTERNS. List pattern number for profiled material, and provide detail profiles for non-standard (special) patterns. Where needed, identify whether tongue and groove (T&G), shiplap (S/L), or other patterns or workings.

SEASONING. Specify "DRY" lumber to assure long range product stability, increased nail-holding power, improved paintability and workability. "DRY" covers both major methods of drying lumber; air dried and kiln dried.

S-DRY MC 15 S-GRN

Any one of the above marks found in a gradestamp denotes the moisture content of lumber at time of surfacing. "S-DRY" indicates a moisture content not exceeding 19 percent. "MC 15" indicates a moisture content not exceeding 15 percent. "S-GRN" indicates that the moisture content exceeded 19 percent.

GRADE STAMPS. Specify WWP grade stamped framing lumber, sheathing and other construction items. Finish lumber and decking may also be grade stamped on backs where the stamps will not be visible in use and may be so specified if desired. Some WWPA mills, located in areas where West Coast Lumber Inspection Bureau Rules may be applicable, also may have the notation (WCLB Rules) on the stamp for some items. This notation indicates that the lumber was graded under WCLIB rules.

Thermal Conductivity

The relatively low thermal conductivity or "k," of Western Softwoods provides for significant insulation value. "k" is the amount of heat (Btu's) transferred in one hour through one square foot of material one inch thick with a difference in temperature of 1° F.

The thermal conductivity of wood increases with increased moisture content and with increased density. The "k" values for the Western Woods are shown in the table below.

Species	"k"*	R/in.
Douglas Fir—Larch	1.06	.94
Douglas Fir South	.99	1.01
Hem-Fir	.92	1.08
Mountain Hemlock	.98	1.02
Alpine Fir	.75	1.33
Engelmann Spruce	.80	1.25
Lodgepole Pine	.92	1.08
Ponderosa Pine—		
Sugar Pine	.89	1.12
Idaho White Pine	.84	1.19
Western Cedars	.75	1.33
Western Hemlock	.99	1.01

*"k" values shown are for wood 12 percent moisture content. For other moisture contents, there is a change in "k" of approximately .01 for each 1 percent moisture content difference — an increase in "k" for an increase in moisture content and a decrease in "k" for a decrease in moisture content. R (reciprocal of k) is the measurement of the resistance to heat flow.

2

Grade Selector Charts

Boards

<table>
<tr><td rowspan="4" style="writing-mode:vertical-lr">APPEARANCE GRADES</td><td>SELECTS</td><td colspan="2">B & BETTER   (IWP—SUPREME)*
C SELECT   (IWP—CHOICE)
D SELECT   (IWP—QUALITY)</td></tr>
<tr><td>FINISH</td><td colspan="2">SUPERIOR
PRIME
E</td></tr>
<tr><td>PANELING</td><td colspan="2">CLEAR (ANY SELECT OR FINISH GRADE)
NO. 2 COMMON SELECTED FOR KNOTTY PANELING
NO. 3 COMMON SELECTED FOR KNOTTY PANELING</td></tr>
<tr><td>SIDING
(BEVEL,
BUNGALOW)</td><td colspan="2">SUPERIOR
PRIME</td></tr>
<tr><td colspan="2">BOARDS
SHEATHING
& FORM
LUMBER</td><td>NO. 1 COMMON (IWP—COLONIAL)
NO. 2 COMMON (IWP—STERLING)
NO. 3 COMMON (IWP—STANDARD)
NO. 4 COMMON (IWP—UTILITY)
NO. 5 COMMON (IWP—INDUSTRIAL)

       ALTERNATE BOARD GRADES
SELECT MERCHANTABLE
CONSTRUCTION
STANDARD
UTILITY
ECONOMY</td></tr>
</table>

*Idaho White Pine carries its own comparable grade designations.

SPECIFICATION CHECK LIST

- ☐ Grades listed in order of quality.
- ☐ Include all species suited to project.
- ☐ Specify lowest grade that will satisfy job requirement.
- ☐ Specify surface texture desired.
- ☐ Specify moisture content suited to project.
- ☐ Specify ⓌⓌⒷ grade stamp. For finish and exposed pieces, specify stamp on back or ends.

Western Red Cedar

FINISH PANELING AND CEILING	**CLEAR HEART** A B
BEVEL SIDING	CLEAR — V.G. HEART A — BEVEL SIDING B — BEVEL SIDING C — BEVEL SIDING

3

Dimension/All Species   2″ to 4″ thick (also applies to finger-jointed stock)

LIGHT FRAMING 2″ to 4″ Thick 2″ to 4″ Wide	CONSTRUCTION STANDARD UTILITY	This category for use where high strength values are **NOT** required; such as studs, plates, sills, cripples, blocking, etc.
STUDS 2″ to 4″ Thick 2″ to 6″ Wide 10′ and Shorter	STUD	An optional all-purpose grade limited to 10 feet and shorter. Characteristics affecting strength and stiffness values are limited so that the "Stud" grade is suitable for all stud uses, including load bearing walls.
STRUCTURAL LIGHT FRAMING 2″ to 4″ Thick 2″ to 4″ Wide	SELECT STRUCTURAL NO. 1 NO. 2 NO. 3	These grades are designed to fit those engineering applications where higher bending strength ratios are needed in light framing sizes. Typical uses would be for trusses, concrete pier wall forms, etc.
STRUCTURAL JOISTS & PLANKS 2″ to 4″ Thick 5″ and Wider	SELECT STRUCTURAL NO. 1 NO. 2 NO. 3	These grades are designed especially to fit in engineering applications for lumber five inches and wider, such as joists, rafters and general framing uses.

Timbers   5″ and thicker

BEAMS & STRINGERS 5″ and thicker Width more than 2″ greater than thickness	SELECT STRUCTURAL NO. 1 NO. 2 (NO. 1 MINING)** NO. 3 (NO. 2 MINING)**	**POSTS & TIMBERS** 5″ x 5″ and larger Width not more than 2″ greater than thickness	SELECT STRUCTURAL NO. 1 NO. 2 (NO. 1 MINING)** NO. 3 (NO. 2 MINING)**

**Design values are not assigned.

Standard Lumber Sizes / Nominal, Dressed, Based on WWPA Rules

Product	Description	Nominal Size: Thickness In.	Nominal Size: Width In.	Dressed Dimensions: Thicknesses and Widths In. — Surfaced Dry	Dressed Dimensions: Thicknesses and Widths In. — Surfaced Unseasoned	Lengths Ft.
DIMENSION	S4S	2 3 4	2 3 4 5 6 8 10 12 Over 12	1-½ 2-½ 3-½ 4-½ 5-½ 7-¼ 9-¼ 11-¼ Off ¾	1-9/16 2-9/16 3-9/16 4-⅝ 5-⅝ 7-½ 9-½ 11-½ Off ½	6 ft. and longer in multiples of 1′
SCAFFOLD PLANK	Rough Full Sawn or S4S	1¼ & Thicker	8 and Wider	Same	Same	6 ft. and longer in multiples of 1′
				Thickness In.	**Width In.**	
TIMBERS	Rough or S4S	5 and Larger		½ Off Nominal		6 ft. and longer in multiples of 1′
		Nominal Size: Thickness In.	**Nominal Size: Width In.**	**Dressed Dimensions: Thickness In.**	**Dressed Dimensions: Width In.**	**Lengths Ft.**
DECKING	2″ Single T&G	2	5 6 8 10 12	1½	4 5 6¾ 8¾ 10¾	6 ft. and longer in multiples of 1′
	3″ and 4″ Double T&G	3 4	6	2½ 3½	5¼	
FLOORING	(D & M), (S2S & CM)	⅜ ½ ⅝ 1 1¼ 1½	2 3 4 5 6	5/16 7/16 9/16 ¾ 1 1¼	1⅛ 2⅛ 3⅛ 4⅛ 5⅛	4 ft. and longer in multiples of 1′
CEILING AND PARTITION	(S2S & CM)	⅜ ½ ⅝ ¾	3 4 5 6	5/16 7/16 9/16 11/16	2⅛ 3⅛ 4⅛ 5⅛	4 ft. and longer in multiples of 1′
FACTORY AND SHOP LUMBER	S2S	1 (4/4) 1¼ (5/4) 1½ (6/4) 1¾ (7/4) 2 (8/4) 2½ (10/4) 3 (12/4) 4 (16/4)	5 and wider except (4″ and wider in 4/4 No. 1 Shop and 4/4 No. 2 Shop)	25/32 (4/4) 1 5/32 (5/4) 1 13/32 (6/4) 1 19/32 (7/4) 1 13/16 (8/4) 2⅜ (10/4) 2¾ (12/4) 3¾ (16/4)	Usually sold random width	4 ft. and longer in multiples of 1′

ABBREVIATIONS
Abbreviated descriptions appearing in the size table are explained below.
S1S — Surfaced one side.
S2S — Surfaced two sides.
S4S — Surfaced four sides.
S1S1E — Surfaced one side, one edge.
S1S2E — Surfaced one side, two edges.
CM — Center matched.
D & M — Dressed and matched.
T & G — Tongue and grooved.
Rough Full Sawn — Unsurfaced green lumber cut to full specified size.

4

Product Classification

	thickness in.	width in.		thickness in.	width in.
board lumber	1″	2″ or more	**beams & stringers**	5″ and thicker	more than 2″ greater than thickness
light framing	2″ to 4″	2″ to 4″	**posts & timbers**	5″ x 5″ and larger	not more than 2″ greater than thickness
studs	2″ to 4″	2″ to 6″ 10′ and shorter	**decking**	2″ to 4″	4″ to 12″ wide
structural light framing	2″ to 4″	2″ to 4″	**siding**	thickness expressed by dimension of butt edge	
structural joists & planks	2″ to 4″	5″ and wider	**mouldings**	size at thickest and widest points	

Lengths of lumber generally are 6 feet and longer in multiples of 2′

Nailing Diagram

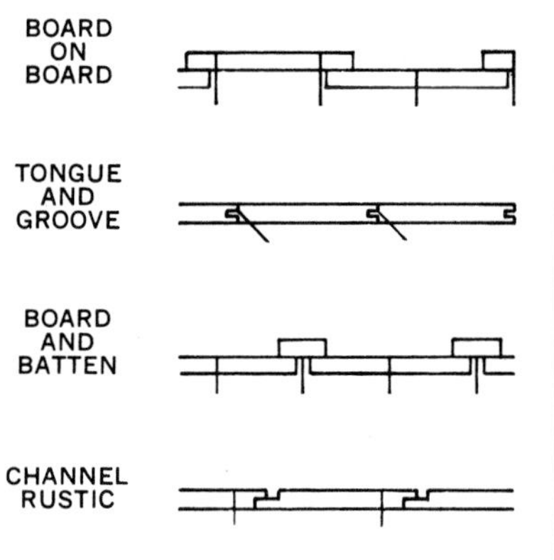
BOARD ON BOARD
TONGUE AND GROOVE
BOARD AND BATTEN
CHANNEL RUSTIC

Standard Lumber Sizes / Nominal, Dressed, Based on WWPA Rules

Product	Description	Nominal Size Thickness In.	Nominal Size Width In.	Dressed Dimensions Thickness In.	Dressed Dimensions Width In.	Dressed Dimensions Lengths Ft.
SELECTS AND COMMONS S-DRY	S1S, S2S, S4S, S1S1E, S1S2E....	4/4 5/4 6/4 7/4 8/4 9/4 10/4 11/4 12/4 16/4	2 3 4 5 6 7 8 and wider	3/4 1 5/32 1 13/32 1 19/32 1 13/16 2 3/32 2 3/8 2 9/16 2 3/4 3 3/4	1 1/2 2 1/2 3 1/2 4 1/2 5 1/2 6 1/2 3/4 Off nominal	6 ft. and longer in multiples of 1' except Douglas Fir and Larch Selects shall be 4' and longer with 3% of 4' and 5' permitted.*
FINISH AND BOARDS S-DRY	S1S, S2S, S4S, S1S1E, S1S2E ... Only these sizes apply to Alternate Board Grades.	3/8 1/2 5/8 3/4 1 1 1/4 1 1/2 1 3/4 2 2 1/2 3 3 1/2 4	2 3 4 5 6 7 8 and wider	5/16 7/16 9/16 5/8 3/4 1 1 1/4 1 3/8 1 1/2 2 2 1/2 3 3 1/2	1 1/2 2 1/2 3 1/2 4 1/2 5 1/2 6 1/2 3/4 off nominal	3' and longer. In Superior grade, 3% of 3' and 4' and 7% of 5' and 6' are permitted. In Prime grade, 20% of 3' to 6' is permitted.
RUSTIC AND DROP SIDING	(D & M) .... If 3/8" or 1/2" T & G specified, same over-all widths apply. (Shiplapped, 3/8-in. or 1/2-in. lap) ..	1	6 8 10 12	23/32	5 3/8 7 1/8 9 1/8 11 1/8	4 ft. and longer in multiples of 1'
PANELING AND SIDING	T&G or Shiplap.................	1	6 8 10 12	23/32	5 7/16 7 1/8 9 1/8 11 1/8	4 ft. and longer in multiples of 1'
CEILING AND PARTITION	T&G	5/8 1	4 6	9/16 23/32	3 3/8 5 3/8	4 ft. and longer in multiples of 1'
BEVEL SIDING	Bevel or Bungalow Siding........ Western Red Cedar Bevel Siding available in 1/2", 5/8", 3/4" nominal thickness. Corresponding thick edge is 15/32", 9/16" and 3/4". Widths for 8" and wider, 1/2" off nominal.	1/2 3/4	4 5 6 8 10 12	15/32 butt, 3/16 tip 3/4 butt, 3/16 tip	3 1/2 4 1/2 5 1/2 7 1/4 9 1/4 11 1/4	3 ft. and longer in multiples of 1' 3 ft. and longer in multiples of 1'

Product	Description	Nominal Thickness In.	Nominal Width In.	Dressed Thickness Surfaced Dry	Dressed Thickness Surfaced Green	Dressed Width Surfaced Dry	Dressed Width Surfaced Green	Lengths Ft.
STRESS RATED BOARDS	S1S, S2S, S4S, S1S1E, S1S2E....	1 1 1/4 1 1/2	2 3 4 5 6 7 8 and Wider	3/4 1 1 1/4	25/32 1 1/32 1 9/32	1 1/2 2 1/2 3 1/2 4 1/2 5 1/2 6 1/2 Off 3/4	1 9/16 2 9/16 3 9/16 4 5/8 5 5/8 6 5/8 Off 1/2	6 ft. and longer in multiples of 1'

See coverage estimator chart below for dressed Shiplap and Tongue and Groove (T&G) widths.

MINIMUM ROUGH SIZES — Thicknesses and Widths Dry or Unseasoned All Lumber

80% of the pieces in a shipment shall be at least 1/8" thicker than the standard surfaced size, the remaining 20% at least 3/32" thicker than the surfaced size. Widths shall be at least 1/8" wider than standard surfaced widths.

When specified to be full sawn, lumber may not be manufactured to a size less than the size specified.

5

Coverage Estimator

The following estimator provides factors for determining the exact amount of material needed for the five basic types of wood paneling. Multiply square footage to be covered by factor (length x width x factor).*

	Nominal Size	WIDTH Overall	WIDTH Face	AREA FACTOR		Nominal Size	WIDTH Overall	WIDTH Face	AREA FACTOR
SHIPLAP	1 x 6 1 x 8 1 x 10 1 x 12	5 1/2 7 1/4 9 1/4 11 1/4	5 1/8 6 7/8 8 7/8 10 7/8	1.17 1.16 1.13 1.10	**PANELING PATTERNS**	1 x 6 1 x 8 1 x 10 1 x 12	5 7/16 7 1/8 9 1/8 11 1/8	5 1/16 6 3/4 8 3/4 10 3/4	1.19 1.19 1.14 1.12
TONGUE AND GROOVE	1 x 4 1 x 6 1 x 8 1 x 10 1 x 12	3 3/8 5 3/8 7 1/8 9 1/8 11 1/8	3 1/8 5 1/8 6 7/8 8 7/8 10 7/8•	1.28 1.17 1.16 1.13 1.10	**BEVEL SIDING**	1 x 4 1 x 6 1 x 8 1 x 10 1 x 12	3 1/2 5 1/2 7 1/4 9 1/4 11 1/4	3 1/2 5 1/2 7 1/4 9 1/4 11 1/4	1.60 1.33 1.28 1.21 1.17
S4S	1 x 4 1 x 6 1 x 8 1 x 10 1 x 12	3 1/2 5 1/2 7 1/4 9 1/4 11 1/4	3 1/2 5 1/2 7 1/4 9 1/4 11 1/4	1.14 1.09 1.10 1.08 1.07					

*Allowance for trim and waste should be added.

Design Values/WWPA Standard Grading Rules

Table 1   LIGHT FRAMING and STUDS—2″ to 4″ Thick, 2″ to 4″ Wide   Grades Described in Sections 40.00 and 41.00.
Design Values in Pounds Per Square Inch*   Also Stress Rated Boards.
See Section 30.60 WWPA Grading Rules.

Species or Group	Grade	Extreme Fiber Stress in Bending "Fb"[2]		Tension Parallel to Grain "Ft"	Horizontal Shear "Fv"	Compression		Modulus of Elasticity "E"
		Single	Repetitive			Perpendicular "Fc ⊥"	Parallel to Grain "Fc"[2]	
DOUGLAS FIR-LARCH	Construction[1]	1050	1200	625	95	385	1150	1,500,000
	Standard[1]	600	675	350	95	385	925	1,500,000
	Utility[1]	275	325	175	95	385	600	1,500,000
	Stud	800	925	475	95	385	600	1,500,000
DOUGLAS FIR SOUTH	Construction[1]	1000	1150	600	90	335	1000	1,100,000
	Standard[1]	550	650	325	90	335	850	1,100,000
	Utility[1]	275	300	150	90	335	550	1,100,000
	Stud	775	875	450	90	335	550	1,100,000
HEM-FIR	Construction[1]	825	975	500	75	245	925	1,200,000
	Standard[1]	475	550	275	75	245	775	1,200,000
	Utility[1]	225	250	125	75	245	500	1,200,000
	Stud	650	725	375	75	245	500	1,200,000
MOUNTAIN HEMLOCK	Construction[1]	875	1000	525	95	370	900	1,000,000
	Standard[1]	500	575	275	95	370	725	1,000,000
	Utility[1]	225	275	125	95	370	475	1,000,000
	Stud	675	775	400	95	370	475	1,000,000
MOUNTAIN HEMLOCK-HEM-FIR	Construction[1]	825	975	500	75	245	900	1,000,000
	Standard[1]	475	550	275	75	245	725	1,000,000
	Utility[1]	225	250	125	75	245	475	1,000,000
	Stud	650	725	375	75	245	475	1,000,000
WESTERN HEMLOCK	Construction[1]	925	1050	550	90	280	1050	1,300,000
	Standard[1]	525	600	300	90	280	850	1,300,000
	Utility[1]	250	275	150	90	280	550	1,300,000
	Stud	700	800	425	90	280	550	1,300,000
ENGELMANN SPRUCE-ALPINE FIR (Engelmann Spruce-Lodgepole Pine)	Construction[1]	700	800	400	70	195	675	1,000,000
	Standard[1]	375	450	225	70	195	550	1,000,000
	Utility[1]	175	200	100	70	195	375	1,000,000
	Stud	525	600	300	70	195	375	1,000,000
LODGEPOLE PINE	Construction[1]	775	875	450	70	250	800	1,000,000
	Standard[1]	425	500	250	70	250	675	1,000,000
	Utility[1]	200	225	125	70	250	425	1,000,000
	Stud	600	675	350	70	250	425	1,000,000
PONDEROSA PINE-SUGAR PINE (Ponderosa Pine-Lodgepole Pine)	Construction[1]	725	825	425	70	235	775	1,000,000
	Standard[1]	400	450	225	70	235	625	1,000,000
	Utility[1]	200	225	100	70	235	400	1,000,000
	Stud	550	625	325	70	235	400	1,000,000
IDAHO WHITE PINE	Construction[1]	675	775	400	70	190	775	1,200,000
	Standard[1]	375	425	225	70	190	650	1,200,000
	Utility[1]	175	200	100	70	190	425	1,200,000
	Stud	525	600	300	70	190	425	1,200,000
WESTERN CEDARS	Construction[1]	775	875	450	75	265	850	900,000
	Standard[1]	425	500	250	75	265	700	900,000
	Utility[1]	200	225	125	75	265	450	900,000
	Stud	600	675	350	75	265	450	900,000
WHITE WOODS (Western Woods)	Construction[1]	675	775	400	70	190	675	900,000
	Standard[1]	375	425	225	70	190	550	900,000
	Utility[1]	175	200	100	70	190	375	900,000
	Stud	525	600	300	70	190	375	900,000

*These design values were calculated in accordance with ASTM standards. For information about use of these values, see Sections 100.00 through 170.00 in WWPA Grading Rules.

[1]Fb, Ft and Fc design values apply only to 4″ width of these grades. See also Tables 1a and 1b.

Single Member Design Values

The design values shown in Tables 1 through 6 on pages 6 through 12 have been calculated in accordance with ASTM Standards D-2555 and D-245. Adjustment factors shown on page 8 and 9 are also derived from ASTM standards.

Sections 100.00 through 170.00 of the WWPA Grading Rules delineate, in detail, the development, use and qualifications pertaining to design values. In single member design, where accuracy is an important consideration, users should consult the WWPA Rule Book.

Stresses Illustrated

Diagrams to the right of this column will help you understand the factors that determine design values in Western Woods.

Extreme Fiber Stress In Bending "Fb"

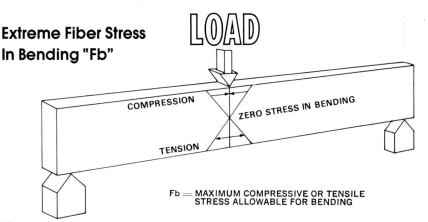

Fb = MAXIMUM COMPRESSIVE OR TENSILE STRESS ALLOWABLE FOR BENDING

When loads are applied, structural members bend, producing tension in the fibers along the faces farthest from the applied load and compression in the fibers along the face nearest to the applied load. These induced stresses in the fibers are designated as "extreme fiber stress in bending." ("Fb").

Single member "Fb" design values are used in design where the strength of an individual piece, such as a beam, girder, post or truss chord, is or may be solely responsible for carrying a specific design load.

Repetitive member "Fb" design values are used in design when three or more load sharing members such as joists, rafters, or beams are spaced no more than 24 inches apart and are joined by flooring, sheathing or other load distributing elements. Repetitive members are also used where pieces are adjacent, such as in decking.

6

Design Values/WWPA Standard Grading Rules

Table 1a LIGHT FRAMING—2″ Thick, 2″ Wide
Design Values in Pounds Per Square Inch*

Horizontal Shear "Fv", Compression Perpendicular "Fc ⊥"
and Modulus of Elasticity "E" values are shown in Table 1, Light Framing.

Grades Described in Section 40.00.
Also Stress Rated Boards.
See Section 30.60 WWPA Grading Rules.

Species or Group	Grade	Extreme Fiber Stress in Bending "Fb"		Tension Parallel to Grain "Ft"	Compression Parallel to Grain "Fc"
		Single	Repetitive		
DOUGLAS FIR-LARCH	Construction Standard Utility	950 450 125	1100 500 150	500 225 75	1150 925 375
DOUGLAS FIR SOUTH	Construction Standard Utility	900 425 125	1050 475 150	475 225 75	1000 850 350
HEM-FIR	Construction Standard Utility	750 350 100	875 400 125	400 175 50	925 775 325
MOUNTAIN HEMLOCK	Construction Standard Utility	800 375 125	925 425 125	425 200 50	900 725 300
MOUNTAIN HEMLOCK-HEM-FIR	Construction Standard Utility	750 350 100	875 400 125	400 175 50	900 725 300
WESTERN HEMLOCK	Construction Standard Utility	825 375 125	950 450 125	450 200 75	1050 850 350
ENGELMANN SPRUCE—ALPINE FIR (Engelmann Spruce-Lodgepole Pine)	Construction Standard Utility	625 300 100	725 325 100	325 150 50	675 550 225
LODGEPOLE PINE	Construction Standard Utility	700 325 100	800 375 125	375 175 50	800 675 275
PONDEROSA PINE-SUGAR PINE (Ponderosa Pine Lodgepole Pine)	Construction Standard Utility	650 300 100	750 350 100	350 150 50	775 625 250
IDAHO WHITE PINE	Construction Standard Utility	600 275 75	700 325 100	325 150 50	775 650 275
WESTERN CEDARS	Construction Standard Utility	700 325 100	800 375 125	375 175 50	850 700 300
WHITE WOODS (Western Woods)	Construction Standard Utility	600 275 75	700 325 100	325 150 50	675 550 225

*These design values were calculated in accordance with ASTM standards. For information about use of these values, see Sections 100.00 through 170.00 in WWPA Grading Rules.

7

modulus of elasticity symbol "E"

The modulus of elasticity ("E") is a ratio of the amount a material will deflect in proportion to an applied load.

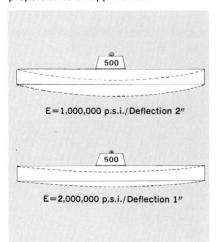

E=1,000,000 p.s.i./Deflection 2″

E=2,000,000 p.s.i./Deflection 1″

compression perpendicular to grain—"Fc⊥"

Where a joist, beam or similar piece of lumber bears on supports, the loads tend to compress the fibers. It is therefore necessary that the bearing area is sufficient to prevent side grain crushing.

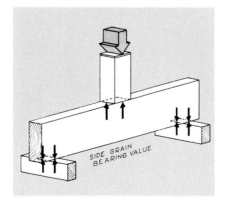

SIDE GRAIN BEARING VALUE

compression parallel to grain—"Fc"

In many parts of a structure, stress-grades are used with the loads supported on the ends of the pieces. Such uses are as studs, posts, columns and struts. The internal stress induced by this kind of loading is the same across the whole cross-section and the fibers are uniformly stressed parallel to and along the full length of the piece.

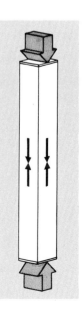

Design Values / WWPA Standard Grading Rules

Table 1b — LIGHT FRAMING—2" to 3" Thick, 3" Wide
Design Values in Pounds Per Square Inch*

Horizontal Shear "Fv", Compression Perpendicular "Fc⊥"
and Modulus of Elasticity "E" values are shown in Table 1, Light Framing.

Grades Described in Section 40.00.
Also Stress Rated Boards.
See Section 30.60 WWPA Grading Rules.

Species or Group	Grade	Extreme Fiber Stress in Bending "Fb"		Tension Parallel to Grain "Ft"	Compression Parallel to Grain "Fc"
		Single	Repetitive		
DOUGLAS FIR-LARCH	Construction	875	1000	500	1150
	Standard	550	625	300	925
	Utility	150	175	100	450
DOUGLAS FIR SOUTH	Construction	825	950	475	1000
	Standard	525	600	300	850
	Utility	150	175	75	400
HEM-FIR	Construction	700	800	400	925
	Standard	425	500	250	775
	Utility	125	150	75	375
MOUNTAIN HEMLOCK	Construction	725	825	400	900
	Standard	450	525	250	725
	Utility	125	150	75	350
MOUNTAIN HEMLOCK- HEM-FIR	Construction	700	800	400	900
	Standard	425	500	250	725
	Utility	125	150	75	350
WESTERN HEMLOCK	Construction	750	875	425	1050
	Standard	475	550	275	850
	Utility	150	150	75	400
ENGELMANN SPRUCE— ALPINE FIR (Engelmann Spruce-Lodgepole Pine)	Construction	575	650	325	675
	Standard	350	425	200	550
	Utility	100	125	50	275
LODGEPOLE PINE	Construction	625	725	350	800
	Standard	400	450	225	675
	Utility	125	125	75	325
PONDEROSA PINE-SUGAR PINE (Ponderosa-Pine- Lodgepole Pine)	Construction	600	675	325	775
	Standard	375	425	200	625
	Utility	100	125	50	300
IDAHO WHITE PINE	Construction	550	650	325	775
	Standard	350	400	200	650
	Utility	100	125	50	300
WESTERN CEDARS	Construction	625	725	350	850
	Standard	400	450	225	700
	Utility	125	125	75	325
WHITE WOODS (Western Woods)	Construction	550	650	325	675
	Standard	350	400	200	550
	Utility	100	125	50	275

*These design values were calculated in accordance with ASTM standards. For information about use of these values, see Sections 100.00 through 170.00 in WWPA Grading Rules.

8

CC Code Acceptability, Certification

Lumber Grades

Grading practices of WWPA member mills are closely supervised by the Association to assure uniformity. The resulting grades provide the specifier with a dependable measure for determining the value of lumber.

The many mills manufacturing lumber from the same or similar woods apply the grade stamp to indicate that they employ stringent quality control standards to achieve a better than 95 percent probability that an individual piece of lumber will equal the predicted average strength for the grade.

The official WWPA grade stamp on a piece of lumber is assurance of its assigned grade. It is recommended wherever possible that grademarked stock be specified. This includes lumber manufactured from 12 commercially important species in the 12 Western states.

The official Association mark (a.) on WWPA Region lumber species indicates

(Continued on page 9)

Adjustment Factors

MC-15
When 2" to 4" thick lumber is manufactured at a maximum moisture content of 15 percent and used in a condition where the moisture content does not exceed 15 percent the design values shown in Tables 1, 1a, 1b, 2, 3, and 6 may be multiplied by the following factors:

Extreme fiber in "Fb"	Tension parallel to grain "Ft"	Horizontal shear "Fv"	Compression perpendicular to grain "Fc⊥"	Compression parallel to grain "Fc"	Modulus of elasticity "E"
1.08	1.08	1.05	1.00	1.17	1.05

exposed uses—lumber 2" to 4" thick
When 2" to 4" thick lumber is designed for use where the moisture content will exceed 19 percent for an extended period of time, the values shown in Tables 1, 1a, 1b, 2, 3, and 6 should be multiplied by the following factors:

0.86	0.84	0.97	0.67	0.70	0.97

exposed uses—lumber 5" and thicker
When lumber 5" and thicker is designed for use where the moisture content will exceed 19 percent for an extended period of time, the values shown in Tables 4, 5 and 6 should be multiplied by the following factors:

1.00	1.00	1.00	0.67	0.91	1.00

horizontal shear "Fv"
The tabulated horizontal shear values shown in Tables 1 through 5 are based on the conservative assumption of the most severe checks, shakes or splits possible, as if a piece were split full length. When lumber 4" and thinner is manufactured unseasoned the tabulated values should be multiplied by a factor of 0.92.

Specific horizontal shear values for any grade and species of lumber may be established by use of the following tables when the length of split or check is known:

Nominal 2" Thick Lumber When length of split on wide face is:	Multiply tabulated "Fv" value by:
No split	2.00
½ x wide face	1.66
¾ x wide face	1.50
1 x wide face	1.34
1½ x wide face or more	1.00

Nominal 3" and Thicker Lumber When length of split on wide face is:	Multiply tabulated "Fv" value by:
No split	2.00
½ x narrow face	1.68
1 x narrow face	1.36
1½ x narrow face	1.04
2 x narrow face or more	1.00

Design Values / WWPA Standard Grading Rules

| Table 2 | STRUCTURAL LIGHT FRAMING and APPEARANCE— 2" to 4" Thick, 2" to 4" Wide Design Values in Pounds Per Square Inch* | | | | | | | | Grades Described in Sections 42.00 and 50.00. Also Stress Rated Boards. See Section 30.60 WWPA Grading Rules. |

| Species or Group | Grade | Extreme Fiber Stress in Bending "Fb" | | Tension Parallel to Grain "Ft" | Hori-zontal Shear "Fv" | Compression | | Modulus of Elasticity "E" |
		Single	Repetitive			Perpen-dicular "Fc ⊥"	Parallel to Grain "Fc"	
DOUGLAS FIR-LARCH	Select Structural[1]	2100	2400	1200	95	385	1600	1,800,000
	No. 1[1]/Appearance	1750	2050	1050	95	385	1250/1500	1,800,000
	No. 2[1]	1450	1650	850	95	385	1000	1,700,000
	No. 3	800	925	475	95	385	600	1,500,000
DOUGLAS FIR SOUTH	Select Structural	2000	2300	1150	90	335	1400	1,400,000
	No. 1/Appearance	1700	1950	975	90	335	1150/1350	1,400,000
	No. 2	1400	1600	825	90	335	900	1,300,000
	No. 3	775	875	450	90	335	550	1,100,000
HEM-FIR	Select Structural	1650	1900	975	75	245	1300	1,500,000
	No. 1/Appearance	1400	1600	825	75	245	1050/1250	1,500,000
	No. 2	1150	1350	675	75	245	825	1,400,000
	No. 3	650	725	375	75	245	500	1,200,000
MOUNTAIN HEMLOCK	Select Structural	1750	2000	1000	95	370	1250	1,300,000
	No. 1/Appearance	1450	1700	850	95	370	1000/1200	1,300,000
	No. 2	1200	1400	700	95	370	775	1,100,000
	No. 3	675	775	400	95	370	475	1,000,000
MOUNTAIN HEMLOCK-HEM-FIR	Select Structural	1650	1900	975	75	245	1250	1,300,000
	No. 1/Appearance	1400	1600	825	75	245	1000/1200	1,300,000
	No. 2	1150	1350	675	75	245	775	1,100,000
	No. 3	650	725	375	75	245	475	1,000,000
WESTERN HEMLOCK	Select Structural	1800	2100	1050	90	280	1450	1,600,000
	No. 1/Appearance	1550	1800	900	90	280	1150/1350	1,600,000
	No. 2	1300	1450	750	90	280	900	1,400,000
	No. 3	700	800	425	90	280	550	1,300,000
ENGELMANN SPRUCE-ALPINE FIR (Engelmann Spruce-Lodgepole Pine)	Select Structural	1350	1550	800	70	195	950	1,300,000
	No. 1/Appearance	1150	1350	675	70	195	750/900	1,300,000
	No. 2	950	1100	550	70	195	600	1,100,000
	No. 3	525	600	300	70	195	375	1,000,000
LODGEPOLE PINE	Select Structural	1500	1750	875	70	250	1150	1,300,000
	No. 1/Appearance	1300	1500	750	70	250	900/1050	1,300,000
	No. 2	1050	1200	625	70	250	700	1,200,000
	No. 3	600	675	350	70	250	425	1,000,000
PONDEROSA PINE-SUGAR PINE (Ponderosa Pine-Lodgepole Pine)	Select Structural	1400	1650	825	70	235	1050	1,200,000
	No. 1/Appearance	1200	1400	700	70	235	850/1000	1,200,000
	No. 2	1000	1150	575	70	235	675	1,100,000
	No. 3	550	625	325	70	235	400	1,000,000
IDAHO WHITE PINE	Select Structural	1350	1550	775	70	190	1100	1,400,000
	No. 1/Appearance	1150	1300	650	70	190	875/1050	1,400,000
	No. 2	925	1050	550	70	190	675	1,300,000
	No. 3	525	600	300	70	190	425	1,200,000
WESTERN CEDARS	Select Structural	1500	1750	875	75	265	1200	1,100,000
	No. 1/Appearance	1300	1500	750	75	265	950/1100	1,100,000
	No. 2	1050	1200	625	75	265	750	1,000,000
	No. 3	600	675	350	75	265	450	900,000
WHITE WOODS (Western Woods)	Select Structural	1350	1550	775	70	190	950	1,100,000
	No. 1/Appearance	1150	1300	650	70	190	750/900	1,100,000
	No. 2	925	1050	550	70	190	600	1,000,000
	No. 3	525	600	300	70	190	375	900,000

*These design values were calculated in accordance with ASTM standards. For information about use of these values, see Sections 100.00 through 170.00 in WWPA Grading Rules.

[1]For dense values, see Table 6, page 12.

9

Effect of Depth on Design Values

ASTM standards now provide means to adjust fiber stress in bending values depending on width, thickness and how a piece of lumber is used (on edge or flatwise). For stress rated boards and dimension 2" to 4" in thickness when used flatwise, the recommended design values for fiber stress in bending shown in Tables 1, 2, 3 and 6 in this booklet may be multiplied by the factors shown in the following table:

Adjustment Factors For Depth Effect

(Apply to Design Values for Extreme Fiber in Bending "Fb")

| Lumber Width | When used as a plank Nominal Thickness | | | |
	1"	2"	3"	4"
2" to 4"	1.19	1.10	1.04	1.00
5" and wider	1.32	1.22	1.16	1.11

For all widths of Decking and Scaffold Plank, use factors listed above for 2" to 4" widths.

(Continued from page 8)

that standard grading rules of the Association have been applied under its supervision. Each mill is assigned a permanent number (b.) for grade stamp purposes. In lieu of the mill number the mill name is often used. The official grade name (c.) as defined by the Association is part of the stamp and gives positive identification to graded lumber. The species mark (d.) identifies the wood. The symbol S-DRY (e.) indicates that the lumber was surfaced at a moisture content of 19% or less.

See **"SEASONING"** page 2, column 3, for alternative symbols at (e).

When a Lumber Inspector's certificate issued by the Association is required on a shipment of lumber and specific grade marks are not used, the stock is identified with the Association mark and the number of the shipping mill.

More Product Information

WWPA has a complete set of detailed product use publications covering the wide range of end-use applications for Western Woods. Consult the following for additional information:

Catalog E, FENCING, DECKING, STORAGE
Catalog F, EXTERIOR SIDING
Catalog G, INTERIOR PANELING
Catalog J, CONCRETE FORMS
Catalog K, SOUND CONTROL

Design Values / WWPA Standard Grading Rules

Table 3 — STRUCTURAL JOISTS and PLANKS and APPEARANCE—
2″ to 4″ Thick, 5″ and Wider
Design Values in Pounds Per Square Inch*

Grades Described in Sections 62.00 and 50.00. Also Stress Rated Boards. See Section 30.60 WWPA Grading Rules.

Species or Group	Grade	Extreme Fiber Stress in Bending "Fb" Single	Extreme Fiber Stress in Bending "Fb" Repetitive	Tension Parallel to Grain "Ft"**	Horizontal Shear "Fv"	Compression Perpendicular "Fc⊥"	Compression Parallel to Grain "Fc"	Modulus of Elasticity "E"
DOUGLAS FIR-LARCH	Select Structural[1]	1800	2050	1200	95	385	1400	1,800,000
	No. 1[1]/Appearance	1500	1750	1000	95	385	1250/1500	1,800,000
	No. 2[1]	1250	1450	650	95	385	1050	1,700,000
	No. 3/Stud	725	850	375	95	385	675	1,500,000
DOUGLAS FIR SOUTH	Select Structural	1700	1950	1150	90	335	1250	1,400,000
	No. 1/Appearance	1450	1650	975	90	335	1150/1350	1,400,000
	No. 2	1200	1350	625	90	335	950	1,300,000
	No. 3/Stud	700	800	350	90	335	600	1,100,000
HEM-FIR	Select Structural	1400	1650	950	75	245	1150	1,500,000
	No. 1/Appearance	1200	1400	800	75	245	1050/1250	1,500,000
	No. 2	1000	1150	525	75	245	875	1,400,000
	No. 3/Stud	575	675	300	75	245	550	1,200,000
MOUNTAIN HEMLOCK	Select Structural	1500	1700	1000	95	370	1100	1,300,000
	No. 1/Appearance	1250	1450	850	95	370	1000/1200	1,300,000
	No. 2	1050	1200	550	95	370	825	1,100,000
	No. 3/Stud	625	700	325	95	370	525	1,000,000
MOUNTAIN HEMLOCK-HEM-FIR	Select Structural	1400	1650	950	75	245	1100	1,300,000
	No. 1/Appearance	1200	1400	800	75	245	1000/1200	1,300,000
	No. 2	1000	1150	525	75	245	825	1,100,000
	No. 3/Stud	575	675	300	75	245	525	1,000,000
WESTERN HEMLOCK	Select Structural	1550	1800	1050	90	280	1300	1,600,000
	No. 1/Appearance	1350	1550	900	90	280	1150/1350	1,600,000
	No. 2	1100	1250	575	90	280	975	1,400,000
	No. 3/Stud	650	750	325	90	280	625	1,300,000
ENGELMANN SPRUCE-ALPINE FIR (Engelmann Spruce-Lodgepole Pine)	Select Structural	1200	1350	775	70	195	850	1,300,000
	No. 1/Appearance	1000	1150	675	70	195	750/900	1,300,000
	No. 2	825	950	425	70	195	625	1,100,000
	No. 3/Stud	475	550	250	70	195	400	1,000,000
LODGEPOLE PINE	Select Structural	1300	1500	875	70	250	1000	1,300,000
	No. 1/Appearance	1100	1300	750	70	250	900/1050	1,300,000
	No. 2	925	1050	475	70	250	750	1,200,000
	No. 3/Stud	525	625	275	70	250	475	1,000,000
PONDEROSA PINE-SUGAR PINE (Ponderosa Pine-Lodgepole Pine)	Select Structural	1200	1400	825	70	235	950	1,200,000
	No. 1/Appearance	1050	1200	700	70	235	850/1000	1,200,000
	No. 2	850	975	450	70	235	700	1,100,000
	No. 3/Stud	500	575	250	70	235	450	1,000,000
IDAHO WHITE PINE	Select Structural	1150	1300	775	70	190	950	1,400,000
	No. 1/Appearance	975	1100	650	70	190	875/1050	1,400,000
	No. 2	800	925	425	70	190	725	1,300,000
	No. 3/Stud	475	550	250	70	190	450	1,200,000
WESTERN CEDARS	Select Structural	1300	1500	875	75	265	1050	1,100,000
	No. 1/Appearance	1100	1300	750	75	265	950/1100	1,100,000
	No. 2	925	1050	475	75	265	800	1,000,000
	No. 3/Stud	525	625	275	75	265	500	900,000
WHITE WOODS (Western Woods)	Select Structural	1150	1300	775	70	190	850	1,100,000
	No. 1/Appearance	975	1100	650	70	190	750/900	1,100,000
	No. 2	800	925	425	70	190	625	1,000,000
	No. 3/Stud	475	550	250	70	190	400	900,000

*These design values were calculated in accordance with ASTM standards. For information about use of these values, see Sections 100.00 through 170.00 in WWPA Grading Rules.
**Tabulated values apply to 5″ and 6″ widths. For 8″ width, use 90% of tabulated tension parallel to grain value for Select Structural and 80% for all other grades. For 10″ and wider widths, use 80% of tabulated tension parallel to grain value for Select Structural and 60% for all other grades.
[1]For Dense values, see Table 6, page 12.

Example of Brief Lumber Specification (Applicable to all Species)

Rough Carpentry

GENERAL:

1. Store lumber off ground, well ventilated and covered.
2. Current Edition, Association Grading Rules govern.
3. All lumber shall bear the grade mark of an ALSC Board of Review approved agency.
4. Any species allowed, unless otherwise noted.
5. Sizes shown are nominal. Actual sizes shall conform to American Lumber Standard PS 20-70.
6. All lumber shall be S4S (surfaced four sides) unless otherwise indicated.
7. Moisture content of lumber 2″ or less in thickness shall be 19% or less at time of enclosure.

MATERIALS: (By Use Category)	MINIMUM GRADE
1. Light Framing (4 x 4 and smaller) A. General Framing	Standard or "Stud"
B. Plates, Blocking, and Nailers	Utility
2. Studs (4 x 4 and smaller) A. Load Bearing	Standard, No. 3 or "Stud"
B. Non-Load Bearing (or bearing roof & ceiling load only)	Utility
2.1 Studs (2″ to 4″ thick, 5″ and 6″ wide) A. Load bearing or non-load bearing.	No. 3 or "Stud"
3. Structural Joists and Planks (2″ to 4″ thick, 5″ & wider) A. Joists, both Floor and Ceiling B. Rafters (Where joist and rafter size and loading conditions apply, spans shall conform to "SPAN TABLES for JOISTS & RAFTERS," 1970 edition, as published by National Forest Products Association.) C. For all other structural framing material (or for loading conditions not listed in above span tables)	Specify by minimum "E" and "Fb" (Single or Repetative) values required*
D. 2 x 5″ and wider Plates, Blocking, and Nailers	No. 3
E. Stair Stringers	No. 1
4. Posts, Beams and Timbers (5 x 5″ and larger)	No. 1—F.O.H.C.
5. Boards A. Shall be suitable for intended use by reasonable carpentry standards.	

*The architect is cautioned **not** to limit his design so that only the higher values apply. This reduces competitive bidding. The higher value grades are somewhat limited in supply and would command much higher prices.

Design Values/WWPA Standard Grading Rules

Table 4 — BEAMS and STRINGERS—5″ and Thicker
Width More Than 2″ Greater Than Thickness
Design Values in Pounds Per Square Inch*

Grades Described in Section 70.00 WWPA Grading Rules

Species or Group	Grade	Extreme Fiber Stress in Bending "Fb" Single Members	Tension Parallel to Grain "Ft"	Horizontal Shear "Fv"	Compression Perpendicular "Fc ⊥"	Compression Parallel to Grain "Fc"	Modulus of Elasticity "E"
DOUGLAS FIR-LARCH	Select Structural¹	1600	1050	85	385	1100	1,600,000
	No. 1¹	1350	900	85	385	925	1,600,000
DOUGLAS FIR SOUTH	Select Structural	1550	1050	85	335	1000	1,200,000
	No. 1	1300	850	85	335	850	1,200,000
HEM-FIR	Select Structural	1250	850	70	245	925	1,300,000
	No. 1	1050	725	70	245	775	1,300,000
MOUNTAIN HEMLOCK	Select Structural	1350	900	90	370	875	1,100,000
	No. 1	1100	750	90	370	750	1,100,000
MOUNTAIN HEMLOCK— HEM-FIR	Select Structural	1250	850	70	245	875	1,100,000
	No. 1	1050	725	70	245	750	1,100,000
WESTERN HEMLOCK	Select Structural	1400	950	85	280	1000	1,400,000
	No. 1	1150	775	85	280	850	1,400,000
ENGELMANN SPRUCE— ALPINE FIR (Engelmann Spruce-Lodgepole Pine)	Select Structural	1050	700	65	195	675	1,100,000
	No. 1	875	600	65	195	550	1,100,000
LODGEPOLE PINE	Select Structural	1150	775	65	250	800	1,100,000
	No. 1	975	650	65	250	675	1,100,000
PONDEROSA PINE- SUGAR PINE (Ponderosa Pine-Lodgepole Pine)	Select Structural	1100	725	65	235	750	1,100,000
	No. 1	925	625	65	235	625	1,100,000
IDAHO WHITE PINE	Select Structural	1000	700	65	190	775	1,300,000
	No. 1	850	575	65	190	650	1,300,000
WESTERN CEDARS	Select Structural	1150	775	70	265	875	1,000,000
	No. 1	975	650	70	265	725	1,000,000
WHITE WOODS (Western Woods)	Select Structural	1000	700	65	190	675	1,000,000
	No. 1	850	575	65	190	550	1,000,000

*These design values were calculated in accordance with ASTM standards. For information about use of these values, see Sections 100.00 through 170.00 in WWPA Grading Rules.
¹For Dense values, see Table 6, page 12.

Decking
2″ to 4″ Thick. 4″ to 12″ Wide Design Values in Pounds Per Square Inch For Flatwise Use Only.*

Species	Grade	DRY(1) Extreme Fiber Stress in Bending "Fb" Repetitive	DRY(1) Modulus of Elasticity "E"	MC 15(2) Extreme Fiber Stress in Bending "Fb" Repetitive	MC 15(2) Modulus of Elasticity "E"
Douglas Fir— Larch	Selected Decking	2000	1,800,000	2150	1,900,000
	Commercial Decking	1650	1,700,000	1800	1,700,000
Douglas Fir South	Selected Decking	1900	1,400,000	2050	1,500,000
	Commercial Decking	1600	1,300,000	1750	1,300,000
Hem-Fir	Selected Decking	1600	1,500,000	1700	1,600,000
	Commercial Decking	1350	1,400,000	1450	1,400,000
Mountain Hemlock	Selected Decking	1650	1,300,000	1800	1,300,000
	Commercial Decking	1400	1,100,000	1500	1,200,000
Mountain Hemlock— Hem-Fir	Selected Decking	1600	1,300,000	1750	1,300,000
	Commercial Decking	1350	1,100,000	1450	1,200,000
Western Hemlock	Selected Decking	1750	1,600,000	1900	1,700,000
	Commercial Decking	1450	1,400,000	1600	1,500,000
Engelmann Spruce, Alpine Fir (Engelmann Spruce— Lodgepole Pine)	Selected Decking	1300	1,300,000	1400	1,300,000
	Commercial Decking	1100	1,100,000	1200	1,200,000
Lodgepole Pine	Selected Decking	1450	1,300,000	1550	1,400,000
	Commercial Decking	1200	1,200,000	1300	1,200,000
Ponderosa Pine—Sugar Pine (Ponderosa Pine— Lodgepole Pine)	Selected Decking	1350	1,200,000	1450	1,300,000
	Commercial Decking	1150	1,100,000	1250	1,100,000
Idaho White Pine	Selected Decking	1300	1,400,000	1400	1,500,000
	Commercial Decking	1050	1,300,000	1150	1,400,000
Western Cedars	Selected Decking	1450	1,100,000	1550	1,100,000
	Commercial Decking	1200	1,000,000	1300	1,000,000
White Woods (Western Woods)	Selected Decking	1300	1,100,000	1400	1,100,000
	Commercial Decking	1050	1,000,000	1150	1,000,000

*These design values were calculated in accordance with ASTM standards. For information about use of these values, see Sections 100.00 through 170.00 in WWPA Grading Rules.
(1) DRY design values apply to lumber manufactured and used at a maximum moisture content of 19%. For other conditions of use, See Section 140.00, Para. 2, WWPA Grading Rules.
(2) MC 15 design values apply to lumber manufactured and used at a maximum moisture content of 15%. For other conditions of use, See Section 140.00, Para. 4, WWPA Grading Rules.

11

Standard decking patterns in 2″ single T&G and 3″ and 4″ double T&G are available in vee or eased joints or grooved faces to meet most architectural design requirements.

For diagrams of available patterns and sizes order STANDARD PATTERNS booklet G-16 from Western Wood Products Association, Yeon Building, Portland, Oregon 97204.

Decking, with tongue-and-groove edges and decorative face patterns, is a standard building product for residential, commercial, and institutional construction.

Known and used as "roof decking," its load-bearing capacities make it also useful as floor decking and solid sidewall construction.

Specified loads are carried satisfactorily through various combinations of support spacing, deck thickness, and span arrangement. Although two-span continuous lay-up offers structural efficiency, use of random-length planks is the most economical application.

Random length double tongue-and-groove decking is used only in conjunction with three or more spans and each piece should bear on at least one support. It's not intended for use over single spans and is not recommended for use over double spans.

Design Values / WWPA Standard Grading Rules

Table 5

POSTS and TIMBERS—5" x 5" and Larger
Width Not More than 2" Greater Than Thickness
Design Values in Pounds Per Square Inch*

Grades Described
in Section 80.00
WWPA Grading Rules

Species or Group	Grade	Extreme Fiber Stress in Bending "Fb" Single Members	Tension Parallel to Grain "Ft"	Horizontal Shear "Fv"	Compression Perpendicular "Fc ⊥"	Compression Parallel to Grain "Fc"	Modulus of Elasticity "E"
DOUGLAS FIR-LARCH	Select Structural¹ No. 1¹	1500 1200	1000 825	85 85	385 385	1150 1000	1,600,000 1,600,000
DOUGLAS FIR SOUTH	Select Structural No. 1	1400 1150	950 775	85 85	335 335	1050 925	1,200,000 1,200,000
HEM-FIR	Select Structural No. 1	1200 950	800 650	70 70	245 245	975 850	1,300,000 1,300,000
MOUNTAIN HEMLOCK	Select Structural No. 1	1250 1000	825 675	90 90	370 370	925 800	1,100,000 1,100,000
MOUNTAIN HEMLOCK—HEM-FIR	Select Structural No. 1	1200 950	800 650	70 70	245 245	925 800	1,100,000 1,100,000
WESTERN HEMLOCK	Select Structural No. 1	1300 1050	875 700	85 85	280 280	1100 950	1,400,000 1,400,000
ENGELMANN SPRUCE-ALPINE FIR (Engelmann Spruce-Lodgepole Pine)	Select Structural No. 1	975 800	650 525	65 65	195 195	700 625	1,100,000 1,100,000
LODGEPOLE PINE	Select Structural No. 1	1100 875	725 600	65 65	250 250	850 725	1,100,000 1,100,000
PONDEROSA PINE—SUGAR PINE (Ponderosa Pine-Lodgepole Pine)	Select Structural No. 1	1000 825	675 550	65 65	235 235	800 700	1,100,000 1,100,000
IDAHO WHITE PINE	Select Structural No. 1	950 775	650 525	65 65	190 190	800 700	1,300,000 1,300,000
WESTERN CEDARS	Select Structural No. 1	1100 875	725 600	70 70	265 265	925 800	1,000,000 1,000,000
WHITE WOODS (Western Woods)	Select Structural No. 1	950 775	650 525	65 65	190 190	700 625	1,000,000 1,000,000

*These design values were calculated in accordance with ASTM standards. For information about use of these values, see Sections 100.00 through 170.00 in WWPA Grading Rules.
¹For Dense values, see Table 6, below.

12

Table 6

DENSE DOUGLAS FIR—LARCH
Recommended Design Values in Pounds Per Square Inch*

Grades Described
in Section 53.00
WWPA Grading Rules

Species or Group	Grade	Extreme Fiber Stress in Bending "Fb" Single	Extreme Fiber Stress in Bending "Fb" Repetitive	Tension Parallel to Grain "Ft"	Horizontal Shear "Fv"	Compression Perpendicular "Fc ⊥"	Compression Parallel to Grain "Fc"	Modulus of Elasticity "E"
STRUCTURAL LIGHT FRAMING	Dense Sel. Struc. Dense No. 1 Dense No. 2	2450 2050 1700	2800 2400 1950	1400 1200 1000	95 95 95	455 455 455	1850 1450 1150	1,900,000 1,900,000 1,700,000
STRUCTURAL JOISTS AND PLANKS	Dense Sel. Struc. Dense No. 1 Dense No. 2	2100 1800 1450	2400 2050 1700	1400** 1200** 775**	95 95 95	455 455 455	1650 1450 1250	1,900,000 1,900,000 1,700,000
BEAMS AND STRINGERS	Dense Sel. Struc. Dense No. 1	1900 1550		1250 1050	85 85	455 455	1300 1100	1,700,000 1,700,000
POSTS AND TIMBERS	Dense Sel. Struc. Dense No. 1	1750 1400		1150 950	85 85	455 455	1350 1200	1,700,000 1,700,000

*These design values were calculated in accordance with ASTM standards. For information about use of these values, see Sections 100.00 through 170.00 in WWPA Grading Rules.
**Tabulated values apply to 5" and 6" widths. For 8" width, use 90% of tabulated tension parallel to grain value for Select Structural and 80% for all other grades. For 10" and wider widths, use 80% of tabulated tension parallel to grain value for Select Structural and 60% for all other grades.

Span Computer

Send for WWPA's Slide Rule that quickly figures spans, spacing and loading of Western lumber joists, rafters and beams. Gives you correct spans for all sizes, grades and species of Western lumber 2" to 4" thickness, and 4" and wider widths, helping you check correct span usage. 4 x 9¼.

Price $1.00 each

Properties of Standard Dressed Sizes (See pages 13 and 14)

Certain mathematical expressions of the properties or elements of sections are used in computing the values of structural members of various shapes for the various conditions under which they are subjected to stress. The properties or elements of sections of Standard sizes of joists, planks, beams, stringers, posts, timbers and decking are given in the following tables.

NEUTRAL AXIS, in the cross section of a beam or column in a state of flexure, is the line on which there is neither tension nor compression.

The neutral axis, X-X in the following tables of properties of the rectangular and square sections of lumber has been as-

sumed as perpendicular to the depth of the section at its center, the depth "h" being parallel to and in the direction of the application of the force or load.

MOMENT OF INERTIA, I, of the cross section of a beam is the sum of the products of each of its elementary areas by the square of their distance from the neutral axis of the section.

SECTION MODULUS, S, is the moment of inertia divided by the distance from the neutral axis to extreme fiber of the section.

CROSS SECTION is a section taken through the member perpendicular to its longitudinal axis.

Properties of Sections (S4S)

Joists and Beams

Nominal Size in Inches b h	Surfaced Size for Design in Inches b h	Area. (A) $A = bh$ (In²)	Section Modulus. (S) $S = \dfrac{bh^2}{6}$ (In³)	Moment of Inertia. (I) $I = \dfrac{bh^3}{12}$ (In⁴)	Board Feet Per Lineal Foot of Piece
2 x 2	1.5 x 1.5	2.25	0.562	0.422	0.33
2 x 3	1.5 x 2.5	3.75	1.56	1.95	0.50
2 x 4	1.5 x 3.5	5.25	3.06	5.36	0.67
2 x 5	1.5 x 4.5	6.75	5.06	11.39	.83
2 x 6	1.5 x 5.5	8.25	7.56	20.80	1.00
2 x 8	1.5 x 7.25	10.88	13.14	47.63	1.33
2 x 10	1.5 x 9.25	13.88	21.39	98.93	1.67
2 x 12	1.5 x 11.25	16.88	31.64	177.98	2.00
2 x 14	1.5 x 13.25	19.88	43.89	290.78	2.33.
3 x 3	2.5 x 2.5	6.25	2.60	3.26	0.75
3 x 4	2.5 x 3.5	8.75	5.10	8.93	1.00
3 x 5	2.5 x 4.5	11.25	8.44	18.98	1.25
3 x 6	2.5 x 5.5	13.75	12.60	34.66	1.50
3 x 8	2.5 x 7.25	18.12	21.90	79.39	2.00
3 x 10	2.5 x 9.25	23.12	35.65	164.89	2.50
3 x 12	2.5 x 11.25	28.12	52.73	296.63	3.00
3 x 14	2.5 x 13.25	33.12	73.15	484.63	3.50
3 x 16	2.5 x 15.25	38.12	96.90	738.87	4.00
4 x 4	3.5 x 3.5	12.25	7.15	12.51	1.33
4 x 5	3.5 x 4.5	15.75	11.81	26.58	1.67
4 x 6	3.5 x 5.5	19.25	17.65	48.53	2.00
4 x 8	3.5 x 7.25	25.38	30.66	111.15	2.67
4 x 10	3.5 x 9.25	32.38	49.91	230.84	3.33
4 x 12	3.5 x 11.25	39.38	73.83	415.28	4.00
4 x 14	3.5 x 13.25	46.38	102.41	678.48	4.67
4 x 16	3.5 x 15.25	53.38	135.66	1034.42	5.33
6 x 6	5.5 x 5.5	30.25	27.73	76.26	3.00
6 x 8	5.5 x 7.5	41.25	51.56	193.36	4.00
6 x 10	5.5 x 9.5	52.25	82.73	392.96	5.00
6 x 12	5.5 x 11.5	63.25	121.23	697.07	6.00
6 x 14	5.5 x 13.5	74.25	167.06	1127.67	7.00
6 x 16	5.5 x 15.5	85.25	220.23	1706.78	8.00
6 x 18	5.5 x 17.5	96.25	280.73	2456.38	9.00
6 x 20	5.5 x 19.5	107.25	348.56	3398.48	10.00
8 x 8	7.5 x 7.5	56.25	70.31	263.67	5.33
8 x 10	7.5 x 9.5	71.25	112.81	535.86	6.67
8 x 12	7.5 x 11.5	86.25	165.31	950.55	8.00
8 x 14	7.5 x 13.5	101.25	227.81	1537.73	9.33
8 x 16	7.5 x 15.5	116.25	300.31	2327.42	10.67
8 x 18	7.5 x 17.5	131.25	382.81	3349.61	12.00
8 x 20	7.5 x 19.5	146.25	475.31	4634.30	13.33
8 x 22	7.5 x 21.5	161.25	577.81	6211.48	14.67
8 x 24	7.5 x 23.5	176.25	690.31	8111.17	16.00
10 x 10	9.5 x 9.5	90.25	142.90	678.76	8.33
10 x 12	9.5 x 11.5	109.25	209.40	1204.03	10.00
10 x 14	9.5 x 13.5	128.25	288.56	1947.80	11.67
10 x 16	9.5 x 15.5	147.25	380.40	2948.07	13.33
10 x 18	9.5 x 17.5	166.25	484.90	4242.84	15.00
10 x 20	9.5 x 19.5	185.25	602.06	5870.11	16.67
10 x 22	9.5 x 21.5	204.25	731.90	7867.88	18.33
12 x 12	11.5 x 11.5	132.25	253.48	1457.51	12.00
12 x 14	11.5 x 13.5	155.25	349.31	2357.86	14.00
12 x 16	11.5 x 15.5	178.25	460.48	3568.71	16.00
12 x 18	11.5 x 17.5	201.25	586.98	5136.07	18.00
12 x 20	11.5 x 19.5	224.25	728.81	7105.92	20.00
12 x 22	11.5 x 21.5	247.25	885.98	9524.28	22.00
12 x 24	11.5 x 23.5	270.25	1058.48	12437.13	24.00

13

Properties of Sections (S4S) —Continued

Planks

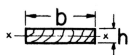

Nominal Size in Inches b h ▽ ▽	Surfaced Size for Design in Inches b h ▽ ▽	Area. (A) A = bh (In²)	Section Modulus. (S) S = $\frac{bh^2}{6}$ (In³)	Moment of Inertia. (I) I = $\frac{bh^3}{12}$ (In⁴)	Board Feet Per Lineal Foot of Piece
3 x 2	2.5 x 1.5	3.75	0.938	0.703	0.50
4 x 2	3.5 x 1.5	5.25	1.312	0.984	0.67
5 x 2	4.5 x 1.5	6.75	1.688	1.266	0.83
6 x 2	5.5 x 1.5	8.25	2.062	1.547	1.00
8 x 2	7.25 x 1.5	10.88	2.719	2.039	1.33
10 x 2	9.25 x 1.5	13.88	3.469	2.602	1.67
12 x 2	11.25 x 1.5	16.88	4.219	3.164	2.00
4 x 3	3.5 x 2.5	8.75	3.646	4.557	1.00
5 x 3	4.5 x 2.5	11.25	4.688	5.859	1.25
6 x 3	5.5 x 2.5	13.75	5.729	7.161	1.50
8 x 3	7.25 x 2.5	18.12	7.552	9.440	2.00
10 x 3	9.25 x 2.5	23.12	9.635	12.044	2.50
12 x 3	11.25 x 2.5	28.12	11.719	14.648	3.00
14 x 3	13.25 x 2.5	33.12	13.802	17.253	3.50
16 x 3	15.25 x 2.5	38.12	15.885	19.857	4.00
5 x 4	4.5 x 3.5	15.75	9.188	16.078	1.67
6 x 4	5.5 x 3.5	19.25	11.229	19.651	2.00
8 x 4	7.25 x 3.5	25.38	14.802	25.904	2.67
10 x 4	9.25 x 3.5	32.38	18.885	33.049	3.33
12 x 4	11.25 x 3.5	39.38	22.969	40.195	4.00
14 x 4	13.25 x 3.5	46.38	27.052	47.341	4.67
16 x 4	15.25 x 3.5	53.38	31.135	54.487	5.33

Decking

2	12 x 1.5	18.00	4.50	3.375	2.00
3	2.5	30.00	12.50	15.625	3.00
4	3.5	42.00	24.50	42.875	4.00

14

Weight Per Lineal Foot

To calculate the weight per lineal foot for a particular size and species multiply the area of the member by the species weight factor shown below. The weight factors apply to lumber when used at a maximum moisture content of 19% such as in most covered structures. For convenience, increase factors for exposed use conditions are also listed.

SPECIES OR SPECIES GROUP	WEIGHT FACTOR
DOUGLAS FIR—LARCH	.252
DOUGLAS FIR SOUTH	.226
HEM-FIR	.221
MOUNTAIN HEMLOCK—HEM-FIR	.221
WESTERN HEMLOCK	.221
ENGELMANN SPRUCE—ALPINE FIR	.173
LODGEPOLE PINE	.205
PONDEROSA PINE—SUGAR PINE	.205
IDAHO WHITE PINE	.184
WESTERN CEDARS	.184

EXPOSED USE

Moisture Content	Increase Factor
30%	1.073
40%	1.156
50%	1.238
60%	1.321
70%	1.403

Weight factors are based on the latest wood density data published by the U.S. Department of Agriculture.

Allowable Stresses / Machine Stress Rated Lumber

2″ and Less in Thickness, 2″ and Wider.
Design Values In Pounds Per Square Inch

Grades Described
In Section 52.00
WWPA 1970 Grading Rules

"f—E" Classification	Extreme Fiber Stress in Bending "Fb" (1)		Modulus of Elasticity "E"	Tension Parallel to Grain "Ft"	Compression Parallel to Grain "Fc"
	Single	Repetitive			
1200f — 1.2 E	1200	1400	1,200,000	600	950
1500f — 1.4 E	1500	1750	1,400,000	900	1200
1650f — 1.5 E	1650	1900	1,500,000	1020	1320
1800f — 1.6 E	1800	2050	1,600,000	1175	1450
2100f — 1.8 E	2100	2400	1,800,000	1575	1700
2400f — 2.0 E	2400	2750	2,000,000	1925	1925
2700f — 2.2 E	2700	3100	2,200,000	2150	2150
3000f — 2.4 E	3000	3450	2,400,000	2400	2400
3300f — 2.6 E	3300	3800	2,600,000	2650	2650

	Douglas Fir & Larch	Douglas Fir S	Hem-Fir	Western Hemlock	Pine (2)	Engelmann Spruce	Cedar (3)
Compression Perpendicular to Grain "Fc ⊥"							
	385	335	245	280	190	195	265
Horizontal Shear "Fv" (DRY)							
	95	90	75	90	70	70	75

The classifications listed below are designed to provide MOE levels with corresponding lower Fb requirements, especially for joist use. Although the tables are separated primarily on the basis of rafter and joist use, any f-E classification may be ordered which meets the requirement of design.

"f—E" Classification		Extreme Fiber Stress in Bending "Fb" (1)	Modulus of Elasticity "E"	Tension Parallel to Grain "Ft"	Compression Parallel to Grain "Fc"
900f — 1.0 E	900	1050	1,000,000	350	725
900f — 1.2 E	900	1050	1,200,000	350	725
1200f — 1.5 E	1200	1400	1,500,000	600	950
1350f — 1.8 E	1350	1550	1,800,000	750	1075
1800f — 2.1 E	1800	2050	2,100,000	1175	1450

(1) The tabulated Extreme Fiber in Bending values "Fb" are applicable to lumber loaded on edge. When loaded flatwise, these values may be increased by multiplying by the following factors:

Nominal Width (In.)	3″	4″	6″	8″	10″	12″	14″
Factor	1.06	1.10	1.15	1.19	1.22	1.25	1.28

(2) Idaho White, Lodgepole, Ponderosa or Sugar Pine.

(3) Incense or Western Red Cedar.

Rules for Machine Stress-Rated Lumber

All Species 2″ and Less in Thickness, 4″ and Wider

Machine stress-rated lumber is lumber that has been evaluated by mechanical stress rating equipment. MSR lumber is distinguished from visually stress graded lumber in that each piece is nondestructively tested and marked to indicate the modulus of elasticity. MSR lumber is also required to meet certain visual requirements as set forth in the Grading Rules.

To meet structural needs for a broad range of engineered construction, 14 "f-E" classifications are available. "E" designates the modulus of elasticity in one million pounds per square inch and "f" indicates a correlated fiber stress in bending for edge loading in pounds per square inch.

The appropriate "f-E" classification should be specified in the order, acknowledgment and invoice. All design values are shown in the table above.

Grade Stamp Example
Machine Stress-Rated Lumber

```
MACHINE  RATED
(W)    12     HEM
 WP  S-DRY    FIR
1650f 1.5E
```

Grade Marking Requirements

A grade stamp on machine stress-rated lumber indicates the stress rating system used meets requirements of the grading agency's certification and quality control procedures. The grade stamp will show the agency trademark, the mill name or number, will include the phrase "Machine Rated," the species identification and condition of seasoning or moisture content at time of surfacing (manufacture).

Uses

One of the prime uses for machine stress-rated lumber is trussed rafters, but this product is also used as floor and ceiling joists, as rafters and for other structural purposes where assured strength capabilities are primary product considerations.

With the increased utilization of trussed-rafters in modern-day roof systems, machine stress-rated lumber is an ideal product to specify. It may be used in the upper and lower chords, and the web members where individual piece strength is important. It may be fabricated with nailed metal plates, punched metal plates with long teeth, punched metal plates with short teeth, and plywood gussets.

How to Specify MSR

The correct specification for Machine Stress-Rated Lumber is simple. Strength is the important factor and controls the specification rather than species. WWPA Rule 52.00 shows the Strengths (stress levels) which are available.

To order, specify MACHINE RATED, WWPA grade-stamped and list the Strength "f" Value and corresponding "E" (Modulus of Elasticity) values, nominal sizes and lengths required. Values

are shown in the chart on this page. Nominal sizes include 2x4, 2x6, 2x8, 2x10, 2x12.

MSR Quality Control

In addition to requiring conformance to the Grading Rules for Machine Rated lumber, the Association maintains rigid quality control standards and procedures over the testing machines which include:

WWPA

Certification of Machines
Calibration of test equipment
Plant use regulations
Continual quality inspections
Laboratory tests
Product appearance considerations

Producer

Strict adherence to WWPA procedures
Strength level checks every shift
Constant quality checks
Regular tests of rated material
Maintenance of detailed test records

Finger-Jointed Lumber Use Criteria

Approved end-jointed lumber (finger-jointed) may be used interchangeably with solid sawn members of the same species and grade. Such use shall include but not be limited to light framing, joists, planks and decking.

The grade stamp on such lumber shall include the notation PS-56 indicating conformance with Product Standard PS-56 except that STUD grade may be marked with a grade stamp including the notation "Certified Glued Joints Stud Use Only."

15

Floor Joists Allowable clear spans for joists spaced 16″ and 24″ o.c.

| Species | Grade | Span (feet and inches) | | | | | |
| | | 2 x 8 | | 2 x 10 | | 2 x 12 | |
		16″ oc	24″ oc	16″ oc	24″ oc	16″ oc	24″ oc
DOUGLAS FIR-LARCH	2 & Better 3	13-1 10-7	11-3 8-8	16-9 13-6	14-5 11-0	20-4 16-5	17-6 13-5
DOUGLAS FIR SOUTH	2 & Better 3	12-0 10-3	10-6 8-4	15-3 13-1	13-4 10-8	18-7 15-11	16-3 13-0
HEM-FIR	2 & Better 3	12-3 9-5	10-0 7-8	15-8 12-0	12-10 9-10	19-1 14-7	15-7 11-11
MOUNTAIN HEMLOCK	2 & Better 3	11-4 9-7	9-11 7-10	14-6 12-3	12-8 10-0	17-7 14-11	15-4 12-2
MOUNTAIN HEMLOCK-HEM-FIR	2 & Better 3	11-4 9-5	9-11 7-8	14-6 12-0	12-8 9-10	17-7 14-7	15-4 11-11
WESTERN HEMLOCK	2 & Better 3	12-3 9-11	10-6 8-1	15-8 12-8	13-4 10-4	19-1 15-5	16-3 12-7
ENGELMANN SPRUCE ALPINE FIR (Engelmann Spruce-Lodgepole Pine)	2 & Better 3	11-2 8-6	9-1 6-11	14-3 10-10	11-7 8-10	17-3 13-2	14-2 10-9
LODGEPOLE PINE	2 & Better 3	11-8 9-1	9-7 7-5	14-11 11-7	12-3 9-5	18-1 14-1	14-11 11-6
PONDEROSA PINE-SUGAR PINE (Ponderosa Pine-Lodgepole Pine)	2 & Better 3	11-4 8-8	9-3 7-1	14-5 11-1	11-9 9-1	17-7 13-6	14-4 11-0
WHITE WOODS (Western Woods)	2 & Better 3	11-0 8-6	9-0 6-11	14-0 10-10	11-6 8-10	17-0 13-2	14-0 10-9
IDAHO WHITE PINE	2 & Better 3	11-0 8-6	9-0 6-11	14-0 10-10	11-6 8-10	17-1 13-2	14-0 10-9
WESTERN CEDARS	2 & Better 3	11-0 9-1	9-7 7-5	14-0 11-6	12-3 9-5	17-0 14-0	14-11 11-6

Design Criteria:
Strength—10 lbs. per sq. ft. dead load plus 40 lbs. per sq. ft. live load.
Deflection—Limited to span in inches divided by 360 for live load only.

16

Ceiling Joists Allowable clear spans for joists spaced 16″ and 24″ o.c.

| Species | Grade | Span (feet and inches) | | | | | |
| | | 2 x 4 | | 2 x 6 | | 2 x 8 | |
		16″ oc	24″ oc	16″ oc	24″ oc	16″ oc	24″ oc
DOUGLAS FIR-LARCH	2 & Better 3	11-6 9-9	10-0 7-11	18-1 14-8	15-7 11-11	23-10 19-4	20-7 15-9
DOUGLAS FIR SOUTH	2 & Better 3	10-6 9-5	9-2 7-9	16-6 14-2	14-5 11-7	21-9 18-9	19-0 15-3
HEM-FIR	2 & Better 3	10-9 8-7	9-5 7-0	16-11 13-1	13-11 10-8	22-4 17-2	18-4 14-0
MOUNTAIN HEMLOCK	2 & Better 3	9-11 8-11	8-8 7-3	15-7 13-3	13-8 10-10	20-7 17-6	18-0 14-4
MOUNTAIN HEMLOCK-HEM-FIR	2 & Better 3	9-11 8-7	8-8 7-0	15-7 13-1	13-8 10-8	20-7 17-2	18-0 14-0
WESTERN HEMLOCK	2 & Better 3	10-9 9-0	9-5 7-5	16-11 13-9	14-6 11-3	22-4 18-1	19-1 14-10
ENGELMANN SPRUCE ALPINE FIR (Engelmann Spruce-Lodgepole Pine)	2 & Better 3	9-11 7-10	8-8 6-5	15-6 11-9	12-8 9-7	20-7 15-6	16-8 12-8
LODGEPOLE PINE	2 & Better 3	10-3 8-4	8-11 6-9	16-1 12-7	13-3 10-3	21-2 16-7	17-6 13-6
PONDEROSA PINE-SUGAR PINE (Ponderosa Pine-Lodgepole Pine)	2 & Better 3	9-11 8-0	8-8 6-6	15-7 12-0	12-10 9-10	20-7 15-10	16-10 12-11
WHITE WOODS (Western Woods)	2 & Better 3	9-7 7-10	8-5 6-5	15-1 11-9	12-6 9-8	20-2 15-6	16-5 12-8
IDAHO WHITE PINE	2 & Better 3	10-3 7-10	8-5 6-5	15-3 11-9	12-6 9-8	20-0 15-6	16-5 12-8
WESTERN CEDARS	2 & Better 3	9-7 8-3	8-5 6-9	15-1 12-7	13-2 10-3	20-0 16-7	17-6 13-7

Design Criteria:
Strength—5 lbs. per sq. ft. dead load plus 10 lbs. per sq. ft. live load.
Deflection—Limited to span in inches divided by 240 for live load only.

2" Decking Spans

Spans are for 4" to 12" wide lumber manufactured and used at a maximum moisture content of 19%. Spans are given in feet-inches for normal load duration.

	Douglas Fir-Larch		Douglas Fir South		Hem-Fir		Mountain Hemlock		Mountain Hemlock Hem-Fir		Western Hemlock		Engelmann Spruce Alpine Fir (Engelmann Spruce-Lodgepole Pine)		Lodgepole Pine		Ponderosa Pine-Sugar Pine (Ponderosa Pine-Lodgepole Pine)		Idaho White Pine		Western Cedars		White Woods (Western Woods)	
	Select	Comm	Select	Comm	Select	Comm	Select	Comm	Select	Comm	Select	Comm	Select	Comm	Select	Comm	Select	Comm	Select	Comm	Select	Comm	Select	Comm
Floor Decking — 10 psf Dead Load/40 psf Live Load/L/360 Deflection Limit																								
Simple	6-1	6-0	5-7	5-5	5-9	5-7	5-5	5-2	5-5	5-2	5-10	5-7	5-5	5-2	5-5	5-4	5-4	5-2	5-7	5-5	5-2	5-0	5-2	5-0
Controlled Random	6-8	6-6	6-1	5-11	6-3	6-1	5-11	5-8	5-11	5-8	6-5	6-1	5-11	5-8	5-11	5-10	5-10	5-8	6-1	5-11	5-8	5-5	5-8	5-5
Roof Decking — 10 psf Dead Load/20 psf Live Load/L/240 Deflection Limit																								
Simple	8-9	8-7	8-1	7-10	8-3	8-1	7-10	7-5	7-10	7-5	8-5	8-1	7-10	7-5	7-10	7-8	7-8	7-5	8-1	7-10	7-5	7-3	7-5	7-3
Controlled Random	9-7	9-5	8-10	8-7	9-0	8-10	8-7	8-1	8-7	8-1	9-2	8-10	8-7	8-1	8-7	8-4	8-4	8-1	8-10	8-7	8-1	7-10	8-1	7-10
Roof Decking — 10 psf Dead Load/30 psf Live Load/L/240 Deflection Limit																								
Simple	7-8	7-6	7-1	6-10	7-3	7-1	6-10	6-6	6-10	6-6	7-4	7-1	6-10	6-6	6-10	6-8	6-8	6-6	7-1	6-10	6-6	6-4	6-6	6-4
Controlled Random	8-4	8-2	7-8	7-6	7-10	7-8	7-6	7-1	7-6	7-1	8-0	7-8	7-6	7-1	7-6	7-4	7-4	7-1	7-8	7-6	7-1	6-10	7-1	6-10
Roof Decking — 10 psf Dead Load/40 psf Live Load/L/240 Deflection Limit																								
Simple	7-0	6-10	6-5	6-3	6-7	6-5	6-3	5-11	6-3	5-11	6-8	6-5	6-3	5-11	6-3	6-1	6-1	5-11	6-5	6-3	5-11	5-9	5-11	5-9
Controlled Random	7-7	7-5	7-0	6-10	7-2	7-0	6-10	6-5	6-10	6-5	7-4	7-0	6-10	6-5	6-10	6-8	6-8	6-5	7-0	6-10	6-5	6-3	6-5	6-3

Joist and Plank grades run to pattern may be used as follows:
No. 1—Use Select spans for all species.
No. 2—Use Commercial spans for all species.
No. 3—Douglas Fir-Larch use Douglas Fir South Select spans.
No. 3—Douglas Fir, South and Western Hemlock use Mountain Hemlock Commercial spans.
No. 3—Hem-Fir and Mountain Hemlock use Western Cedar Commercial spans.

17

3" Decking Spans

Spans are for 4" to 12" wide lumber manufactured and used at a maximum moisture content of 19%. Spans are given in feet-inches for normal load duration.

	Douglas Fir-Larch		Douglas Fir South		Hem-Fir		Mountain Hemlock		Mountain Hemlock Hem-Fir		Western Hemlock		Engelmann Spruce Alpine Fir (Engelmann Spruce-Lodgepole Pine)		Lodgepole Pine		Ponderosa Pine-Sugar Pine (Ponderosa Pine-Lodgepole Pine)		Idaho White Pine		Western Cedars		White Woods (Western Woods)	
	Select	Comm	Select	Comm	Select	Comm	Select	Comm	Select	Comm	Select	Comm	Select	Comm	Select	Comm	Select	Comm	Select	Comm	Select	Comm	Select	Comm
Floor Decking — 10 psf Dead Load/40 psf Live Load/L/360 Deflection Limit																								
Simple	10-2	9-11	9-4	9-1	9-6	9-4	9-1	8-7	9-1	8-7	9-9	9-4	9-1	8-7	9-1	8-10	8-10	8-7	9-4	9-1	8-7	8-4	8-7	8-4
Controlled Random	11-8	11-5	10-8	10-5	10-11	10-8	10-5	9-10	10-5	9-10	11-2	10-8	10-5	9-10	10-5	10-2	10-2	9-10	10-8	10-5	9-10	9-7	9-10	9-7
Roof Decking — 10 psf Dead Load/20 psf Live Load/L/240 Deflection Limit																								
Simple	14-7	14-4	13-5	13-1	13-9	13-5	13-1	12-5	13-1	12-5	14-1	13-5	13-1	12-5	13-1	12-9	12-9	12-5	13-5	13-1	12-5	12-0	12-5	12-0
Controlled Random	16-9	16-5	15-5	15-1	15-9	15-5	15-1	14-3	15-1	14-3	16-1	15-5	15-1	14-3	15-1	14-8	14-8	14-3	15-5	15-1	14-3	13-9	14-3	13-9
Roof Decking — 10 psf Dead Load/30 psf Live Load/L/240 Deflection Limit																								
Simple	12-9	12-6	11-9	11-6	12-0	11-9	11-6	10-10	11-6	10-10	12-3	11-9	11-6	10-10	11-6	11-2	11-2	10-10	11-9	11-6	10-10	10-6	10-10	10-6
Controlled Random	14-8	14-4	13-6	13-2	13-9	13-6	13-2	12-5	13-2	12-5	14-1	13-6	13-2	12-5	13-2	12-10	12-10	12-5	13-6	13-2	12-5	12-0	12-5	12-0
Roof Decking — 10 psf Dead Load/40 psf Live Load/L/240 Deflection Limit																								
Simple	11-7	11-5	10-8	10-5	10-11	10-8	10-5	9-10	10-5	9-10	11-2	10-8	10-5	9-10	10-5	10-2	10-2	9-10	10-8	10-5	9-10	9-6	9-10	9-6
Controlled Random	13-4	13-1	12-3	11-11	12-6	12-3	11-11	11-3	11-11	11-3	12-9	12-3	11-11	11-3	11-11	11-7	11-7	11-3	12-3	11-11	11-3	10-11	11-3	10-11

Joist and Plank grades run to pattern may be used as follows:
No. 1—Use Select spans for all species.
No. 2—Use Commercial spans for all species.
No. 3—Douglas Fir-Larch use Mountain Hemlock Commercial spans.
No. 3—Douglas Fir, South use Western Cedar Commercial spans.

Typical Dimension Grades

NOTE: **Western Wood Species Book Volume 1, Dimension Lumber** *(32 pages in color) is available from WWPA. Single copy FREE, quantities at cost.*

Light Framing / Ponderosa Pine

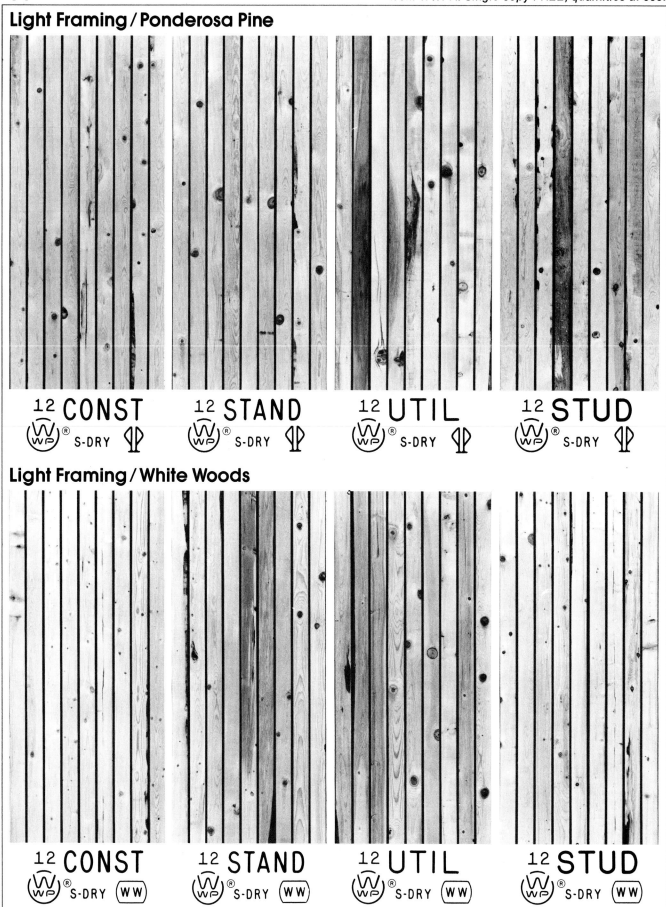

18

¹² CONST
(WWP)® S-DRY

¹² STAND
(WWP)® S-DRY

¹² UTIL
(WWP)® S-DRY

¹² STUD
(WWP)® S-DRY

Light Framing / White Woods

¹² CONST
(WWP)® S-DRY (WW)

¹² STAND
(WWP)® S-DRY (WW)

¹² UTIL
(WWP)® S-DRY (WW)

¹² STUD
(WWP)® S-DRY (WW)

Typical Dimension Grades

Structural Light Framing / Douglas Fir-Larch

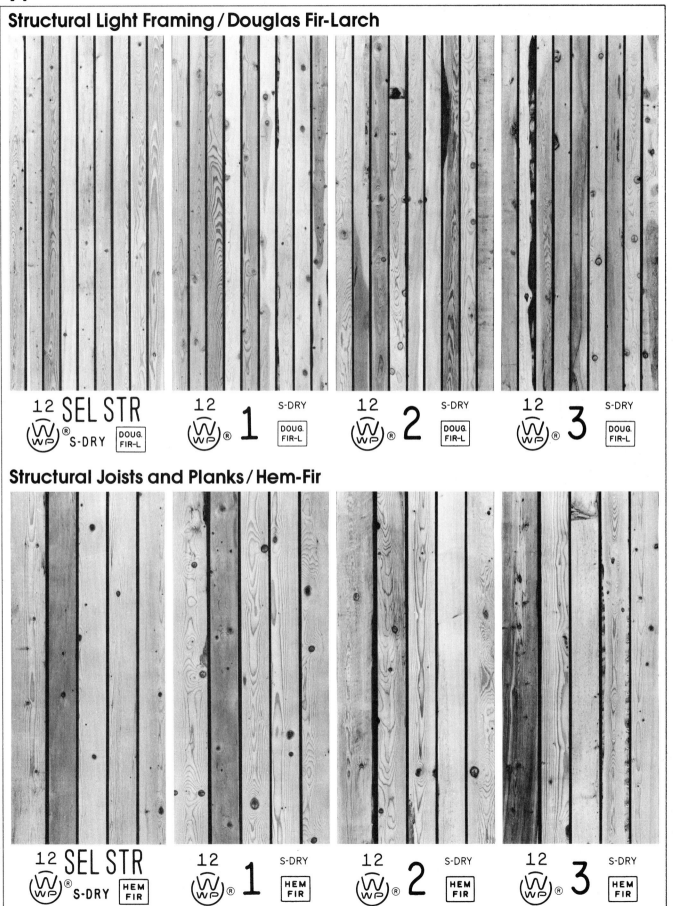

12 SEL STR
Ⓦ (WP)® S-DRY [DOUG. FIR-L]

12 Ⓦ (WP)® 1 S-DRY [DOUG. FIR-L]

12 Ⓦ (WP)® 2 S-DRY [DOUG. FIR-L]

12 Ⓦ (WP)® 3 S-DRY [DOUG. FIR-L]

Structural Joists and Planks / Hem-Fir

12 SEL STR
Ⓦ (WP)® S-DRY [HEM FIR]

12 Ⓦ (WP)® 1 S-DRY [HEM FIR]

12 Ⓦ (WP)® 2 S-DRY [HEM FIR]

12 Ⓦ (WP)® 3 S-DRY [HEM FIR]

The Western Woods Region

The growth range of the 12 Western species extends from the Pacific Ocean east to the Great Plains. This is the Western Woods Region. It covers nearly 30 per cent of the U.S. land surface.

The Western Woods Region contains about 1,364 billion board feet of commercial softwood sawtimber.

Estimated Net Volume of Sawtimber on Commercial Forest Lands of the West*

Douglas Fir ....521 Billion board feet
Ponderosa Pine ....190 Billion board feet
True Firs ....219 Billion board feet
Western Hemlock ..144 Billion board feet
Engelmann Spruce . 64 Billion board feet
Lodgepole Pine .... 65 Billion board feet
Western Red Cedar . 36 Billion board feet
Western Larch ..... 31 Billion board feet
Sugar Pine .... 24 Billion board feet
Idaho White Pine .. 21 Billion board feet
Incense Cedar ..... 14 Billion board feet

Redwood .... 24 Billion board feet
Other Softwoods .... 11 Billion board feet
　Total ....1,364 Billion board feet

Above merchantable timber is on
　78 million acres

New forests, acres under sawtimber size:
　34 million

Total private forest acres: 42 million

Total Certified Tree Farm acres in the
　West: 17,125,944

*Excluding Alaska and Hawaii

Source: Forest Resource Report No. 20, Oct. 1973

Regional Field Managers

For additional help regarding information in this booklet, contact the man in your area:

SAN FRANCISCO
H. H. Hofmann
6019 Blackbird Court
San Jose, Ca. 95120
(408) 997-3615

LOS ANGELES
D. P. Comstock
4258 N. Bresee
Baldwin Park, Ca. 91706
(213) 337-3522

COLUMBUS
L. E. Berry
4350 Wanda Lane
Columbus, Ohio 43224
(614) 262-0933

DALLAS
F. D'Augustine
5621 Belmont Avenue
Apt. 308A
Dallas, Texas 75206
(214) 827-9601

WASHINGTON, D.C.
Craig Larsen
15 Thompson Creek Rd.
Stevensville, Md. 21666
(301) 643-3278

ATLANTA
H. J. Anton
4148 Ashwoody Trail, N.E.
Atlanta, Ga. 30319
(404) 451-2707

Western Wood Products Association
Yeon Building, Portland, Oregon 97204 · 503/224-3930

CATALOG A
LITHO IN U.S.A.
REVISED DEC. 1977

glulam
systems

AITC

1978

AMERICAN INSTITUTE OF TIMBER CONSTRUCTION

Mid Gad Valley Restaurant, Snowbird, Utah.
Architects: Enteleki Architecture, Planning,
Research, Inc., Salt Lake City, Utah.

St. Louis Park Ice Arena, Minneapolis, Minnesota.
Architects: S. C. Smiley & Associates,
Minneapolis, Minnesota.

Temple Beth El, West Palm Beach, Florida
Architect: Alfred Browning Parker, Miami, Florida

Pacifica Marina Shopping Center, Long Beach, California
Architect: Killingsworth, Brady & Associates,
Long Beach, California

Cover: Rimrock Mall, Billings, Montana
Architect: Charles Kober Associates, Los Angeles, California

AMERICAN INSTITUTE OF TIMBER CONSTRUCTION

mr manufacturer

THE AMERICAN INSTITUTE OF TIMBER CONSTRUCTION is the national technical trade association of the structural glued laminating (glulam) industry. Its members manufacture, fabricate, assemble, erect and/or design wood structural systems and related wood products for construction applications.

PRODUCT DESCRIPTION

pp product presentation

Glulam is used as load-carrying structural framing for roofs and other structural portions of buildings, and for other construction, such as bridges, towers and marine installations. The term "structural glued laminated timber" refers to an engineered, stress-rated product of a timber laminating plant, comprising assemblies of suitably selected and prepared wood laminations securely bonded together with adhesives. The grain of all laminations is approximately parallel longitudinally. The individual laminations do not exceed 2 inches in net thickness. Laminations may be comprised of pieces end-joined to form any length, of pieces placed or glued edge to edge to make wider ones, or of pieces bent to a curved form during gluing.

Adhesives for the manufacture of glulam must comply with Voluntary Product Standard PS 56-73. Wet-use adhesives must be used if the members are subject to occasional or continuous wetting, or for applications, either exterior or interior, where the moisture content of the wood will exceed 16%.

Detailed information about the proper use and specification of glulam may be found in the AITC Spec-Data Sheet on Structural Glued Laminated Timber. Refer to "Treating Standard for Structural Timber Framing," AITC 109 for information on preservative treatments for glulam. Copies of these publications are available from AITC.

ADVANTAGES OF GLULAM

pp product presentation

Glued laminated timber permits new uses and has enhanced the natural beauty and extended the enduring qualities of wood. Glulam has made possible the production of structural timbers in a wide variety of sizes and shapes and allows wide latitude in creating forms which are expressive of the struc-

dt document

ture's function and intended use. Following is a partial list of the advantages of using engineered structural timber. The entire list is as varied as your own imagination and your specific applications.

Economy. Timber construction has historically been recognized as an economical type of construction. Laminated wood does not require the added expense of false ceilings to cover or disguise the structural framework. Glulam members can be used to provide long clear spans eliminating interior walls and supports.

Ease of Installation. Because glulam members can be prefabricated at the plant to the job specifications, they arrive at the site ready for immediate installation. Most glulam members are installed by local labor forces with mobile construction equipment and hand tools.

Chemical Resistance. Timber is often used where chemical deterioration eliminates use of other structural materials. Since wood substance is relatively inert chemically, under normal conditions it is not subject to chemical change or deterioration. It is resistant to most acids, rust and other corrosive agents.

Durability. Wood structures, properly designed and constructed, have performed in service with satisfaction for centuries. When recognized principles of design and construction that protect wood from exposure to moisture, decay, fungi and insects are applied, wood is a durable construction material. When wood is not protected from this exposure, it should be pressure treated with chemical preservatives to increase durability.

Safety. Heavy timber sizes used in glulam construction are difficult to ignite. Glulam burns slowly and resists heat penetration by the formation of self-insulating char. In a large member subjected to fire, the uncharred inner portion maintains its strength. Also, glulam does not expand or deform enough to push out supporting walls.

Glulam, with its great capacity for absorbing impact loads and temporary overloads, provides safety under high wind and earthquake conditions.

Thermal Expansion. Wood members change less in dimension with variations in temperature than do other materials. Usually, the effects of thermal expansion are negligible compared to dimensional changes (shrinkage or swelling) due to changes in moisture content and the two changes tend to offset each other. Longitudinal dimensional changes can be neglected for most structural designs.

Unique Physical Properties. Wood's resilience permits it to absorb shocks that could rupture or break other materials. The fatigue limit of wood is above normal design stress levels, and wood resists fatigue due to repeated loading. Wood has excellent natural thermal and electrical insulating qualities. When properly used, glulam will last indefinitely. It can be finished in a wide variety of beautiful textures and colors.

Renewable Resource. The U. S. has abundant forest resources. Trees are potentially the most plentiful industrial raw material in America. Lumber and plywood for housing and construction, and some 5,000 other products are manufactured from wood, the only naturally renewable building material resource. The U. S. still has nearly 75% as much forest land as when Columbus landed. Glulam permits better utilization of available supplies, because the laminating process makes use of several species and grades of lumber. Higher grades of lumber are placed in the areas of highest stress and lower grades are used in areas of lower stress. This efficient utilization insures a continuous available supply of glulam.

Energy Conservation. Conversion of wood from the raw states to finished product consumes less fuel than the production of any comparable industrial building material. Comparisons reveal that the production of a ton of lumber requires about 453 kilowatt hours of electricity or its equivalent, while the production of a ton of steel takes 3,780 kwh of electricity, and to produce a ton of aluminum requires 20,160 kwh.

Our Lady of the Lake Catholic Church, Lake Arrowhead, California
Architect: Vernon H. Johnson, Lake Arrowhead, California

Hayward Field Grandstand, University of Oregon, Eugene, Oregon
Architect: John Amundson, Springfield, Oregon

American Broadcasting Company, Century City, California   Designers: K/S Wilshire, Inc., Los Angeles, California

RECOMMENDED ARCHITECTURAL SPECIFICATIONS

ts technical support

This Guide Specification is applicable to all glued laminated structural members. A more detailed specification may be found in the AITC Spec-Data Sheet on Structural Glued Laminated Timber. In the following, words in parenthesis are explanatory and should not appear in your finished specification.

Scope

All structural glued laminated timber shall be furnished as shown detailed on the plans and specified herein.

Shop Details

Shop details shall be furnished by the fabricator and approval obtained from the buyer before work is commenced.

Manufacture

Materials, Manufacture and Quality Control shall be in conformance with Voluntary Product Standard PS 56-73, "Structural Glued Laminated Timber."

Laminating Combinations

Laminating combinations shall meet the requirements of Product Standard PS 56-73, "Structural Glued Laminated Timber," and shall provide allowable stress values of _____psi in bending (F_b), _____psi in tension parallel to grain (F_t), _____psi in compression parallel to grain (F_c), _____psi in compression perpendicular to grain bottom ($F_{c\perp}$), and _____psi in compression perpendicular to grain top ($F_{c\perp}$) for (check one):

_____DRY condition of service (when the moisture content of the member will be at or below 16% in service).

_____WET condition of service (when the moisture content of the member will be above 16% in service).

Adhesives

Adhesives shall meet the requirements for (check one):

_____DRY condition of service.

_____WET condition of service.
(See explanation of service conditions under laminating combinations above.)

Appearance

Appearance of members shall be (check one):

_____INDUSTRIAL GRADE

_____ARCHITECTURAL GRADE

_____PREMIUM GRADE

Protection

Unless otherwise specified, a coat of end sealer shall be applied to the ends of all members as soon as practicable after end trimming. Surfaces of members shall be (check one):

_____NOT SEALED

_____SEALED WITH PENETRATING SEALER

_____SEALED WITH SEALER COAT

_____OTHER TYPE OF FINISH (specify) _____

Members shall be (check one):

_____NOT WRAPPED

_____BUNDLE WRAPPED

_____INDIVIDUALLY WRAPPED

Quality Marks and Certificates

(check appropriate items):

_____Members shall be marked with a Quality Mark indicating conformance with Product Standard PS 56-73, "Structural Glued Laminated Timber."

_____Members shall be marked with Quality Mark and, in addition, a Certificate of Conformance shall be provided to indicate conformance with Product Standard PS 56-73, "Structural Glued Laminated Timber."

Optional Considerations

The following specifications are sometimes desired. They are covered here briefly for your consideration and convenience.

Preservative Treatment

When the conditions of service are such that pressure preservative treatment to prevent attack by fungi or insects is required, information such as the following should be given in your specification:

The preservative shall be _____

The retention shall be _____

(Note: Refer to AITC 109 "Treating Standard for Structural Timber Framing" for complete data.)

Hardware

The fabricator shall furnish connection steel and hardware for joining timber members to each other and to their supports exclusive of anchorage embedded in masonry, setting plates, and items field-welded to structural steel. Metal shapes to have one coat of shop applied paint containing rust inhibitor.

QUALITY CONTROL AND INSPECTION

Specifying quality inspected materials to assure consistent and dependable structural glued laminated timber is a professional responsibility. The AITC program is based on Voluntary Product Standard PS 56-73 and the INSPECTION MANUAL, AITC 200.

APPEARANCE GRADES

mf materials, finishes

Three appearance grades—Industrial, Architectural and Premium—have a sufficient range to fulfill all use requirements. These grades apply to the surfaces of glued laminated members and include such items as growth characteristics, inserts, wood fillers and surfacing operations. The appearance grades do not apply to laminating procedures, decorative or other finishes, or to protective coverings. They do not modify the design stress, fabrication controls, grades of lumber used, or other provisions of the standards for glued laminated structural members. In specifying appearance grades it is necessary only to state the desired grade without detailed specifications.

For detailed information on appearance grade specifications, refer to AITC Spec-Data Sheet on Structural Glued Laminated Timber.

FINISHES AND COATINGS

cs coatings, surfacings

Available finishes for glued laminated timber include surface sealers, stains and paints. Surface sealers increase resistance to soiling, control grain raising, minimize checking and serve as a moisture retardant. Surface sealers fall into two classifications. Penetrating sealers provide limited protection and are suitable for use when final finish requires staining or a natural finish. Primer and sealer coats provide maximum protection by sealing the surface of the wood. Primer and sealer coats should not be specified when the final finish requires a natural or stained finish.

Precise finger joint cutter insures tight fit for maximum strength after gluing.

This glue extruder gives complete coverage across the face of the lam stock.

Workmen inspect a massive curved beam as it comes from planer.

This information is applicable to laminated members of four or more laminations when the load is applied perpendicular to the wide face of the laminations and to bending values for members of three or more laminations when the load is applied parallel to the wide face of the laminations.

AITC recommends the production of structural glued laminated timber be in compliance with Voluntary Product Standard PS 56-73.

LAMINATING SPECIES

Softwood species commonly used for laminating are Douglas fir and larch, Southern pine, hem-fir and California redwood. (See page 10 for stress information.) Other species, including hardwoods, may be used. Contact AITC for additional information.

The allowable unit stresses given in Tables 1 and 2, and the modifications required for other conditions of use and loading are applicable also to structural glued laminated members that have been pressure impregnated by an approved preservative process in accordance with "Treating Standard for Structural Timber Framing," AITC 109.

The allowable unit stresses given in Tables 1 and 2 are for normal conditions of loading. Modifications for other conditions of loading are given under Modification of Stresses—Duration of Load.

The allowable unit bending stresses (F_b) given in Tables 1 and 2, apply to a 12-inch deep member, uniformly loaded, with a span to depth ratio of 21 to 1. Modifications for other sizes and loading conditions are given under Modification of Stresses—Size Factor.

Allowable Unit Stress Tables: Table 1 is based on an arrangement of laminations best suited for members where the principal stress is bending when the direction of loading is perpendicular to the wide face of the laminations.

Table 2 is based on an arrangement of laminations best suited to members where the principal stress is axial. This table gives allowable unit stresses for such members. In addition, Table 2 gives allowable unit stresses for members stressed in bending when the direction of the load is parallel to the wide face of the laminations. This table also gives allowable unit stresses for members stressed in bending when the direction of the load is perpendicular to the wide face of the laminations.

Condition of Use: Dry condition of use stress values given in Tables 1 and 2 are applicable when the moisture content in service is less than 16%, as in most covered structures.

Wet conditions of use stress values are applicable when the moisture content in service is 16% or more, as may occur in members not covered or in covered locations of high relative humidity.

MODIFICATION OF STRESSES

Duration of Load: Normal load duration contemplates fully stressing a member to the allowable unit stress by the application of the full design load for a duration of approximately 10 years (either continuously or cumulatively).

When a member is fully stressed by maximum design loads for long term loading conditions (greater than 10 years either continuously or cumulatively), the allowable stresses are 90% of the tabulated values.

When the duration of the full design load (either continuously or cumulatively) does not exceed the period indicated, increase the tabulated allowable unit stresses as follows: 15% for 2 months duration, as for snow; 25% for 7 days duration; 33⅓% for wind or earthquake; 100% for impact. These increases are not cumulative.

The allowable unit stress for normal loading may be used without regard to impact if the stress induced by impact does not exceed the allowable unit stress for normal loading.

These adjustments do not apply to modulus of elasticity except when used to determine allowable unit loads for columns.

Curvature Factor: For the curved portion of members, the allowable unit stress in bending is modified through multiplication by the following curvature factor: $C_c = 1 - 2000 (t/R)^2$ in which t = thickness of lamination in inches, R = radius of curvature of lamination in inches and t/R should not exceed 1/100 for hardwoods and Southern pine, nor 1/125 for softwoods other than Southern pine. No curvature factor is applied to stress in the straight portion of an assembly, regardless of curvature elsewhere.

The recommended minimum radii of curvature for curved structural glued laminated members are 9 feet 4 inches for a lamination thickness of ¾ inch; and 27 feet 6 inches for a lamination thickness of 1½ inches. Other radii of curvature may be used with these thicknesses and other radius-thickness combinations may be used. The designer should determine availability before specifying.

Radial Tension or Compression: The radial stress induced by a bending moment in a curved member of constant cross-section is computed by the formula:

$$f_r = \frac{3M}{2Rbd}$$

in which M = bending moment in inch pounds; R = radius of curvature at centerline of member in inches; b = width of cross section in inches; d = depth of cross section in inches.

For procedures for calculating radial stresses in curved beams with varying cross-section, contact AITC.

When M is in the direction tending to decrease curvature (increase the radius), the stress is tension across the grain. For this condition, the allowable tension stress across the grain is limited to ⅓ the allowable unit stress in horizontal shear for Southern pine and California redwood for all load conditions, and for Douglas fir, hem-fir and larch for wind or earthquake loadings. The limit is 15 psi for Douglas fir, hem-fir and larch for other types of loading. These values are subject to modifications for duration of load. If these values are exceeded, mechanical reinforcing sufficient to resist all radial tension stresses is required, but in no case shall the calculated radial tension stress exceed ⅓ the allowable unit stress in horizontal shear.

When M is in the direction tending to increase curvature (decrease the radius), the stress is compression across the grain and is limited to the allowable unit stress in compression perpendicular to the grain for all species included herein, subject to modifications for duration of load.

Size Factor: When the depth of a rectangular beam exceeds 12 inches, the tabulated unit stress in bending F_b, is reduced through multiplication by the size factor, C_F as determined from the following relationship: $C_F = (12/d)^{1/9}$ in which C_F = size factor; d = depth of member in inches (See Section Properties table on page 11 for values of C_F).

This size factor relationship is applicable to a bending member satisfying the following basic assumptions: (a) simply supported beam, (b) uniformly distributed load and (c) span to depth ratio (L/d) of 21. This factor can thus be applied with reasonable accuracy to most commonly encountered design situations. Where greater accuracy is desired for other sizes and conditions of loading, the percentage changes given in the following table may be applied directly to the size factor calculated for the basic conditions as previously stated. Straight line interpolation may be used for other L/d ratios.

SPAN TO DEPTH RATIO L/d	% CHANGE	LOADING CONDITION FOR SIMPLY SUPPORTED BEAMS	% CHANGE
7	+6.2	Single Concentrated Load	+7.8
14	+2.3		
21	0	Uniform Load	0
28	−1.6	Third Point Load	−3.2
35	−2.8		

For information on a more detailed analysis of the size effect factor and its application to the design of bending members contact AITC.

Lateral Stability: The tabulated allowable unit bending stress values are applicable to members which are adequately braced. When deep, slender members not adequately braced are used, a reduction to the allowable unit bending stresses must be applied based on a computation of the slenderness factor of the member. In the check of lateral stability, the slenderness factor should be applied in design as shown in the AITC "Timber Construction Manual."

The reduction in bending stresses determined by applying the slenderness factor is not cumulative with a reduction in stress due to the application of size factor. In no case may the allowable unit bending stress used in design exceed the stress as determined by applying the size factor.

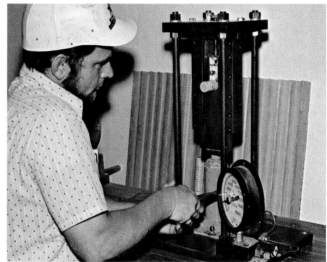
Glue line shear test to assure conformance with Product Standard PS 56-73.

Weathering cycles are accelerated with heat and moisture testing in this autoclave.

UAW Family Education Center, Black Lake, Michigan
Architects: Stonorov & Haws.

Avon Bridge, Avon, Colorado
Engineer: Eldorado Engineering Company,
Glenwood Springs, Colorado

The Andersons Fertilizer Warehouse, Maumee, Ohio
Engineers: Andersons Engineering Department.

GLULAM IS FIRE SAFE
ts technical support

How well a building performs in protecting life and property in a fire, rather than the structural materials used, is the most important consideration in judging the ultimate fire safety of a structure.

Buildings of engineered heavy timber construction perform extremely well in a fire and have excellent fire resistive qualities when fire safety provisions, as required by modern building codes, are followed.

While timber will burn, it retains its strength under fire longer than unprotected metals which are rated noncombustible. Unprotected metals lose their strength quickly and collapse suddenly under extreme heat.

Steel loses strength rapidly as its temperature is raised above about 480° F. At about 1020° F it has less than one-half of its original strength and loses 90% of its strength at about 1380° F.

These temperatures are significant since ordinary building fires attain temperatures of from 1290° F to 1650° F.

Wood does not lose strength in the same way; it loses strength only as material is lost through the charring of the surface. Wood does not normally ignite until a temperature of about 480° F is attained.

Experience and tests have shown that if adequate fire protective measures are not incorporated, smoke from burning contents can make a building untenable to human life in from 2 to 6 minutes. Temperatures of 150° F may be reached in 5 to 11 minutes. At such low temperatures, wood and other common structural materials would not be ignited nor damaged by heat.

FIRE INSURANCE RATES

Questions are sometimes raised concerning fire insurance rates for wood construction and their effect on the overall cost of a building.

A comparison between engineered timber construction and other structural framing materials often favors the wood structure in several respects, especially construction cost. When fire insurance rates are introduced as an operating cost factor rate differentials between timber construction and so-called "noncombustible" construction materials often exist. The lower construction cost gives an interest savings that frequently offsets the insurance rate differential.

Most insurance rating bureaus recognize the excellent fire resistive properties of heavy timber construction in assigning fire insurance rates. In those cases where a comparison between a heavy timber construction system and alternate materials reveals that the initial construction cost is lower for heavy timber, but that fire insurance rates for the competing structural material are lower, the following factors should be considered in evaluating relative costs:

1. When the cost of competing structural framing materials is greater than that of an engineered timber construction system, even if by only a small amount, financial benefits derived from a lower fire insurance rate may be eliminated.

2. Interest on the additional construction cost will usually compensate if there are higher insurance rates on engineered timber construction. Therefore, using more costly construction to secure a lower insurance rate may actually result in an annual loss rather than a financial gain. It may take a number of years for the slight savings on insurance premiums to repay the additional construction costs, plus interest.

Another factor to consider in relation to fire insurance rates for various construction materials is the use of automatic sprinklers. Not only does the installation of sprinklers reduce fire insurance rates for heavy timber construction, it tends to equalize rates for all construction materials.

Dramatic illustration of wood's actual fire performance.

After one-half hour fire test, 75% of original cross section of glulam beam remains undamaged.

THE FILENE CENTER AT WOLF TRAP FARM— A CASE STUDY

What happens when a building framed with glulam catches fire? An answer to this question was provided at the Filene Center for the Performing Arts, a multi-purpose outdoor theater located at Wolf Trap Farm, Virginia, near Washington, D.C.

The roof framing plan on this project consisted of four unique glulam and steel queen-post trusses with a span of 150 feet from the proscenium arch to the rear of the balcony. Additional glulam and steel king-post trusses framed intermediate spans of 60-100 feet. Exposed 2 x 6 roof decking, two-inch sheathing on wall surfaces and steel H-columns boxed in wood completed the framing system at the Filene Center.

Near the end of construction, a fire started at the base of the steel H-columns, which spread quickly up and then across the entire face of the stage house. Heat from the fire caused the H-columns to buckle. These columns were later classified beyond repair by inspectors, resulting in their complete replacement. The steel plate girders required subsequent reinforcement with new steel trusses.

The condition of the major glulam members after the fire gave a dramatic example of how their use as structural components saved both time and money. After requiring total replacement of the twisted structural steel, inspectors then determined that the laminated wood component framing had retained its design structural capabilities and required only in-place sandblasting of its charred surfaces. This was indeed good news for both the insurance underwriters and the owner, who joined in the applause of the patrons when the opening night curtain raised on schedule, less than three months after the fire.

STRESS TABLES

ts technical support

1. The tabulated stresses in this table are primarily applicable to members stressed in bending due to a load applied perpendicular to the wide face of the laminations. For combinations and stresses applicable to members loaded primarily axially or parallel to wide face of the laminations, see Table 2.
2. The tabulated bending stresses are applicable to members 12 inches or less in depth. For members greater than 12 inches in depth, the size factor modifications apply.
3. The tabulated combinations are applicable to arches, compression members, tension members and also bending members less than 16¼ inches in depth. For bending members 16¼ inches or more in depth, AITC tension lamination restrictions apply.
4. To obtain wet-use stresses, multiply dry-use stresses by the following factors:

Type of stress	:	Wet-use factor
Bending and tension parallel to grain	:	0.80
Compression parallel to grain	:	0.73
Compression perpendicular to grain	:	0.67
Shear	:	0.88
Modulus of elasticity	:	0.83

5. The tabulated stresses in this table are primarily applicable to members loaded axially or parallel to the wide face of the laminations. For combinations and stresses applicable to members stressed principally in bending due to a load applied perpendicular to the wide face of the laminations, see Table 1.
6. The tabulated stresses are applicable to members containing four (4) or more laminations.
7. The tabulated stresses are applicable to members containing three (3) or more laminations.
8. It is not intended that these combinations be used for deep bending members, but if bending members 16¼ inches or deeper are used, AITC tension lamination restrictions apply.

STANDARD SIZES

ts technical support

To the extent that other considerations will permit, the finished sizes of structural glued laminated timber as given in the Section Properties table constitute normal industry practice. **Industry standards do, however, permit the use of any width of glued laminated timber.** Dimension lumber of 1½ inch net thickness is normally used to laminate straight members and those curved members having radii of curvature within the bending radius limitations for the species. Boards of ¾ inch net thickness are recommended for laminating curved members when the bending radius is too short to permit the use of dimension lumber, provided the bending radius limitations for the species are observed. Other lamination thicknesses may be used to obtain the specified depth of the member or to meet special requirements.

When the depth of a rectangular beam exceeds 12 inches, the allowable unit stress in bending must be reduced by multiplication by a size factor. The size factor values given in the Section Properties table are based on the formula and basic assumptions given on pages 6 and 7.

Weight per linear foot of section may be determined by multiplying the volume per linear foot by the following values — Douglas fir and larch: 35 pcf; Southern pine: 36 pcf; hem-fir and California redwood: 27 pcf.

NOTE: Expanded table available
An expanded Section Properties Table is available from AITC.

TABLE 1: GLULAM BENDING STRESSES   DRY CONDITIONS OF USE

Allowable Unit Stresses (psi) For Normal Conditions Of Loading, Members Stressed Principally In Bending, Loaded Perpendicular To The Wide Face of the Laminations[1,2,3,4]

Combination Symbol	Allowable Unit Stresses, psi						Modulus of Elasticity E psi
	Extreme Fiber in Bending F_b	Tension Parallel to Grain F_t	Compression Parallel to Grain F_c	Compression Perpendicular to Grain $F_{c\perp}$		Horizontal Shear F_v	
				Tension Face	Comp. Face		
DOUGLAS FIR AND LARCH							
16F	1600	900	1500	385	385	165	1,600,000
18F	1800	900	1500	385	385	165	1,700,000
20F	2000	1000	1500	385	385	165	1,700,000
	2000	1000	1500	410	410	165	1,700,000
	2000	1000	1500	450	450	165	1,700,000
22F	2200	1000	1500	410	410	165	1,800,000
	2200	1000	1500	450	385	165	1,800,000
24F	2400	1000	1500	450	385	165	1,800,000
NOTE: The 26F combination is only available by special inquiry to the manufacturer. Other combinations are generally available from all laminators.							
26F	2600	1100	1500	450	410	165	1,800,000
HEM-FIR							
18F	1800	900	1250	245		155	1,600,000
20F	2000	900	1250	245		155	1,600,000
24F	2400	900	1250	245		155	1,700,000
SOUTHERN PINE							
16F	1600	800	700	385		140	1,500,000
18F	1800	900	1500	385		200	1,600,000
20F	2000	800	700	385		140	1,600,000
	2000	1000	1500	385		200	1,700,000
	2000	1000	1500	450		200	1,700,000
22F	2200	1000	1500	385		200	1,700,000
	2200	1000	1500	450		200	1,700,000
24F	2400	1000	1000	385		140	1,700,000
	2400	1000	1500	385		200	1,800,000
	2400	1000	1500	450		200	1,800,000
NOTE: The 26F combination is only available by special inquiry to the manufacturer. Other combinations are generally available from all laminators.							
26F	2600	1100	1500	385		200	1,800,000
	2600	1100	1500	450		200	1,800,000
CALIFORNIA REDWOOD							
16F	1600	1200	2000	325		125	1,400,000
NOTE: The 16F combination is generally available. The 22F combinations are generally available only in members without end joints and the designer should check with the laminator prior to specifying this stress level.							
22F	2200	1200	2000	325		125	1,400,000

TABLE 2: GLULAM AXIAL STRESSES   DRY CONDITIONS OF USE

Allowable Unit Stresses (psi) For Normal Conditions of Loading, Members Stressed Principally In Axial Tension, Axial Compression Or Loaded In Bending Parallel Or Perpendicular To the Wide Face [4,5]

Combination Symbol	Allowable Unit Stresses, psi							Modulus of Elasticity E psi
	Tension Parallel to Grain[7] F_t	Compression Parallel to Grain[6] F_c	Extreme Fiber in Bending F_b When Loaded		Compression Perpendicular to Grain[7] $F_{c\perp}$	Horizontal Shear F_v, When Loaded		
			Parallel to Wide Face[7]	Perpendicular to Wide Face[6,8]		Parallel to Wide Face[7]	Perpendicular to Wide Face[7]	
DOUGLAS FIR AND LARCH								
1	900	1500	900	1200	385	145	165	1,600,000
2	1300	1800	1500	1800	385	145	165	1,800,000
3	1400	2100	1900	2200	450	145	165	1,900,000
4	1500	2000	2100	2400	410	145	165	2,000,000
5	1600	2200	2300	2600	450	145	165	2,100,000
HEM-FIR								
1	700	1250	700	1000	245	125	155	1,300,000
2	1000	1500	1200	1400	245	125	155	1,400,000
3	1100	1550	1550	1800	245	125	155	1,600,000
4	1300	1800	1800	2400	245	125	155	1,700,000
SOUTHERN PINE								
1	900	1400	900	1100	385	165	200	1,500,000
2	1200	1900	1500	1800	385	165	200	1,700,000
3	1400	2200	1800	2100	450	165	200	1,800,000
4	1400	2100	1900	2400	385	165	200	1,900,000
5	1600	2200	2200	2600	450	165	200	2,000,000
CALIFORNIA REDWOOD								
1	1200	1800	1000	1400	325	115	125	1,300,000
2	1200	1800	1000	1400	325	115	125	1,300,000
3	1300	2000	1400	2000	325	125	125	1,400,000
4	1500	2200	2200	2200	325	125	125	1,400,000
5	1500	2200	2200	2200	325	125	125	1,400,000

SECTION PROPERTIES Use 1½" columns in table for straight beams; use ¾" columns in table for curved arches.

3⅛" WIDTH

No. of Lams 1½"	No. of Lams ¾"	Depth, d (inches)	Size Factor, C_F	Area, A (inches²)	Section Modulus, S (inches³)	Moment of Inertia, I (inches⁴)
2	4	3.00	1.00	9.4	4.7	7.0
	5	3.75	1.00	11.7	7.3	13.7
3	6	4.50	1.00	14.1	10.5	23.7
	7	5.25	1.00	16.4	14.4	37.7
4	8	6.00	1.00	18.8	18.8	56.3
	9	6.75	1.00	21.1	23.7	80.1
5	10	7.50	1.00	23.4	29.3	109.9
	11	8.25	1.00	25.8	35.4	146.2
6	12	9.00	1.00	28.1	42.2	189.8
	13	9.75	1.00	30.5	49.5	241.4
7	14	10.50	1.00	32.8	57.4	301.5
	15	11.25	1.00	35.2	65.9	370.8
8	16	12.00	1.00	37.5	75.0	450.0
	17	12.75	0.99	39.8	84.7	539.8
9	18	13.50	0.99	42.2	94.9	640.7
	19	14.25	0.98	44.5	105.8	753.6
10	20	15.00	0.98	46.9	117.2	878.9
	21	15.75	0.97	49.2	129.2	1,017.4
11	22	16.50	0.97	51.6	141.8	1,169.8
	23	17.25	0.96	53.9	155.0	1,336.7
12	24	18.00	0.96	56.3	168.8	1,518.8
	25	18.75	0.95	58.6	183.1	1,716.6
13	26	19.50	0.95	60.9	198.0	1,931.0
	27	20.25	0.94	63.3	213.6	2,162.4
14	28	21.00	0.94	65.6	229.7	2,411.7
	29	21.75	0.94	68.0	246.4	2,679.5
15	30	22.50	0.93	70.3	263.7	2,966.3
	31	23.25	0.93	72.7	281.5	3,272.9
16	32	24.00	0.93	75.0	300.0	3,600.0

5⅛" WIDTH

No. of Lams 1½"	No. of Lams ¾"	Depth, d (inches)	Size Factor, C_F	Area, A (inches²)	Section Modulus, S (inches³)	Moment of Inertia, I (inches⁴)
3	6	4.50	1.00	23.1	17.3	38.9
	7	5.25	1.00	26.9	23.5	61.8
4	8	6.00	1.00	30.8	30.8	92.3
	9	6.75	1.00	34.6	38.9	131.3
5	10	7.50	1.00	38.4	48.0	180.2
	11	8.25	1.00	42.3	58.1	239.8
6	12	9.00	1.00	46.1	69.2	311.3
	13	9.75	1.00	50.0	81.2	395.8
7	14	10.50	1.00	53.8	94.2	494.4
	15	11.25	1.00	57.7	108.1	608.1
8	16	12.00	1.00	61.5	123.0	738.0
	17	12.75	0.99	65.3	138.9	885.2
9	18	13.50	0.99	69.2	155.7	1,050.8
	19	14.25	0.98	73.0	173.4	1,235.8
10	20	15.00	0.98	76.9	192.2	1,441.4
	21	15.75	0.97	80.7	211.9	1,668.6
11	22	16.50	0.97	84.6	232.5	1,918.5
	23	17.25	0.96	88.4	254.2	2,192.2
12	24	18.00	0.96	92.3	276.8	2,490.8
	25	18.75	0.95	96.1	300.3	2,815.2
13	26	19.50	0.95	99.9	324.8	3,166.8
	27	20.25	0.94	103.8	350.3	3,546.4
14	28	21.00	0.94	107.6	376.7	3,955.2
	29	21.75	0.94	111.5	404.1	4,394.3
15	30	22.50	0.93	115.3	432.4	4,864.7
	31	23.25	0.93	119.2	461.7	5,367.6
16	32	24.00	0.93	123.0	492.0	5,904.0
	33	24.75	0.92	126.8	523.2	6,475.0
17	34	25.50	0.92	130.7	555.4	7,081.6
	35	26.25	0.92	134.5	588.6	7,725.0
18	36	27.00	0.91	138.4	622.7	8,406.3
	37	27.75	0.91	142.2	657.8	9,126.4
19	38	28.50	0.91	146.1	693.8	9,886.6
	39	29.25	0.91	149.9	730.8	10,687.8
20	40	30.00	0.90	153.8	768.8	11,531.3
	41	30.75	0.90	157.6	807.7	12,417.9
21	42	31.50	0.90	161.4	847.5	13,348.9
	43	32.25	0.90	165.3	888.4	14,325.2
22	44	33.00	0.89	169.1	930.2	15,348.1
	45	33.75	0.89	173.0	972.9	16,418.5
23	46	34.50	0.89	176.8	1,016.7	17,537.6
	47	35.25	0.89	180.7	1,061.4	18,706.4
24	48	36.00	0.88	184.5	1,107.0	19,926.0

6¾" WIDTH

No. of Lams 1½"	No. of Lams ¾"	Depth, d (inches)	Size Factor, C_F	Area, A (inches²)	Section Modulus, S (inches³)	Moment of Inertia, I (inches⁴)
4	8	6.00	1.00	40.5	40.5	121.5
	9	6.75	1.00	45.6	51.3	173.0
5	10	7.50	1.00	50.6	63.3	237.3
	11	8.25	1.00	55.7	76.6	315.9
6	12	9.00	1.00	60.8	91.1	410.1
	13	9.75	1.00	65.8	106.9	521.4
7	14	10.50	1.00	70.9	124.0	651.2
	15	11.25	1.00	75.9	142.4	800.9
8	16	12.00	1.00	81.0	162.0	972.0
	17	12.75	0.99	86.1	182.9	1,165.9
9	18	13.50	0.99	91.1	205.0	1,384.0
	19	14.25	0.98	96.2	228.4	1,627.7
10	20	15.00	0.98	101.3	253.1	1,898.4
	21	15.75	0.97	106.3	279.1	2,197.7
11	22	16.50	0.97	111.4	306.3	2,526.8
	23	17.25	0.96	116.4	334.8	2,887.3
12	24	18.00	0.96	121.5	364.5	3,280.5
	25	18.75	0.95	126.6	395.5	3,707.9
13	26	19.50	0.95	131.6	427.8	4,170.9
	27	20.25	0.94	136.7	461.3	4,670.9
14	28	21.00	0.94	141.8	496.1	5,209.3
	29	21.75	0.94	146.8	532.2	5,787.6
15	30	22.50	0.93	151.9	569.5	6,407.2
	31	23.25	0.93	156.9	608.1	7,069.5
16	32	24.00	0.93	162.0	648.0	7,776.0
	33	24.75	0.92	167.1	689.1	8,528.0
17	34	25.50	0.92	172.1	731.5	9,327.0
	35	26.25	0.92	177.2	775.2	10,174.4
18	36	27.00	0.91	182.3	820.1	11,071.7
	37	27.75	0.91	187.3	866.3	12,020.2
19	38	28.50	0.91	192.4	913.8	13,021.4
	39	29.25	0.91	197.4	962.5	14,076.7
20	40	30.00	0.90	202.5	1,012.5	15,187.5
	41	30.75	0.90	207.6	1,063.8	16,355.3
21	42	31.50	0.90	212.6	1,116.3	17,581.4
	43	32.25	0.90	217.7	1,170.1	18,867.4
22	44	33.00	0.89	222.8	1,225.1	20,214.6
	45	33.75	0.89	227.8	1,281.4	21,624.4
23	46	34.50	0.89	232.9	1,339.0	23,098.3
	47	35.25	0.89	237.9	1,397.9	24,637.7
24	48	36.00	0.88	243.0	1,458.0	26,244.0
	49	36.75	0.88	248.1	1,519.4	27,918.7
25	50	37.50	0.88	253.1	1,582.0	29,663.1
	51	38.25	0.88	258.2	1,645.9	31,478.7
26	52	39.00	0.88	263.3	1,711.1	33,366.9
	53	39.75	0.88	268.3	1,777.6	35,329.2
27	54	40.50	0.87	273.4	1,845.3	37,367.0
	55	41.25	0.87	278.4	1,914.3	39,481.6
28	56	42.00	0.87	283.5	1,984.5	41,674.5
	57	42.75	0.87	288.6	2,056.0	43,947.2
29	58	43.50	0.87	293.6	2,128.8	46,301.0
	59	44.25	0.87	298.7	2,202.8	48,737.4
30	60	45.00	0.86	303.8	2,278.1	51,257.8
	61	45.75	0.86	308.8	2,354.7	53,863.7
31	62	46.50	0.86	313.9	2,432.5	56,556.4
	63	47.25	0.86	318.9	2,511.6	59,337.3
32	64	48.00	0.86	324.0	2,592.0	62,208.0

8¾" WIDTH

No. of Lams 1½"	No. of Lams ¾"	Depth, d (inches)	Size Factor, C_F	Area, A (inches²)	Section Modulus, S (inches³)	Moment of Inertia, I (inches⁴)
6	12	9.00	1.00	78.8	118.1	531.6
	13	9.75	1.00	85.3	138.6	675.8
7	14	10.50	1.00	91.9	160.8	844.1
	15	11.25	1.00	98.4	184.6	1,038.2
8	16	12.00	1.00	105.0	210.0	1,260.0
	17	12.75	0.99	111.6	237.1	1,511.3
9	18	13.50	0.99	118.1	265.8	1,794.0
	19	14.25	0.98	124.7	296.1	2,109.9
10	20	15.00	0.98	131.3	328.1	2,460.9
	21	15.75	0.97	137.8	361.8	2,848.8
11	22	16.50	0.97	144.4	397.0	3,275.5
	23	17.25	0.96	150.9	433.9	3,742.8
12	24	18.00	0.96	157.5	472.5	4,252.5
	25	18.75	0.95	164.1	512.7	4.806.5
13	26	19.50	0.95	170.6	554.5	5,406.7
	27	20.25	0.94	177.2	598.0	6,054.8
14	28	21.00	0.94	183.8	643.1	6,752.8
	29	21.75	0.94	190.3	689.9	7,502.5
15	30	22.50	0.93	196.9	738.3	8,305.7
	31	23.25	0.93	203.4	788.3	9,164.2
16	32	24.00	0.93	210.0	840.0	10,080.0
	33	24.75	0.92	216.6	893.3	11,054.8
17	34	25.50	0.92	223.1	948.3	12,090.6
	35	26.25	0.92	229.7	1,004.9	13,189.1
18	36	27.00	0.91	236.3	1,063.1	14,352.2
	37	27.75	0.91	242.8	1,123.0	15,581.7
19	38	28.50	0.91	249.4	1,184.5	16,879.6
	39	29.25	0.91	255.9	1,247.7	18,247.5
20	40	30.00	0.90	262.5	1,312.5	19,687.5
	41	30.75	0.90	269.1	1,378.9	21,201.3
21	42	31.50	0.90	275.6	1,447.0	22,790.7
	43	32.25	0.90	282.2	1,516.8	24,457.7
22	44	33.00	0.89	288.8	1,588.1	26,204.1
	45	33.75	0.89	295.3	1,661.1	28,031.6
23	46	34.50	0.89	301.9	1,735.8	29,942.2
	47	35.25	0.89	308.4	1,812.1	31,937.7
24	48	36.00	0.88	315.0	1,890.0	34,020.0
	49	36.75	0.88	321.6	1,969.6	36,190.9
25	50	37.50	0.88	328.1	2,050.8	38,452.2
	51	38.25	0.88	334.7	2,133.6	40,805.7
26	52	39.00	0.88	341.3	2,218.1	43,253.4
	53	39.75	0.88	347.8	2,304.3	45,797.1
27	54	40.50	0.87	354.4	2,392.0	48,438.6
	55	41.25	0.87	360.9	2,481.4	51,179.8
28	56	42.00	0.87	367.5	2,572.5	54,022.5
	57	42.75	0.87	374.1	2,665.2	56,968.6
29	58	43.50	0.87	380.6	2,759.5	60,019.8
	59	44.25	0.87	387.2	2,855.5	63,178.1
30	60	45.00	0.86	393.8	2,953.1	66,445.3
	61	45.75	0.86	400.3	3,052.4	69,823.3
31	62	46.50	0.86	406.9	3,153.3	73,313.8
	63	47.25	0.86	413.4	3,255.8	76,918.8
32	64	48.00	0.86	420.0	3,360.0	80,640.0
	65	48.75	0.86	426.6	3,465.8	84,479.4
33	66	49.50	0.85	433.1	3,573.3	88,438.7
	67	50.25	0.85	439.7	3,682.4	92,519.9
34	68	51.00	0.85	446.3	3,793.1	96,724.7
	69	51.75	0.85	452.8	3,905.5	101,055.0
35	70	52.50	0.85	459.4	4,019.5	105,512.7
	71	53.25	0.85	465.9	4,135.2	110,099.6
36	72	54.00	0.85	472.5	4,252.5	114,817.5
	73	54.75	0.85	479.1	4,371.4	119,668.3
37	74	55.50	0.84	485.6	4,492.0	124,653.9
	75	56.25	0.84	492.2	4,614.3	129,776.0
38	76	57.00	0.84	498.8	4,738.1	135,036.6
	77	57.75	0.84	505.3	4,863.6	140,437.4
39	78	58.50	0.84	511.9	4,990.8	145,980.4
	79	59.25	0.84	518.4	5,119.6	151,667.3
40	80	60.00	0.84	525.0	5,250.0	157,500.0
	81	60.75	0.84	531.6	5,382.1	163,480.4
41	82	61.50	0.83	538.1	5,515.8	169,610.3
	83	62.25	0.83	544.7	5,651.1	175,891.5
42	84	63.00	0.83	551.3	5,788.1	182,326.0

10¾" WIDTH

No. of Lams 1½"	No. of Lams ¾"	Depth, d (inches)	Size Factor, C_F	Area, A (inches²)	Section Modulus, S (inches³)	Moment of Inertia, I (inches⁴)
7	14	10.50	1.00	112.9	197.5	1,037.0
	15	11.25	1.00	120.9	226.8	1,275.5
8	16	12.00	1.00	129.0	258.0	1,548.0
	17	12.75	0.99	137.1	291.3	1,856.8
9	18	13.50	0.99	145.1	326.5	2,204.1
	19	14.25	0.98	153.2	363.8	2,592.2
10	20	15.00	0.98	161.3	403.1	3,023.4
	21	15.75	0.97	169.3	444.4	3,500.0
11	22	16.50	0.97	177.4	487.8	4,024.2
	23	17.25	0.96	185.4	533.1	4,598.3
12	24	18.00	0.96	193.5	580.5	5,224.5
	25	18.75	0.95	201.6	629.9	5,905.2
13	26	19.50	0.95	209.6	681.3	6,642.5
	27	20.25	0.94	217.7	734.7	7,438.8
14	28	21.00	0.94	225.8	790.1	8,296.3
	29	21.75	0.94	233.8	847.6	9,217.3
15	30	22.50	0.93	241.9	907.0	10,204.1
	31	23.25	0.93	249.9	968.5	11,258.9
16	32	24.00	0.93	258.0	1,032.0	12,384.0
	33	24.75	0.92	266.1	1,097.5	13,581.7
17	34	25.50	0.92	274.1	1,165.0	14,854.1
	35	26.25	0.92	282.2	1,234.6	16,203.7
18	36	27.00	0.91	290.3	1,306.1	17,632.7
	37	27.75	0.91	298.3	1,379.7	19,143.3
19	38	28.50	0.91	306.4	1,455.3	20,737.8
	39	29.25	0.91	314.4	1,532.9	22,418.4
20	40	30.00	0.90	322.5	1,612.5	24,187.5
	41	30.75	0.90	330.6	1,694.1	26,047.3
21	42	31.50	0.90	338.6	1,777.8	28,000.1
	43	32.25	0.90	346.7	1,863.4	30,048.1
22	44	33.00	0.89	354.8	1,951.1	32,193.6
	45	33.75	0.89	362.8	2,040.8	34,438.8
23	46	34.50	0.89	370.9	2,132.5	36,786.2
	47	35.25	0.89	378.9	2,226.3	39,237.8
24	48	36.00	0.88	387.0	2,322.0	41,796.0
	49	36.75	0.88	395.1	2,419.8	44,463.1
25	50	37.50	0.88	403.1	2,519.5	47,241.2
	51	38.25	0.88	411.2	2,621.3	50,132.8
26	52	39.00	0.88	419.3	2,725.1	53,139.9
	53	39.75	0.88	427.3	2,830.9	56,265.0
27	54	40.50	0.87	435.4	2,938.8	59,510.3
	55	41.25	0.87	443.4	3,048.6	62,878.1
28	56	42.00	0.87	451.5	3,160.5	66,370.5
	57	42.75	0.87	459.6	3,274.4	69,989.9
29	58	43.50	0.87	467.6	3,390.3	73,738.6
	59	44.25	0.87	475.7	3,508.2	77,618.8
30	60	45.00	0.86	483.8	3,628.1	81,632.8
	61	45.75	0.86	491.8	3,750.1	85,782.9
31	62	46.50	0.86	499.9	3,874.0	90,071.2
	63	47.25	0.86	507.9	4,000.0	94,500.2
32	64	48.00	0.86	516.0	4,128.0	99,072.0
	65	48.75	0.86	524.1	4,258.0	103,789.0
33	66	49.50	0.85	532.1	4,390.0	108,653.3
	67	50.25	0.85	540.2	4,524.1	113,667.3
34	68	51.00	0.85	548.3	4,660.1	118,833.2
	69	51.75	0.85	556.3	4,798.2	124,153.3
35	70	52.50	0.85	564.4	4,938.3	129,629.9
	71	53.25	0.85	572.4	5,080.4	135,265.2
36	72	54.00	0.85	580.5	5,224.5	141,061.5
	73	54.75	0.85	588.6	5,370.6	147,021.1
37	74	55.50	0.84	596.6	5,518.8	153,146.2
	75	56.25	0.84	604.7	5,668.9	159,439.1
38	76	57.00	0.84	612.8	5,821.1	165,902.1
	77	57.75	0.84	620.8	5,975.3	172,537.4
39	78	58.50	0.84	628.9	6,131.5	179,347.3
	79	59.25	0.84	636.9	6,289.8	186,334.1
40	80	60.00	0.84	645.0	6,450.0	193,500.0
	81	60.75	0.84	653.1	6,612.3	200,847.4
41	82	61.50	0.83	661.1	6,776.5	208,378.4
	83	62.25	0.83	669.2	6,942.8	216,095.3
42	84	63.00	0.83	677.3	7,111.1	224,000.5
	85	63.75	0.83	685.3	7,281.4	232,096.1
43	86	64.50	0.83	693.4	7,453.8	240,384.5
	87	65.25	0.83	701.4	7,628.1	248,867.9
44	88	66.00	0.83	709.5	7,804.5	257,548.5
	89	66.75	0.83	717.6	7,982.9	266,428.8
45	90	67.50	0.83	725.6	8,163.3	275,510.8
	91	68.25	0.82	733.7	8,345.7	284,796.9
46	92	69.00	0.82	741.8	8,530.1	294,289.3
	93	69.75	0.82	749.8	8,716.6	303,990.5
47	94	70.50	0.82	757.9	8,905.0	313,902.4
	95	71.25	0.82	765.9	9,095.5	324,027.5
48	96	72.00	0.82	774.0	9,288.0	334,368.0
	97	72.75	0.82	782.1	9,482.5	344,926.3
49	98	73.50	0.82	790.1	9,679.0	355,704.5
	99	74.25	0.82	798.2	9,877.6	366,704.8
50	100	75.00	0.82	806.3	10,078.1	377,929.7

STRUCTURAL GLUED LAMINATED TIMBER
FOR INFORMATION CALL 800/525-1625

SIMPLE SPAN BEAM TABLE

ts technical support

TABLE SPECIFICATIONS

This beam design table applies for straight, simply-supported, laminated timber beams. Other beam support systems may be employed to meet varying design conditions.

Roofs should have a minimum slope of ¼ inch per foot to eliminate water ponding.

Total load carrying capacity includes beam weight. Floor beams are designed for uniform loads of 40 psf live load and 10 psf dead load.

Allowable stresses:
Bending stress, Fb = 2400 psi (reduced by size factor). C_F

Shear stress, Fv = 165 psi.
Modulus of elasticity, E = 1,800,000 psi.
For roof beams, Fb and Fv were increased 15% for short duration of loading.

Deflection limits:
Roof beams — 1/180 span for total load.
Floor beams — 1/360 span for 40 psf live load only.

Values for preliminary design purposes only. For more complete design information, see the AITC "Timber Construction Manual."

SPAN FT.	SPACING FT.	ROOF BEAMS—TOTAL LOAD CARRYING CAPACITY								FLOOR BEAMS TOTAL LOAD
		20 PSF	25 PSF	30 PSF	35 PSF	40 PSF	45 PSF	50 PSF	55 PSF	50 PSF
8	4	—	—	3⅛x4½	3⅛x4½	3⅛x6	3⅛x6	3⅛x6	3⅛x6	3⅛x6
	6	—	—	3⅛x4½	3⅛x4½	3⅛x6	3⅛x6	3⅛x6	3⅛x6	3⅛x6
	8	—	—	3⅛x4½	3⅛x4½	3⅛x6	3⅛x6	3⅛x6	3⅛x6	3⅛x7½
10	4	—	—	3⅛x4½	3⅛x4½	3⅛x6	3⅛x6	3⅛x6	3⅛x6	3⅛x7½
	6	—	—	3⅛x4½	3⅛x6	3⅛x6	3⅛x6	3⅛x6	3⅛x7½	3⅛x7½
	8	—	—	3⅛x6	3⅛x6	3⅛x7½	3⅛x7½	3⅛x7½	3⅛x7½	3⅛x9
	10	—	—	3⅛x6	3⅛x7½	3⅛x7½	3⅛x7½	3⅛x7½	3⅛x9	3⅛x9
12	6	—	—	3⅛x6	3⅛x6	3⅛x7½	3⅛x7½	3⅛x7½	3⅛x7½	3⅛x9
	8	—	—	3⅛x6	3⅛x7½	3⅛x9	3⅛x9	3⅛x9	3⅛x9	3⅛x10½
	10	—	—	3⅛x7½	3⅛x7½	3⅛x9	3⅛x9	3⅛x9	3⅛x10½	3⅛x10½
	12	—	—	3⅛x7½	3⅛x9	3⅛x9	3⅛x9	3⅛x10½	3⅛x10½	3⅛x12
14	8	—	—	3⅛x7½	3⅛x9	3⅛x9	3⅛x9	3⅛x10½	3⅛x10½	3⅛x12
	10	—	—	3⅛x9	3⅛x9	3⅛x10½	3⅛x10½	3⅛x10½	3⅛x12	3⅛x12
	12	—	—	3⅛x9	3⅛x10½	3⅛x10½	3⅛x10½	3⅛x12	3⅛x12	3⅛x13½
	14	—	—	3⅛x10½	3⅛x10½	3⅛x12	3⅛x12	3⅛x12	3⅛x13½	3⅛x13½
16	8	—	—	3⅛x9	3⅛x9	3⅛x10½	3⅛x10½	3⅛x12	3⅛x12	3⅛x13½
	12	—	—	3⅛x10½	3⅛x12	3⅛x12	3⅛x12	3⅛3x1½	3⅛x13½	3⅛x15
	14	—	3⅛x10½	3⅛x12	3⅛x12	3⅛x13½	3⅛x13½	3⅛x15	3⅛x15	3⅛x15
	16	—	3⅛x10½	3⅛x12	3⅛x13½	3⅛x13½	3⅛x15	3⅛x15	3⅛x16½	3⅛x15
18	8	—	—	3⅛x9	3⅛x10½	3⅛x12	3⅛x12	3⅛x12	3⅛x13½	3⅛x15
	12	—	3⅛x10½	3⅛x12	3⅛x12	3⅛x13½	3⅛x13½	3⅛x15	3⅛x16½	3⅛x16½
	16	—	3⅛x12	3⅛x13½	3⅛x15	3⅛x15	3⅛x16½	5⅛x13½	5⅛x13½	5⅛x15
	20	—	3⅛x13½	3⅛x15	3⅛x16½	3⅛x18	3⅛x18	5⅛x15	5⅛x16½	5⅛x16½
20	8	—	—	3⅛x12	3⅛x12	3⅛x13½	3⅛x13½	3⅛x13½	3⅛x15	3⅛x16½
	12	—	3⅛x12	3⅛x13½	3⅛x13½	3⅛x15	3⅛x16½	3⅛x16½	5⅛x13½	5⅛x15
	16	—	3⅛x13½	3⅛x15	3⅛x16½	3⅛x18	3⅛x18	5⅛x15	5⅛x16½	5⅛x18
	20	—	3⅛x15	3⅛x16½	3⅛x18	5⅛x15	5⅛x16½	5⅛x16½	5⅛x18	5⅛x18
24	8	—	—	3⅛x13½	3⅛x15	3⅛x15	3⅛x16½	3⅛x16½	3⅛x18	5⅛x16½
	12	—	3⅛x15	3⅛x16½	3⅛x16½	3⅛x18	5⅛x15	5⅛x16½	5⅛x16½	5⅛x18
	16	—	3⅛x16½	3⅛x18	5⅛x16½	5⅛x16½	5⅛x18	5⅛x18	5⅛x19½	5⅛x21
	20	—	3⅛x18	5⅛x16½	5⅛x16½	5⅛x18	5⅛x19½	5⅛x19½	5⅛x21	5⅛x22½
28	8	—	3⅛x13½	3⅛x16½	3⅛x16½	3⅛x18	3⅛x18	5⅛x16½	5⅛x16½	5⅛x19½
	12	—	3⅛x18	3⅛x18	5⅛x16½	5⅛x18	5⅛x18	5⅛x18	5⅛x19½	5⅛x21
	16	—	5⅛x16½	5⅛x18	5⅛x18	5⅛x19½	5⅛x19½	5⅛x21	5⅛x22½	5⅛x24
	20	—	5⅛x18	5⅛x18	5⅛x19½	5⅛x21	5⅛x22½	5⅛x24	5⅛x25½	5⅛x25½
32	8	—	3⅛x18	3⅛x18	5⅛x16½	5⅛x18	5⅛x18	5⅛x18	5⅛x19½	5⅛x21
	12	—	5⅛x16½	5⅛x18	5⅛x19½	5⅛x19½	5⅛x21	5⅛x21	5⅛x22½	5⅛x24
	16	—	5⅛x18	5⅛x19½	5⅛x21	5⅛x22½	5⅛x22½	5⅛x24	5⅛x25½	5⅛x27
	20	5⅛x18	5⅛x19½	5⅛x21	5⅛x22½	5⅛x24	5⅛x25½	5⅛x27	5⅛x28½	6¾x27
36	12	—	5⅛x19½	5⅛x19½	5⅛x21	5⅛x22½	5⅛x22½	5⅛x24	5⅛x25½	6¾x25½
	16	—	5⅛x21	5⅛x22½	5⅛x24	5⅛x24	5⅛x25½	5⅛x27	5⅛x28½	6¾x27
	20	5⅛x21	5⅛x22½	5⅛x24	5⅛x25½	5⅛x27	5⅛x30	6¾x27	6¾x28½	6¾x30
	24	5⅛x22½	5⅛x24	5⅛x25½	5⅛x28½	5⅛x30	6¾x27	6¾x28½	6¾x30	6¾x31½
40	12	5⅛x19½	5⅛x21	5⅛x22½	5⅛x24	5⅛x24	5⅛x25½	5⅛x27	6¾x25½	6¾x28½
	16	5⅛x21	5⅛x22½	5⅛x24	5⅛x25½	5⅛x27	5⅛x28½	6¾x27	6¾x28½	6¾x31½
	20	5⅛x22½	5⅛x25½	5⅛x27	5⅛x28½	6¾x27	6¾x28½	6¾x30	6¾x31½	6¾x33
	24	5⅛x24	5⅛x27	5⅛x28½	6¾x27	6¾x28½	6¾x31½	6¾x33	6¾x34½	6¾x36
44	12	5⅛x21	5⅛x22½	5⅛x24	5⅛x25½	5⅛x27	5⅛x27	6¾x25½	6¾x27	6¾x31½
	16	5⅛x24	5⅛x25½	5⅛x27	5⅛x28½	5⅛x30	6¾x28½	6¾x30	6¾x31½	6¾x33
	20	5⅛x25½	5⅛x27	5⅛x30	6¾x27	6¾x30	6¾x30	6¾x33	6¾x34½	6¾x36
	24	5⅛x27	5⅛x28½	6¾x28½	6¾x30	6¾x31½	6¾x34½	6¾x36	6¾x37½	6¾x39
48	12	5⅛x24	5⅛x25½	5⅛x27	5⅛x28½	5⅛x30	5⅛x30	6¾x28½	6¾x30	6¾x33
	16	5⅛x25½	5⅛x27	5⅛x30	6¾x28½	6¾x30	6¾x30	6¾x31½	6¾x34½	6¾x37½
	20	5⅛x27	5⅛x30	6¾x28½	6¾x30	6¾x31½	6¾x34½	6¾x36	6¾x37½	8¾x36
	24	5⅛x30	6¾x28½	6¾x30	6¾x33	6¾x34½	6¾x37½	6¾x39	8¾x36	8¾x39

SPAN FT.	SPACING FT.	ROOF BEAMS—TOTAL LOAD CARRYING CAPACITY								FLOOR BEAMS TOTAL LOAD
		20 PSF	25 PSF	30 PSF	35 PSF	40 PSF	45 PSF	50 PSF	55 PSF	50 PSF
52	12	5⅛x25½	5⅛x27	5⅛x28½	5⅛x30	6¾x28½	6¾x30	6¾x31½	6¾x31½	6¾x36
	16	5⅛x28½	5⅛x30	6¾x28½	6¾x30	6¾x31½	6¾x33	6¾x34½	6¾x37½	8¾x36
	20	5⅛x30	6¾x30	6¾x31½	6¾x33	6¾x34½	6¾x37½	6¾x39	8¾x36	8¾x39
	24	6¾x28½	6¾x31½	6¾x33	6¾x36	6¾x37½	6¾x40½	8¾x37½	8¾x39	8¾x42
56	12	5⅛x27	5⅛x28½	6¾x28½	6¾x30	6¾x31½	6¾x33	6¾x33	6¾x34½	8¾x36
	16	5⅛x30	6¾x30	6¾x31½	6¾x33	6¾x34½	6¾x36	6¾x37½	8¾x34½	8¾x39
	20	6¾x28½	6¾x31½	6¾x33	6¾x36	6¾x37½	8¾x34½	8¾x37½	8¾x39	8¾x42
	24	6¾x31½	6¾x33	6¾x36	6¾x39	8¾x36	8¾x39	8¾x40½	8¾x42	8¾x45
60	12	5⅛x28½	6¾x28½	6¾x30	6¾x31½	6¾x33	6¾x34½	6¾x36	6¾x37½	8¾x39
	16	6¾x28½	6¾x31½	6¾x33	6¾x34½	6¾x36	6¾x39	8¾x36	8¾x37½	8¾x42
	20	6¾x31½	6¾x34½	6¾x36	6¾x37½	8¾x36	8¾x37½	8¾x40½	8¾x42	8¾x45
	24	6¾x33	6¾x36	6¾x39	8¾x36	8¾x39	8¾x42	8¾x43½	8¾x45	8¾x48
64	12	6¾x28½	6¾x30	6¾x33	6¾x34½	6¾x36	6¾x37½	6¾x39	6¾x40½	8¾x40½
	16	6¾x31½	6¾x33	6¾x36	6¾x37½	6¾x39	6¾x40½	8¾x39	8¾x40½	8¾x45
	20	6¾x33	6¾x36	6¾x37½	6¾x40½	8¾x39	8¾x40½	8¾x42	8¾x45	8¾x48
	24	6¾x36	6¾x37½	6¾x40½	8¾x39	8¾x42	8¾x43½	8¾x46½	8¾x49½	8¾x51
68	12	6¾x30	6¾x33	6¾x34½	6¾x36	6¾x37½	6¾x39	6¾x40½	8¾x39	8¾x43½
	16	6¾x33	6¾x36	6¾x37½	6¾x39	8¾x37½	8¾x39	8¾x40½	8¾x43½	8¾x48
	20	6¾x36	6¾x37½	6¾x40½	8¾x39	8¾x40½	8¾x43½	8¾x45	8¾x48	8¾x51
	24	6¾x37½	6¾x40½	8¾x39	8¾x42	8¾x45	8¾x46½	8¾x49½	8¾x52½	10¾x51
72	12	6¾x31½	6¾x34½	6¾x36	6¾x37½	6¾x40½	8¾x37½	8¾x39	8¾x40½	8¾x46½
	16	6¾x34½	6¾x37½	6¾x40½	8¾x39	8¾x40½	8¾x42	8¾x43½	8¾x45	8¾x51
	20	6¾x37½	6¾x40½	8¾x39	8¾x42	8¾x43½	8¾x45	8¾x48	8¾x51	10¾x51
	24	6¾x40½	8¾x39	8¾x42	8¾x43½	8¾x46½	8¾x49½	8¾x52½	10¾x49½	10¾x54
76	12	6¾x33	6¾x36	6¾x37½	6¾x40½	8¾x39	8¾x40½	8¾x42	8¾x43½	8¾x48
	16	6¾x37½	6¾x39	8¾x39	8¾x40½	8¾x42	8¾x43½	8¾x45	8¾x48	8¾x52½
	20	6¾x39	8¾x39	8¾x42	8¾x43½	8¾x45	8¾x48	8¾x51	10¾x48	10¾x54
	24	8¾x39	8¾x42	8¾x43½	8¾x46½	8¾x49½	8¾x52½	10¾x49½	10¾x52½	10¾x57
80	12	6¾x34½	6¾x37½	6¾x40½	8¾x39	8¾x40½	8¾x42	8¾x43½	8¾x45	8¾x51
	16	6¾x39	8¾x37½	8¾x40½	8¾x42	8¾x45	8¾x45	8¾x48	8¾x51	10¾x52½
	20	8¾x37½	8¾x40½	8¾x43½	8¾x46½	8¾x48	8¾x51	10¾x48	10¾x51	10¾x57
	24	8¾x40½	8¾x43½	8¾x46½	8¾x49½	8¾x52½	10¾x49½	10¾x52½	10¾x55½	10¾x60
84	12	6¾x37½	6¾x39	8¾x39	8¾x40½	8¾x42	8¾x43½	8¾x46½	8¾x48	10¾x49½
	16	6¾x40½	8¾x40½	8¾x42	8¾x45	8¾x46½	8¾x48	8¾x51	8¾x52½	10¾x55½
	20	8¾x40½	8¾x43½	8¾x46½	8¾x48	8¾x51	10¾x49½	10¾x51	10¾x54	10¾x58½
	24	8¾x42	8¾x46½	8¾x48	8¾x51	10¾x49½	10¾x52½	10¾x55½	10¾x58½	10¾x63
88	12	6¾x39	8¾x37½	8¾x40½	8¾x42	8¾x45	8¾x46½	8¾x48	8¾x49½	10¾x52½
	16	8¾x39	8¾x42	8¾x45	8¾x46½	8¾x49½	8¾x51	8¾x52½	10¾x51	10¾x57
	20	8¾x42	8¾x45	8¾x48	8¾x51	8¾x52½	10¾x51	10¾x54	10¾x55½	10¾x61½
	24	8¾x45	8¾x48	8¾x51	10¾x49½	10¾x52½	10¾x55½	10¾x61½	—	—
92	12	6¾x40½	8¾x40½	8¾x42	8¾x45	8¾x46½	8¾x48	8¾x51	8¾x52½	10¾x54
	16	8¾x40½	8¾x43½	8¾x46½	8¾x49½	8¾x51	8¾x52½	10¾x51	10¾x54	10¾x60
	20	8¾x43½	8¾x46½	8¾x49½	8¾x52½	10¾x51	10¾x54	10¾x55½	10¾x58½	10¾x64½
	24	8¾x46½	8¾x49½	8¾x52½	10¾x52½	10¾x54	10¾x58½	10¾x61½	10¾x64½	—
96	12	8¾x39	8¾x42	8¾x43½	8¾x46½	8¾x48	8¾x51	8¾x52½	10¾x51	10¾x57
	16	8¾x42	8¾x45	8¾x48	8¾x51	10¾x49½	10¾x52½	10¾x54	10¾x55½	10¾x63
	20	8¾x45	8¾x49½	8¾x52½	10¾x51	10¾x54	10¾x55½	10¾x58½	10¾x61½	—
	24	8¾x48	8¾x52½	10¾x52½	10¾x54	10¾x57	10¾x60	10¾x64½	—	—
100	12	8¾x40½	8¾x43½	8¾x46½	8¾x48	8¾x51	8¾x52½	10¾x51	10¾x52½	10¾x60
	16	8¾x43½	8¾x48	8¾x51	8¾x52½	10¾x52½	10¾x54	10¾x55½	10¾x58½	10¾x64½
	20	8¾x48	8¾x51	10¾x51	10¾x54	10¾x55½	10¾x58½	10¾x61½	10¾x64½	—
	24	8¾x51	10¾x51	10¾x54	10¾x57	10¾x60	10¾x63	—	—	—

CANTILEVERED AND CONTINUOUS SPAN SYSTEMS

Cantilever beam systems may be comprised of any of the various types and combinations of beam illustrated below. Cantilever systems permit longer spans or larger loads for a given size member than do simple span systems, provided member size is not controlled by compression perpendicular to grain at the supports or by horizontal shear. Substantial design economies can be effected by decreasing the depths of the members in the suspended portions of a cantilever system.

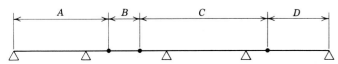

CANTILEVERED BEAM SYSTEMS. A is single cantilever, B is a suspended beam, C has a double cantilever, and D is a beam with one end suspended.

For economy, the negative bending moment at the supports of a cantilevered beam should be equal in magnitude to the positive moment.

Consideration must be given to deflection and camber in cantilevered multiple spans. When possible, roofs should be sloped the equivalent of ¼ inch per foot of horizontal distance between the level of the drain and the high point of the roof to eliminate water pockets, or provisions should be made to ensure that accumulation of water does not produce greater deflection and live loads than anticipated. Unbalanced loading conditions should be investigated for maximum bending moment, deflection, and stability.

Continuous span beams are commonly used in both building and bridge construction to reduce maximum moments, thus reducing the section size required.

Design aids for cantilever and continuous span beam systems may be found in the AITC "Timber Construction Manual."

Glued laminated timber beams are often tapered or curved to meet architectural requirements, to provide pitched roofs, or to provide a minimum depth of beam at the point of bearing.

CANTILEVER BEAM DESIGN TABLE

ts technical support

CANTILEVER BEAM TABLE① BEAM SPACING 20' — SEE FOOTNOTES FOR OTHER DESIGN SPECIFICATIONS.

Main Support Spacing②, ft.	Dead Load,③ psf	Live Load, psf	TWO-SPAN SYSTEM ④		THREE-SPAN SYSTEM ⑤		THREE-SPAN SYSTEM ⑥	
			Suspended Beam	Cantilevered Beam	Suspended Beam	Cantilevered Beams	Suspended Beams	Double Cantilevered Beam
32	10	12	5⅛ x 15	5⅛ x 16½	5⅛ x 10½	5⅛ x 16½	5⅛ x 15	5⅛ x 15
		20	5⅛ x 16½	5⅛ x 19½	5⅛ x 10½	5⅛ x 19½	5⅛ x 18	5⅛ x 19½
		30	5⅛ x 19½	5⅛ x 25½	5⅛ x 12	5⅛ x 24	5⅛ x 21	5⅛ x 24
	12	12	5⅛ x 15	5⅛ x 16½	5⅛ x 10½	5⅛ x 16½	5⅛ x 15	5⅛ x 16½
		20	5⅛ x 18	5⅛ x 21	5⅛ x 12	5⅛ x 21	5⅛ x 18	5⅛ x 19½
		30	5⅛ x 21	5⅛ x 27	5⅛ x 12	5⅛ x 24	5⅛ x 21	5⅛ x 25½
	15	20	5⅛ x 19½	5⅛ x 22½	5⅛ x 12	5⅛ x 21	5⅛ x 19½	5⅛ x 21
		30	5⅛ x 21	5⅛ x 28½	5⅛ x 13½	5⅛ x 25½	5⅛ x 22½	5⅛ x 27
36	10	12	5⅛ x 16½	5⅛ x 18	5⅛ x 10½	5⅛ x 18	5⅛ x 16½	5⅛ x 16½
		20	5⅛ x 19½	5⅛ x 22½	5⅛ x 12	5⅛ x 22½	5⅛ x 19½	5⅛ x 21
		30	5⅛ x 22½	5⅛ x 28½	5⅛ x 13½	5⅛ x 27	5⅛ x 22½	5⅛ x 27
	12	12	5⅛ x 16½	5⅛ x 19½	5⅛ x 12	5⅛ x 19½	5⅛ x 18	5⅛ x 18
		20	5⅛ x 19½	5⅛ x 24	5⅛ x 12	5⅛ x 24	5⅛ x 21	5⅛ x 21
		30	5⅛ x 22½	5⅛ x 30	5⅛ x 13½	5⅛ x 27	5⅛ x 24	5⅛ x 28½
	15	20	5⅛ x 21	5⅛ x 25½	5⅛ x 13½	5⅛ x 24	5⅛ x 22½	5⅛ x 24
		30	5⅛ x 24	5⅛ x 33	5⅛ x 15	5⅛ x 28½	5⅛ x 25½	5⅛ x 31½
40	10	12	5⅛ x 18	5⅛ x 21	5⅛ x 12	5⅛ x 21	5⅛ x 18	5⅛ x 18
		20	5⅛ x 21	5⅛ x 25½	5⅛ x 13½	5⅛ x 25½	5⅛ x 22½	5⅛ x 24
		30	5⅛ x 25½	5⅛ x 31½	5⅛ x 15	5⅛ x 30	5⅛ x 25½	5⅛ x 30
	12	12	5⅛ x 18	5⅛ x 21	5⅛ x 12	5⅛ x 21	5⅛ x 19½	5⅛ x 19½
		20	5⅛ x 22½	5⅛ x 25½	5⅛ x 13½	5⅛ x 25½	5⅛ x 22½	5⅛ x 24
		30	5⅛ x 25½	5⅛ x 33	5⅛ x 15	5⅛ x 30	5⅛ x 27	5⅛ x 31½
	15	20	5⅛ x 24	5⅛ x 28½	5⅛ x 15	5⅛ x 27	5⅛ x 24	5⅛ x 27
		30	5⅛ x 27	5⅛ x 36	5⅛ x 16½	5⅛ x 31½	5⅛ x 28½	5⅛ x 34½
44	10	12	5⅛ x 19½	5⅛ x 22½	5⅛ x 12	5⅛ x 22½	5⅛ x 21	5⅛ x 21
		20	5⅛ x 24	5⅛ x 28½	5⅛ x 15	5⅛ x 28½	5⅛ x 25½	5⅛ x 25½
		30	5⅛ x 27	5⅛ x 34½	5⅛ x 16½	5⅛ x 33	5⅛ x 28½	5⅛ x 33
	12	12	5⅛ x 21	5⅛ x 22½	5⅛ x 13½	5⅛ x 24	5⅛ x 21	5⅛ x 21
		20	5⅛ x 24	5⅛ x 28½	5⅛ x 15	5⅛ x 28½	5⅛ x 25½	5⅛ x 27
		30	5⅛ x 28½	5⅛ x 36	5⅛ x 18	5⅛ x 33	5⅛ x 30	5⅛ x 34½
	15	20	5⅛ x 25½	5⅛ x 31½	5⅛ x 16½	5⅛ x 30	5⅛ x 27	5⅛ x 30
		30	5⅛ x 30	6¾ x 30	5⅛ x 18	5⅛ x 34½	5⅛ x 30	6¾ x 30
48	10	12	5⅛ x 21	5⅛ x 24	5⅛ x 13½	5⅛ x 24	5⅛ x 22½	5⅛ x 22½
		20	5⅛ x 25½	5⅛ x 30	5⅛ x 16½	5⅛ x 30	5⅛ x 27	5⅛ x 28½
		30	5⅛ x 30	5⅛ x 37½	5⅛ x 18	5⅛ x 36	5⅛ x 31½	5⅛ x 36
	12	12	5⅛ x 22½	5⅛ x 25½	5⅛ x 13½	5⅛ x 25½	5⅛ x 24	5⅛ x 24
		20	5⅛ x 27	5⅛ x 31½	5⅛ x 16½	5⅛ x 31½	5⅛ x 28½	5⅛ x 30
		30	5⅛ x 31½	6¾ x 31½	5⅛ x 19½	5⅛ x 36	5⅛ x 31½	6¾ x 30
	15	20	5⅛ x 28½	5⅛ x 34½	5⅛ x 18	5⅛ x 33	5⅛ x 30	5⅛ x 33
		30	5⅛ x 33	6¾ x 33	5⅛ x 19½	5⅛ x 37½	5⅛ x 33	6¾ x 31½
52	10	12	5⅛ x 24	5⅛ x 27	5⅛ x 15	5⅛ x 27	5⅛ x 24	5⅛ x 25½
		20	5⅛ x 28½	6¾ x 28½	5⅛ x 18	6¾ x 28½	5⅛ x 30	5⅛ x 31½
		30	5⅛ x 33	6¾ x 33	5⅛ x 19½	6¾ x 34½	5⅛ x 34½	6¾ x 31½
	12	12	5⅛ x 24	5⅛ x 27	5⅛ x 15	5⅛ x 27	5⅛ x 25½	5⅛ x 25½
		20	5⅛ x 30	6¾ x 30	5⅛ x 18	6¾ x 30	5⅛ x 30	5⅛ x 33
		30	5⅛ x 33	6¾ x 34½	5⅛ x 21	6¾ x 34½	5⅛ x 34½	6¾ x 33
	15	20	5⅛ x 31½	6¾ x 30	5⅛ x 19½	6¾ x 31½	5⅛ x 33	5⅛ x 36
		30	5⅛ x 34½	6¾ x 36	5⅛ x 21	6¾ x 36	5⅛ x 36	6¾ x 34½

CANTILEVER BEAM TABLE① BEAM SPACING 20' — SEE FOOTNOTES FOR OTHER DESIGN SPECIFICATIONS.

Main Support Spacing②, ft.	Dead Load③, psf	Live Load, psf	TWO-SPAN SYSTEM ④		THREE-SPAN SYSTEM ⑤		THREE-SPAN SYSTEM ⑥	
			Suspended Beam	Cantilevered Beam	Suspended Beam	Cantilevered Beams	Suspended Beams	Cantilevered Double Beam
56	10	12	5⅛ x 25½	5⅛ x 28½	5⅛ x 15	5⅛ x 28½	5⅛ x 27	5⅛ x 25½
		20	5⅛ x 31½	5⅛ x 36	5⅛ x 19½	6¾ x 31½	5⅛ x 31½	5⅛ x 33
		30	5⅛ x 36	6¾ x 36	5⅛ x 22½	6¾ x 36	5⅛ x 37½	6¾ x 34½
	12	12	5⅛ x 27	5⅛ x 30	5⅛ x 16½	5⅛ x 30	5⅛ x 27	5⅛ x 27
		20	5⅛ x 31½	6¾ x 31½	5⅛ x 19½	6¾ x 31½	5⅛ x 33	5⅛ x 34½
		30	5⅛ x 36	6¾ x 37½	5⅛ x 22½	6¾ x 37½	5⅛ x 37½	6¾ x 34½
	15	20	5⅛ x 33	6¾ x 33	5⅛ x 21	6¾ x 33	5⅛ x 34½	6¾ x 30
		30	5⅛ x 37½	6¾ x 39	5⅛ x 24	6¾ x 39	6¾ x 34½	6¾ x 37½
60	10	12	5⅛ x 27	5⅛ x 31½	5⅛ x 16½	5⅛ x 31½	5⅛ x 28½	5⅛ x 28½
		20	5⅛ x 33	6¾ x 33	5⅛ x 21	6¾ x 33	5⅛ x 34½	5⅛ x 36
		30	5⅛ x 37½	6¾ x 39	5⅛ x 24	6¾ x 39	6¾ x 34½	6¾ x 37½
	12	12	5⅛ x 28½	5⅛ x 31½	5⅛ x 18	5⅛ x 31½	5⅛ x 30	5⅛ x 30
		20	5⅛ x 34½	6¾ x 34½	5⅛ x 21	6¾ x 34½	5⅛ x 36	5⅛ x 37½
		30	6¾ x 34½	8¾ x 34½	5⅛ x 24	8¾ x 34½	6¾ x 34½	6¾ x 37½
	15	20	5⅛ x 36	6¾ x 36	5⅛ x 22½	6¾ x 36	5⅛ x 37½	6¾ x 33
		30	6¾ x 36	8¾ x 36	5⅛ x 25½	8¾ x 36	6¾ x 36	8¾ x 33
64	10	12	5⅛ x 28½	5⅛ x 33	5⅛ x 18	5⅛ x 33	5⅛ x 30	5⅛ x 30
		20	5⅛ x 36	6¾ x 36	5⅛ x 21	6¾ x 36	5⅛ x 36	6¾ x 33
		30	6¾ x 36	8¾ x 36	5⅛ x 25½	8¾ x 36	6¾ x 36	8¾ x 34½
	12	12	5⅛ x 30	5⅛ x 34½	5⅛ x 19½	5⅛ x 34½	5⅛ x 31½	5⅛ x 31½
		20	5⅛ x 36	6¾ x 36	5⅛ x 22½	6¾ x 36	6¾ x 33	6¾ x 33
		30	6¾ x 36	8¾ x 37½	5⅛ x 25½	8¾ x 37½	6¾ x 37½	8¾ x 34½
	15	20	6¾ x 33	6¾ x 37½	5⅛ x 24	6¾ x 39	6¾ x 34½	6¾ x 34½
		30	6¾ x 37½	8¾ x 39	5⅛ x 27	8¾ x 39	6¾ x 39	8¾ x 36

① This beam design table applies for straight, cantilevered, laminated timber beams. Member sizes are governed by either bending or shear. **Where building code deflection requirements apply, the member sizes must be checked.** A minimum roof slope of ¼ in. per foot should be provided to minimize water ponding.

Specifications and allowable stresses:
  Beam spacing: 20' — 0"
  Bending stress, F = 2400 psi
  Shear stress, F_v = 165 psi
  Compression perpendicular to grain stress, $F_{c\perp}$ = 385 psi
  Modulus of elasticity, E = 1,800,000; psi
  Duration of load factor: 1.25 for 12 psf live loads; and 1.15 for 20 and 30 psf live loads
  Member sizes are checked for full unbalanced live loading.

② Main supports are columns or bearing walls. Table is based on equal spacing of main supports.

③ Does not include weight of glulam.

⑤ Three-span cantilever system: End members cantilevered over intermediate column supports and carrying the suspended beam. Length of cantilevers, ℓ' equal to approximately 0.25 x main support spacing, ℓ.

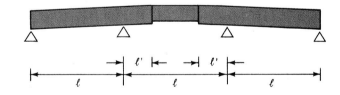

④ Two-span cantilever system: Cantilevered beam extends over center support with the length of cantilever, ℓ' equal to approximately 0.20 x main support spacing, ℓ.

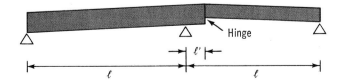

⑥ Three-span cantilever system: Center member double — cantilevered over intermediate column supports and carrying the suspended wall beams. Length of cantilevers, ℓ' equal to approximately 0.17 x main support spacing, ℓ.

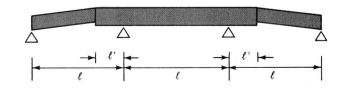

ARCH TABLE

LOADING	ROOF PITCH	WALL HGT. FT.	30′ SPAN WIDTH	30′ BASE	30′ LOWER TANG.	30′ UPPER TANG.	30′ CROWN	35′ SPAN WIDTH	35′ BASE	35′ LOWER TANG.	35′ UPPER TANG.	35′ CROWN	40′ SPAN WIDTH	40′ BASE	40′ LOWER TANG.	40′ UPPER TANG.	40′ CROWN	50′ SPAN WIDTH	50′ BASE	50′ LOWER TANG.	50′ UPPER TANG.	50′ CROWN
VERTICAL DEAD + LIVE LOAD = 400#/FT.	3/12	10	3⅛	8¼	12	10¾	7½	3⅛	10½	13¼	12	7½	3⅛	13¼	14½	13¼	7½	5⅛	11¾	14	13¾	7½
		12	5⅛	7½	11	10¾	7½	5⅛	7½	12	12	7½	5⅛	7½	13¼	13	7½	5⅛	10½	14¾	14½	7½
		14	5⅛	7½	12	12	7½	5⅛	7½	13½	13¼	7½	5⅛	7½	14¾	14½	7½	5⅛	9½	16¾	16¼	7½
		16	5⅛	7½	13¼	13	7½	5⅛	7½	14¾	14½	7½	5⅛	7½	16	16	7½	5⅛	8¾	18¾	17½	7½
		18	5⅛	7½	14¼	14¼	7½	5⅛	7½	16	15¾	7½	5⅛	7½	17½	17¼	7½	5⅛	8	20½	19	7½
	4/12	10	3⅛	7½	11¾	12¾	7½	3⅛	9¾	13½	12¾	7½	3⅛	12	15¼	12¾	7½	5⅛	10½	13	12¾	7½
		12	5⅛	7½	10¾	10¾	7½	5⅛	7½	11¾	11¾	7½	5⅛	7½	12¾	12½	7½	5⅛	9½	14½	13½	7½
		14	5⅛	7½	12	12	7½	5⅛	7½	13¼	13	7½	5⅛	7½	14¼	14¼	7½	5⅛	8¾	16¾	15	7½
		16	5⅛	7½	13¼	13	7½	5⅛	7½	14½	14½	7½	5⅛	7½	15¾	15½	7½	5⅛	8	18½	16½	7½
		18	5⅛	7½	14¼	14	7½	5⅛	7½	15¾	15½	7½	5⅛	7½	17	17	7½	5⅛	7½	20¼	18	7½
	6/12	12	5⅛	7½	10½	10½	7½	5⅛	7½	11½	11¼	7½	5⅛	7½	12¼	11½	7½	5⅛	8	14¾	11¾	7½
		14	5⅛	7½	11¾	11¾	7½	5⅛	7½	12¾	12¾	7½	5⅛	7½	13¾	13¼	7½	5⅛	7½	16½	12¾	7½
		16	5⅛	7½	13	12¾	7½	5⅛	7½	14	14	7½	5⅛	7½	15	15	7½	5⅛	7½	18¼	14¼	7½
		18	5⅛	7½	14	14	7½	5⅛	7½	15¼	15¼	7½	5⅛	7½	16½	16¼	7½	5⅛	7½	19¾	16	7½
	8/12	12	5⅛	7½	10¼	10	7½	5⅛	7½	11	10½	7½	5⅛	7½	12	10¼	7½	5⅛	7½	14¼	11½	7½
		14	5⅛	7½	11½	11¼	7½	5⅛	7½	12¼	12	7½	5⅛	7½	13½	11¾	7½	5⅛	7½	16	12¼	7½
		16	5⅛	7½	12¾	12½	7½	5⅛	7½	13½	13½	7½	5⅛	7½	14¾	13½	7½	5⅛	7½	17¾	13	7½
		18	5⅛	7½	13¾	13½	7½	5⅛	7½	14¾	14¾	7½	5⅛	7½	16	15	7½	5⅛	7½	19¼	14	7½
VERTICAL DEAD + LIVE LOAD = 600#/FT.	3/12	10	3⅛	12	14½	12¾	7½	5⅛	9¾	12	12¾	7½	5⅛	12¼	14	13¾	12¼	5⅛	17½	17½	15½	12¼
		12	5⅛	7½	12	12	7½	5⅛	8½	13½	13	7½	5⅛	10¾	15	13½	7½	5⅛	15½	17½	16	7½
		14	5⅛	7½	13½	13¼	7½	5⅛	7¾	15½	14¼	7½	5⅛	9¾	17½	14½	7½	5⅛	14	21	16½	7½
		16	5⅛	7½	14¾	14¾	7½	5⅛	7½	17¼	15¼	7½	5⅛	8¾	19¼	15¾	7½	5⅛	12¾	23½	17	7½
		18	5⅛	7½	16	16	7½	5⅛	7½	18¾	16¼	7½	5⅛	8	21¼	16¾	7½	6¾	9	20½	20¼	7½
	4/12	10	3⅛	11	15	15½	7½	5⅛	9	10¼	15½	7½	5⅛	11	11¼	15½	12	5⅛	15½	15½	15½	12
		12	5⅛	7½	12	12	7½	5⅛	8	13¾	12¼	7½	5⅛	9¾	15¼	12¾	7½	5⅛	14	18	15¼	7½
		14	5⅛	7½	13½	13¼	7½	5⅛	7½	15½	13¾	7½	5⅛	9	17½	13¾	7½	5⅛	12¾	21	16	7½
		16	5⅛	7½	14¾	14¾	7½	5⅛	7½	17	15	7½	5⅛	8¼	19¼	15¼	7½	5⅛	11¾	23½	16½	7½
		18	5⅛	7½	16	16	7½	5⅛	7½	18½	16¼	7½	5⅛	7½	21	16½	7½	5⅛	10¾	25½	16¾	7½
	6/12	12	5⅛	7½	12	11¼	7½	5⅛	7½	13¾	11¼	7½	5⅛	8½	15¼	11	7½	5⅛	11¾	18¼	14½	7¾
		14	5⅛	7½	13½	12¾	7½	5⅛	7½	15½	12½	7½	5⅛	7¾	17¼	12½	7½	5⅛	10¾	20¾	15¼	7½
		16	5⅛	7½	14¾	14	7½	5⅛	7½	17	14	7½	5⅛	7½	19	14	7½	5⅛	10	23	15¾	7½
		18	5⅛	7½	16	15¼	7½	5⅛	7½	18¼	15½	7½	5⅛	7½	20½	15¼	7½	5⅛	9½	25	16½	7½
	8/12	12	5⅛	7½	12	10½	7½	5⅛	7½	13½	10¼	7½	5⅛	7½	15¼	11	7½	5⅛	10	18	14	9½
		14	5⅛	7½	13¼	12¼	7½	5⅛	7½	15¼	11½	7½	5⅛	7½	17	11¾	7½	5⅛	9¼	20¼	15	8
		16	5⅛	7½	14½	13½	7½	5⅛	7½	16½	13¼	7½	5⅛	7½	18½	12¾	7½	5⅛	8¾	22¼	15¾	7½
		18	5⅛	7½	15¾	14¾	7½	5⅛	7½	18	14¼	7½	5⅛	7½	20¼	13¾	7½	5⅛	8¼	24¼	16¼	7½
VERTICAL DEAD + LIVE LOAD = 800#/FT.	3/12	10	5⅛	10	12¼	12¼	12¼	5⅛	13	13¾	13¾	12¼	5⅛	16	16	14½	12¼	5⅛	22¾	22¾	18½	12¼
		12	5⅛	8¾	13¾	12	7½	5⅛	11¼	15¾	12½	7½	5⅛	14	17¼	13¼	7½	5⅛	20½	20½	18½	12¼
		14	5⅛	7¾	15¾	12¾	7½	5⅛	10	18¼	13¼	7½	5⅛	12¾	20½	13¾	7½	5⅛	18½	24½	19	12¼
		16	5⅛	7½	17½	13¾	7½	5⅛	9¼	20¼	14	7½	5⅛	11½	22¾	14½	7½	6¾	13	22	18¾	12¼
		18	5⅛	7½	19¼	14¼	7½	5⅛	8¼	22¼	14¾	7½	5⅛	10½	25	15¼	7½	6¾	12	24	20	12¼
	4/12	10	5⅛	9¼	9¾	18½	12	5⅛	11¾	11¾	18½	12	5⅛	14½	14½	18½	12	5⅛	20½	20½	18½	12
		12	5⅛	8	14	11½	7½	5⅛	10½	16	11¾	7½	5⅛	12¾	17¾	13	7½	5⅛	18½	20¾	17½	12
		14	5⅛	7½	16	12½	7½	5⅛	9½	18¼	12¾	7½	5⅛	11¾	20½	13½	7½	5⅛	16¾	24¾	18¼	12
		16	5⅛	7½	17½	13½	7½	5⅛	8½	20¼	13¾	7½	5⅛	10¾	22¾	13¾	7½	6¾	12	22	17¾	12
		18	5⅛	7½	19	14½	7½	5⅛	7¾	22	14¾	7½	5⅛	9¾	25	14½	7½	6¾	11	23¾	19¼	12
	6/12	12	5⅛	7½	14¼	10¾	7½	5⅛	9	16¼	10½	7½	5⅛	11	18	12½	7½	5⅛	15¼	21½	16½	11¼
		14	5⅛	7½	16	11¾	7½	5⅛	8¼	18¼	11¾	7½	5⅛	10	20¼	13¼	7½	5⅛	14¼	24½	17¼	11¼
		16	5⅛	7½	17½	13	7½	5⅛	7½	20	13	7½	5⅛	9¼	22½	13¾	7½	6¾	10¼	21½	16	11¼
		18	5⅛	7½	19	14	7½	5⅛	7½	21¾	14	7½	5⅛	8¾	24½	14¼	7½	6¾	9½	23	17½	11¼
	8/12	12	5⅛	7½	14¼	9¾	7½	5⅛	8	16	10¾	7½	5⅛	9½	17¾	12½	8	5⅛	13¼	21¼	16	11
		14	5⅛	7½	15¾	11¼	7½	5⅛	7½	18	11½	7½	5⅛	9	20	13½	7½	5⅛	12½	24	17	10½
		16	5⅛	7½	17¼	12½	7½	5⅛	7½	19¾	12	7½	5⅛	8¼	22	14	7½	6¾	9	20¾	16	10½
		18	5⅛	7½	18¾	13½	7½	5⅛	7½	21½	13	7½	5⅛	7¾	24	14½	7½	6¾	8½	22½	16½	10½
VERTICAL DEAD + LIVE LOAD = 1000#/FT.	3/12	10	5⅛	12½	12½	18½	12¼	5⅛	16	16	18½	12¼	5⅛	19¾	19¾	18½	12¼	5⅛	28¼	28¼	23	17
		12	5⅛	10¾	15½	11¼	7½	5⅛	13¾	17½	13	7½	5⅛	17½	19	16	12¼	5⅛	25	25	22¼	12¼
		14	5⅛	9½	18	11¾	7½	5⅛	12½	20½	12¾	7½	5⅛	15¾	23	15¾	12¼	6¾	17½	22	18¾	12¼
		16	5⅛	8¾	20	12¼	7½	5⅛	11¼	23	12¾	7½	6¾	11	20½	17¼	12¼	6¾	16	24¾	19	12¼
		18	5⅛	8	22	12¾	7½	5⅛	10¼	25¼	13¼	7½	6¾	10	22¼	18½	12¼	6¾	14¾	27	19½	12¼
	4/12	10	5⅛	11½	11½	23	12	5⅛	14½	14½	23	12	5⅛	17¾	17¾	23	12	5⅛	25¼	25¼	23	16¾
		12	5⅛	10	15¾	11	7½	5⅛	12¾	18	13	7½	5⅛	16	19¾	15¾	12	5⅛	22½	22½	21¾	12
		14	5⅛	9	18	11¾	7½	5⅛	11½	20¾	12¾	7½	5⅛	14½	23¼	15½	12	6¾	16	22¼	18	12
		16	5⅛	8¼	20	12¼	7½	5⅛	10½	23	12½	7½	6¾	10¼	20½	16¾	12	6¾	14¾	24¾	18½	12
		18	5⅛	7½	21¾	13¼	7½	5⅛	9¾	25¼	13	7½	6¾	9½	22	18¼	12	6¾	13¾	26¾	19	12
	6/12	12	5⅛	8¾	16¼	10	7½	5⅛	11	18¼	11¾	7½	5⅛	13¾	20½	14¼	11¼	5⅛	19	24	19	11¼
		14	5⅛	8	18	11¼	7½	5⅛	10¼	20¾	12¼	7½	5⅛	12½	23¼	14½	11¼	6¾	13½	22	17¼	11¼
		16	5⅛	7½	20	12	7½	5⅛	9½	22¾	12½	7½	5⅛	11¾	25¾	15	11¼	6¾	12¾	24¼	17¾	11¼
		18	5⅛	7½	21¾	12¾	7½	5⅛	8¾	25	13	7½	6¾	8¼	21¾	17¼	11¼	6¾	11¾	26¼	18½	11¼
	8/12	12	5⅛	7¾	16	9¾	7½	5⅛	9¾	18¼	12	7½	5⅛	12	20¼	14	10½	5⅛	16¼	24	17¾	12½
		14	5⅛	7½	18	10½	7½	5⅛	9	20¼	12¾	7½	5⅛	11	22¾	14¾	10½	6¾	11¾	21½	16¾	10½
		16	5⅛	7½	19¾	11½	7½	5⅛	8½	22½	13¼	7½	5⅛	10¼	25¼	15½	10½	6¾	11	23½	17¾	10½
		18	5⅛	7½	21½	12¼	7½	5⅛	8	24½	13½	7½	6¾	7½	21	16½	10½	6¾	10½	25¼	18½	10½
VERTICAL DEAD = 240#/FT. HORIZONTAL WIND = 320#/FT.	10/12	8	5⅛	7½	7½	11	7½	5⅛	7½	7½	12	10¼	5⅛	7½	8¼	13	12¾	5⅛	7½	9¼	15½	15½
		10	5⅛	7½	9¼	12½	12½	5⅛	7½	10	13¼	8	5⅛	7½	10¾	14¼	11¾	5⅛	7½	12	16¼	16¼
		12	5⅛	7½	11¼	13¾	13¾	5⅛	7½	12	14¾	7½	5⅛	7½	12¾	15¾	9¾	5⅛	7½	14¼	17½	16
	12/12	8	5⅛	7½	7½	12½	8¾	5⅛	7½	8¼	13¼	12	5⅛	7½	8¾	14¾	14½	5⅛	7½	9¾	17½	17½
		10	5⅛	7½	9¾	13¾	9	5⅛	7½	10½	15	10¼	5⅛	7½	11	16¼	13¾	5⅛	7½	12½	18½	18½
		12	5⅛	7½	11¾	15¼	15¼	5⅛	7½	12½	16½	9	5⅛	7½	13¼	17½	11¾	5⅛	7½	14¾	20	18¼
	14/12	8	5⅛	7½	8¾	13¾	10½	5⅛	7½	9	15	13¾	5⅛	7½	9½	16¼	16¼	5⅛	7½	10¼	19½	19½
		10	5⅛	7½	11¼	15¼	8¼	5⅛	7½	11½	16½	12¼	5⅛	7½	12½	18	15¾	5⅛	7¾	13¼	20½	20½
		12	5⅛	7½	13¼	17	17	5⅛	7½	14	18	8¼	5⅛	7½	14½	19½	14¼	5⅛	8¼	16	22	20¾
	16/12	8	5⅛	7½	10	15	12½	5⅛	7½	10½	16¼	15¾	5⅛	7½	11	18	18	5⅛	9	11	21½	21½
		10	5⅛	7½	12¼	16½	9½	5⅛	7½	13	18	14½	5⅛	7¾	14	19½	18	5⅛	9¼	14¾	22¾	22¾
		12	5⅛	7½	14¾	18¼	7½	5⅛	7½	15½	19¾	11½	5⅛	8¼	16¼	21¼	16¾	5⅛	9¾	17½	24	23½
VERTICAL DEAD = 320#/FT. HORIZONTAL WIND = 320#/FT.	10/12	8	5⅛	7½	7½	10¾	9	5⅛	7½	8¼	11¾	11¼	5⅛	7½	9	13	13	5⅛	8	10	15¾	15¾
		10	5⅛	7½	10	12	7½	5⅛	7½	10¾	13	10½	5⅛	7½	11½	14	13½	5⅛	7¾	13	16½	16½
		12	5⅛	7½	12	13¼	13¼	5⅛	7½	12¾	14¼	8½	5⅛	7½	13¾	15¼	12½	5⅛	7¾	15¾	17¼	17¼
	12/12	8	5⅛	7½	8¼	12¼	10¼	5⅛	7½	9	13¼	13¼	5⅛	7½	9½	14¾	14¾	5⅛	7¾	10½	17¾	17¾
		10	5⅛	7½	10½	13½	9	5⅛	7½	11¼	14¾	12¼	5⅛	7½	12	15¾	15¼	5⅛	7¾	13½	18¾	18¾
		12	5⅛	7½	12½	15	9	5⅛	7½	13¼	16	10¼	5⅛	7½	14¼	17¼	14¼	5⅛	7¾	16	19½	19½
	14/12	8	5⅛	7½	8¾	13½	12	5⅛	7½	9¼	14¾	14¾	5⅛	7½	10	16½	16½	5⅛	7¾	10½	19¾	19¾
		10	5⅛	7½	10¾	15	10¼	5⅛	7½	11¾	16¼	14¼	5⅛	7½	12½	17½	17¼	5⅛	7¾	13¾	20¾	20¾
		12	5⅛	7½	12¾	16½	8¼	5⅛	7½	13¾	17¾	12½	5⅛	7½	14¾	19¼	16½	5⅛	8	16½	21¾	21¾
	16/12	8	5⅛	7½	9½	15	13¾	5⅛	7½	9¾	16¼	16¼	5⅛	7½	10¼	18¼	18¼	5⅛	8¼	10¾	22	22
		10	5⅛	7½	11¾	16½	12¼	5⅛	7½	12¾	18	16¼	5⅛	7½	13	19¼	19¼	5⅛	8½	14	23	23
		12	5⅛	7½	14¼	18	7¾	5⅛	7½	14¾	19½	14½	5⅛	7½	15¾	21	18¾	5⅛	9	16¾	24¼	24¼
VERTICAL DEAD = 480#/FT. HORIZONTAL WIND = 320#/FT.	10/12	8	5⅛	7½	9	10½	10½	5⅛	7½	9¾	12	12	5⅛	8	10½	13½	13½	5⅛	10¼	11¼	16½	16½
		10	5⅛	7½	11¼	11½	10¼	5⅛	7½	12¼	12½	12½	5⅛	7¾	13¼	14	14	5⅛	10	15¼	17	17
		12	5⅛	7½	13½	12¾	8¾	5⅛	7½	14¾	13½	12½	5⅛	7¾	16	14¾	14¾	5⅛	9¾	18	17½	17½
	12/12	8	5⅛	7½	9¼	12	12	5⅛	7½	10¼	13½	13½	5⅛	7¾	11	15¼	15¼	5⅛	9¾	11¾	18½	18½
		10	5⅛	7½	11¾	13¼	11½	5⅛	7½	12¾	14¼	14¼	5⅛	7¾	13¾	15¾	15¾	5⅛	9¾	15½	19	19
		12	5⅛	7½	13¾	14½	10	5⅛	7½	15	15½	14	5⅛	7¾	16¼	16¾	16¾	5⅛	9½	18¼	19¾	19¾
	14/12	8	5⅛	7½	9¾	13¼	13¼	5⅛	7½	10½	15	15	5⅛	7¾	11¼	17	17	5⅛	9½	12	20½	20½
		10	5⅛	7½	12	14¾	13	5⅛	7½	13	16	16	5⅛	7¾	14	17¾	17¾	5⅛	9½	15½	21¼	21¼
		12	5⅛	7½	14¼	16	11½	5⅛	7½	15½	17½	15½	5⅛	7¾	16½	18¾	18¾	5⅛	9½	18½	22¼	22¼
	16/12	8	5⅛	7½	10	14¾	14¾	5⅛	7½	10¾	16¾	16¾	5⅛	7¾	11½	18¾	18¾	5⅛	9½	12	22¾	22¾
		10	5⅛	7½	12¼	16¼	14½	5⅛	7½	13¼	17¾	17¾	5⅛	7¾	14¼	19½	19½	5⅛	9½	15½	23½	23½
		12	5⅛	7½	14½	17¾	13¼	5⅛	7½	15¾	19¼	17½	5⅛	7¾	17	20¾	20¾	5⅛	9½	18¾	24½	24½

WALL HGT. FT.	60′ SPAN					70′ SPAN					80′ SPAN					90′ SPAN				
	WIDTH	BASE	LOWER TANG.	UPPER TANG.	CROWN	WIDTH	BASE	LOWER TANG.	UPPER TANG.	CROWN	WIDTH	BASE	LOWER TANG.	UPPER TANG.	CROWN	WIDTH	BASE	LOWER TANG.	UPPER TANG.	CROWN
12	5⅛	14	16¼	16¾	7½	5⅛	17¾	17¾	20	7½	5⅛	21¾	21¾	23	7½	6¾	20	20	22¾	8
14	5⅛	12¾	19½	17½	7½	5⅛	16¼	22	20¾	7½	5⅛	20	24	24	7½	6¾	18½	21½	24	7½
16	5⅛	11¾	22	17¾	7½	5⅛	15	25	21¼	7½	6¾	14¼	22½	22	7½	6¾	17¼	24¾	24¾	7½
18	5⅛	10¾	24	19¼	7½	6¾	10¾	22	21¼	7½	6¾	13¼	24½	22¾	7½	6¾	16	27	25¾	7½
20	6¾	7¾	22	22	7½	6¾	10	23½	23¼	7½	6¾	12½	26½	23	7½	6¾	15	29¼	26	7½
12	5⅛	12½	16¾	15¾	7½	5⅛	15¾	18½	18¾	7¾	5⅛	19¼	20	21½	9½	5⅛	22¾	22¾	24¼	12
14	5⅛	11½	19½	16½	7½	5⅛	14½	22	19½	7½	5⅛	17¾	24¼	22¾	8¼	6¾	16¼	21½	22¼	8½
16	5⅛	10½	21¾	17	7½	5⅛	13½	24½	20¼	7½	6¾	12¾	22	20¾	7½	6¾	15¼	24¼	23¼	7½
18	5⅛	10	23¾	17¾	7½	6¾	9¾	21½	19½	7½	6¾	12	24	21¼	7½	6¾	14¼	26½	24¼	7½
20	5⅛	9¼	25½	19¼	7½	6¾	9	23	21½	7½	6¾	11¼	25¾	22	7½	6¾	13½	28½	24¾	7½
12	5⅛	10¼	16¾	14¼	8¼	5⅛	12¾	18¾	16¾	10½	5⅛	15¼	20½	19	13¼	5⅛	18	22¼	21¼	16
14	5⅛	9½	19	15¼	7½	5⅛	12	21½	17¾	9	5⅛	14½	23¾	20¼	11½	6¾	13	21	19¾	12
16	5⅛	9	21	16	7½	5⅛	11¼	23¾	18¾	7¾	6¾	10½	21¼	18¾	8½	6¾	12¼	23¼	21	10½
18	5⅛	8½	23	16½	7½	6¾	8	20¾	17¼	7½	6¾	9¾	23	19½	7½	6¾	11¾	25¼	22	9¼
12	5⅛	8¾	16½	13½	10	5⅛	10¾	18½	15½	12¾	5⅛	12¾	20¼	17¼	16	5⅛	15	22	19¼	19¼
14	5⅛	8¼	18½	14½	8¾	5⅛	10¼	20¾	16¾	11¼	5⅛	12¼	23	18¾	14	5⅛	14¼	25¼	20¾	17
16	5⅛	7¾	20½	15½	7½	5⅛	9½	23	17¾	9¾	5⅛	11½	25½	20	12½	6¾	10¼	22¼	19½	12¾
18	5⅛	7½	22¼	16¼	7½	5⅛	9¼	25¼	18¾	8¾	6¾	8½	22	18½	9¼	6¾	10	24	20½	11½
12	5⅛	20½	20½	20¼	7½	5⅛	26¼	26¼	24	12¼	6¾	25	25	24½	12¼	6¾	29¾	29¾	27½	12¼
14	5⅛	18¾	24	21	7½	6¾	18½	22	22¼	12¼	6¾	23	23½	26	12¼	6¾	27½	27½	29¼	12¼
16	6¾	13¼	22	19	7½	6¾	17¼	25	23	12¼	6¾	21¼	27½	26¾	12¼	6¾	25½	30	30¼	12¼
18	6¾	12¼	24	20¼	7½	6¾	16	27¼	23½	12¼	6¾	19¾	30½	27¼	12¼	6¾	23¾	33½	31	12¼
20	6¾	11½	25¾	21¾	7½	6¾	14¾	29½	24	12¼	6¾	18½	33	28	12¼	8¾	17½	30	28¼	12¼
12	5⅛	18¼	20¼	19¼	7½	5⅛	23¼	23¼	22¾	12	6¾	21¾	21¾	23	12	6¾	25¾	25¾	25½	12¾
14	5⅛	17	24¼	20	7½	6¾	16½	22	21¼	12	6¾	20¼	24¼	24¼	12	6¾	24	26	27¼	12
16	6¾	12	21¾	18¼	7½	6¾	15½	24¾	21¾	12	6¾	18¾	27¼	25	12	6¾	22½	29¾	28¼	12
18	6¾	11¼	23½	18¾	7½	6¾	14½	27	22½	12	6¾	17¾	30	26	12	6¾	21¼	32¾	29¼	12
20	6¾	10½	25¼	20½	7½	6¾	13½	28¾	23	12	6¾	16¾	32¼	26½	12	8¾	15½	29¼	26¾	12
12	5⅛	15¼	21	17½	10¼	5⅛	18¾	23¼	20½	13¼	5⅛	22¾	25½	23½	16¼	6¾	20½	22¼	22¾	17
14	5⅛	14	24	18½	8¾	6¾	13½	21¾	19¼	11¼	6¾	16¼	23¾	22	12	6¾	19¼	26	24¼	14¾
16	6¾	10¼	21¼	17¼	7½	6¾	12¾	24	20	11¼	6¾	15½	26½	23	11¼	6¾	18¼	29	25½	13
18	6¾	9½	22¾	17¾	7½	6¾	12	26	21	11¼	6¾	14¾	28¾	23¾	11¼	6¾	17¼	31½	26¾	11¾
12	5⅛	13	20¾	16½	12½	5⅛	16	23¼	19	16	5⅛	19	25½	21¼	19¾	6¾	17	22¼	20½	20¼
14	5⅛	12¼	23¼	17¾	10¾	6¾	11½	21	18	12	6¾	13¾	23¼	20¼	14¾	6¾	16	25¼	22¼	18
16	6¾	8¾	20½	16½	8	6¾	11	23	19¼	10½	6¾	13	25½	21½	13¼	6¾	15½	27¾	23¾	16
18	6¾	8¼	22	17½	7½	6¾	10½	25	20	10½	6¾	12½	27½	22½	11¾	6¾	14¾	30¼	25	14½
12	5⅛	27¼	27¼	23	12¼	6¾	26¾	26¾	24¼	12¼	6¾	32½	32½	27¾	12¼	6¾	38¾	38¾	31	12½
14	6¾	19¼	22½	21¼	12¼	6¾	24½	24½	25¾	12¼	6¾	30	30	29½	12¼	8¾	28¼	28¼	29¾	12¼
16	6¾	17½	25¾	21¾	12¼	6¾	22½	28¾	26¼	12¼	6¾	27¾	31¾	30¾	12¼	8¾	26¼	29	30¾	12¼
18	6¾	16¼	28	22¼	12¼	6¾	21	31¾	26¾	12¼	8¾	20¼	29½	27¾	12¼	8¾	24½	32¼	31¾	12¼
20	6¾	15	30¼	22½	12¼	8¾	15¼	28¼	24¾	12¼	8¾	19	31¾	28½	12¼	8¾	23	34¾	32¼	12¼
12	5⅛	24¼	24¼	22	12	6¾	23½	23½	23	12	6¾	28½	28½	26	12½	6¾	33¾	33¾	29¼	15¼
14	6¾	17¼	22¾	20¼	12	6¾	21¾	25¼	24¼	12	6¾	26½	27½	28	12	6¾	31½	31½	31¼	12¾
16	6¾	16	25½	21	12	6¾	20¼	28¾	25	12	6¾	24¾	31¾	28¾	12	8¾	23	29	29	12
18	6¾	14¾	27¾	21½	12	6¾	19	31½	25¾	12	8¾	18¼	29	26½	12	8¾	21¾	31¾	29¾	12
20	6¾	13¾	29¾	22	12	6¾	17¾	33¾	26¼	12	8¾	17	31	27¼	12	8¾	20½	34	30¾	12
12	5⅛	20	24¼	20¼	12	6¾	19	22	21	13	6¾	23	23¾	23¾	16¼	6¾	27	27	26¼	19¾
14	6¾	14¼	22½	18¾	11¼	6¾	17¾	25¼	22	11¼	6¾	21½	27¾	25	14¼	6¾	25½	30	28	17½
16	6¾	13½	24¾	19¾	11¼	6¾	16¾	28	23	11¼	6¾	20¼	31	26¼	12½	6¾	24	33¾	29½	15½
18	6¾	12¾	26¾	20½	11¼	6¾	16	30½	24	11¼	6¾	19¼	33¾	27½	11¼	8¾	17¾	30¼	27¼	11¾
12	5⅛	17	24½	19	14¾	6¾	16	22	19¼	16	6¾	19¼	24	21½	19¾	6¾	22½	25¾	23¾	23¾
14	6¾	12¼	22	18	10¾	6¾	15¼	24½	20¾	14	6¾	18¼	27¼	23¼	17½	6¾	21¼	29½	25¾	21
16	6¾	11½	24	19	10½	6¾	14½	27	22	12¼	6¾	17¼	30	24¾	15½	6¾	20¼	32¾	27¼	19
18	6¾	11	26	20	10½	6¾	13¾	29¼	23	11	6¾	16½	32½	26	13¾	8¾	15¼	29	25½	14½
12	6¾	26	26	22½	12¼	6¾	32¾	32¾	26½	12¼	6¾	40½	40½	30¾	17	8¾	37¾	37¾	30¾	17
14	6¾	23½	25	23¾	12¼	6¾	30	30	28½	12¼	6¾	37¼	37¼	32¾	17	8¾	35	35	32¾	17
16	6¾	21¾	28¾	24¼	12¼	6¾	27¾	32¼	29¼	12¼	8¾	27	29¾	30½	17	8¾	32½	32½	34½	17
18	6¾	20	31½	24¾	12¼	8¾	20¼	29¾	26½	12¼	8¾	25¼	33	31	17	8¾	30¼	36	35½	17
20	8¾	14½	28	23½	12¼	8¾	18¾	31¾	27	12¼	8¾	23½	35½	31¾	17	8¾	28½	39	36	17
12	6¾	23	23	21½	12	6¾	29	29	25¼	12	6¾	35¼	35¼	29¼	16¾	8¾	32¾	32¾	28¾	16¾
14	6¾	21¼	25½	22½	12	6¾	26¾	28	27	12	6¾	33	33	31	16¾	8¾	30½	30½	31	16¾
16	6¾	19¾	28¾	23¼	12	6¾	25	32¼	27¾	12	8¾	24	29¾	28½	16¾	8¾	28¾	32	32¼	16¾
18	6¾	18¼	31¼	24	12	8¾	18¼	29¼	25½	12	8¾	22½	32½	29½	16¾	8¾	27	35½	33¼	16¾
20	6¾	17¼	33¾	24¼	12	8¾	17¼	31¼	26	12	8¾	21¼	35	30¼	16¾	8¾	25½	38¼	34¼	16¾
12	6¾	19	22	19¾	11½	6¾	23½	24¼	23¼	14¾	6¾	28½	28½	26¼	18½	6¾	33¼	33¼	29	22¾
14	6¾	17¾	25¼	21	11¼	6¾	22	28¼	24½	13	6¾	26¾	31	28	16¼	8¾	24¾	28½	27¾	16¾
16	6¾	16½	28	22	11¼	6¾	20¾	31½	25¾	11¼	8¾	19¾	29	26	15¾	8¾	23½	31½	29¼	15¾
18	6¾	15¾	30½	22¾	11¼	8¾	15¼	28¼	23¾	11¼	8¾	18¾	31¼	27	15¾	8¾	22¼	34¼	30¼	15¾
12	6¾	16¼	22	18¾	14	6¾	20	24½	21½	18	6¾	23¾	26¾	24¼	22¼	6¾	27¾	28¾	26¾	26¾
14	6¾	15¼	24¾	20¼	12¼	6¾	18¾	27¾	23¼	15¾	6¾	22½	30¾	26	19¾	6¾	26½	33¼	28¾	24
16	6¾	14¼	27¼	21¼	10¾	6¾	18	30½	24½	14	8¾	16¾	28	24¼	15	8¾	19¾	30½	27	18½
18	6¾	13¾	29½	22¼	10½	6¾	17	33¼	25¾	12½	8¾	16	30	25¾	14¾	8¾	18¾	32¾	28½	16½

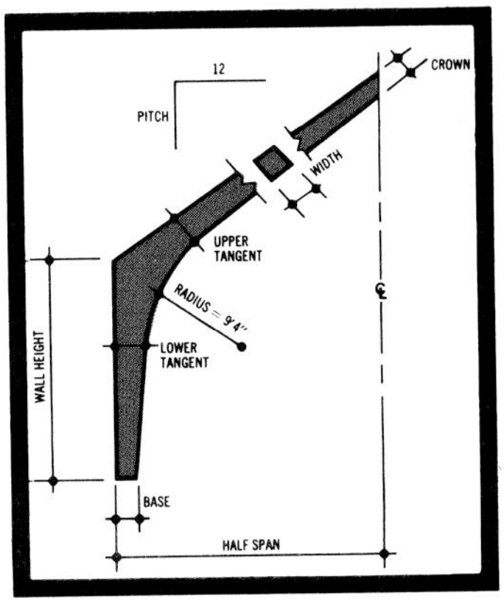

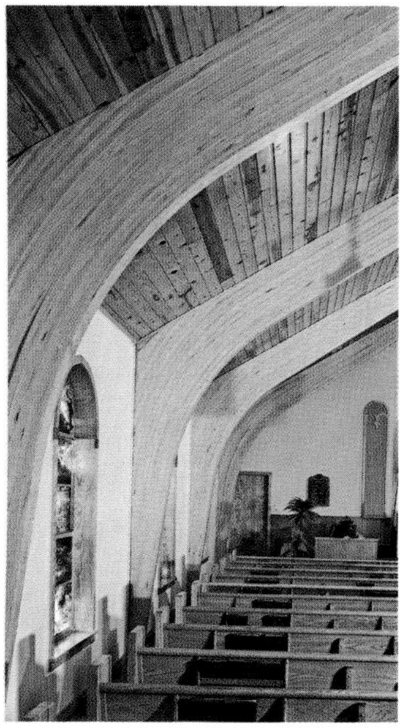

West London Baptist Church,
London, Kentucky.

Values for preliminary design purposes only. For more complete design information see the AITC Timber Construction Manual. Sizes are based on Douglas fir laminated timber, developing an allowable shear stress of 165 psi and with a bending radius of 9 feet 4 inches. For Southern pine laminated timber, an allowable shear stress of 200 psi and a bending radius of 7 feet 0 inches may be used.

For roof pitches less than 10/12, the critical loading is generally the combined dead and live load on the horizontal projection of the full span. For roof pitches of 10/12 or greater, the critical loading is generally a combination of dead load and horizontal wind load. Sizes shown are determined from a uniformly distributed wind load applied on the vertical projection of the roof arm with a concentrated wind load equal to ½ the total wind load on the wall height acting at the haunch.

In the combined stress analysis, it was assumed that the bending portion of the loading exceeded the axial compression portion.

The section sizes shown in this table are in inches and are based on the following design criteria:

1. Uniform loading
2. Radius of curvature at the haunch=9 ft. 4 in.
3. Allowable stresses:

   Bending stress, F_b=2400 psi (reduced by size factor and curvature factor when applicable)

   Shear stress, F_v=165 psi

   Compression parallel to grain stress, F_c=1500 psi (adjusted for l/d ratio)

   Modulus of elasticity, E=1,800,000 psi

   These stresses were increased 15% for short duration of loading and 33⅓% for wind loading when applicable.
4. Deflection limits: 1/180 for dead plus live load; 1/240 for live load only.
5. Vertical arch legs are laterally unsupported with tangent point depth to breadth ratio not exceeding 5 to 1. (When vertical arch legs are laterally supported, tangent point depth to breadth ratio not exceeding 6 to 1 may be used.)
6. Dead load equal to one-third of the total vertical load.

RADIAL ARCH DESIGN

ts technical support

RADIAL ARCHES

Glued laminated radial arches are well suited to achieve large, unobstructed, clear span enclosures for a variety of uses. They may be either buttressed or tied arches depending upon soil conditions and other building requirements. In the buttressed arch type, horizontal and vertical reactions are taken through concrete abutments. In the tied arch type, the horizontal reaction is taken by steel tie rods located at the ceiling height. This type of arch is usually set on masonry walls or columns.

Preliminary Design Procedure

The following procedure may be used for determining radial arch sections for preliminary architectural planning and estimating purposes. This procedure should be used for preliminary design purposes only, since portions of it are empirical and cannot be derived rationally. In all cases, the data is subject to specific design requirements of local building codes or special conditions. A complete design check should be made in accordance with the AITC Timber Construction Manual.

Span (L)	= 90 ft.	
Rise (h)	= 30 ft.	
Spacing	= 16 ft.	
Total Load (TL) (live plus dead load on horizontal projection)	= 50 psf	
Allowable bending stress (F_b)	= 2400 psi	

w = lb. per lineal foot

Max. Moment = 1.5 w(h)²

$$w_{TL} = (spacing)(TL) = (16)(50) = 800 \text{ plf}$$

(1) Determine the required radius (R) either by a graphical procedure or by the formula:

$$R = \frac{4h^2 + L^2}{8h} \qquad R = \frac{(4)(30^2) + (90^2)}{(8)(30)} = 48.75 \text{ ft.}$$

(2) Maximum bending moment (M) due to total loading = 1.5 wh²

$$M = (1.5)(800)(30^2) = 1,080,000 \text{ in. -lb.}$$

(3) Determine the limiting bending stress ($F_b{}'$) using Figure 1

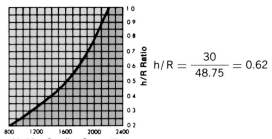

Limiting Bending Stress ($F_b{}'$)

Figure 1

$$h/R = \frac{30}{48.75} = 0.62$$

Entering the graph with h/R = 0.62 determine $F_b{}'$ to be 1800 psi as the limiting bending stress.

(4) Section modulus (S) required $= \dfrac{M}{F_b{}' C_F}$

where C_F = size factor

For preliminary purposes, assume $C_F = 0.90$

$$S = \frac{1,080,000}{(1800)(0.90)} = 667 \text{ in.}^3$$

(5) From the Section Properties table, for a 1½" lamination thickness, select the section having the least area with a section modulus equal to, or greater than, the value calculated and having a depth to width ratio of less than 5 to 1. Select a 6¾" x 25½" section with A = 172 in.²; and S = 732 in.³

A-FRAME DESIGN

A-FRAMES

The A-frame is a popular type of laminated timber construction which can be used to create geometrically simple structures that keep material costs to a minimum without sacrificing quality. At the same time, A-frame structures can also have lofty and dramatic interiors.

Preliminary Design Procedure

The following example of a preliminary design procedure for A-frames if based on uniformly distributed load combinations of dead plus live load, and a dead plus wind load applied as illustrated. This procedure should be used for preliminary design purposes only, since portions of it are empirical and cannot be derived rationally. In all cases, the data is subject to specific design requirements of local building codes or special conditions. A complete design check should be made in accordance with the AITC Timber Construction Manual. The preliminary design should be analyzed as a three-hinged arch using standard engineering methods.

Span (L)	= 60 ft.	
Rise (h)	= 50 ft.	
Spacing	= 15 ft.	
Roof pitch	= 20/12	

Dead Load (DL) (along length of arch leg)	= 15 psf
Live Load (LL) (on horizontal projection)	= 20 psf
Wind Load (WL) (on vertical projection)	= 20 psf
Allowable bending stress (F_b)	= 2400 psi
Modulus of Elasticity (E)	= 1,800,000 psi

TABLE 1

Pitch	k_1	Pitch	k_1
12/12	1.41	21/12	2.02
13/12	1.47	22/12	2.08
14/12	1.54	23/12	2.16
15/12	1.60	24/12	2.24
16/12	1.66	25/12	2.31
17/12	1.73	26/12	2.38
18/12	1.80	27/12	2.46
19/12	1.87	28/12	2.54
20/12	1.94	29/12	2.61

$k_1 = \dfrac{m}{L/2}$ (See Table 1)

k_2 = Allowable bending stress adjustment which accounts for live load duration (assumed to be 1.15 for snow loading), size factor, and axial contribution to combined stress. For preliminary purposes use 0.90

k_3 = Allowable bending stress adjustment which accounts for wind load duration (1.33) and size factor (assumed to be 0.85) = 1.13

w_{DL} = (spacing)(DL)(k_1) = (15)(15)(1.94) = 436 plf

w_{LL} = (spacing)(LL) = (15)(20) = 300 plf

w_{TL} = w_{DL} + w_{LL} = 736 plf

w_{WL} = (spacing)(WL) = (15)(20) = 300 plf

To determine the required cross section at the midpoint of the rafter, determine:

A-Frame Design (continued)

(1) Bending moment — total load $(M_{TL}) = (\frac{3}{8})(w_{TL})(L^2)$
= (0.375)(736)(60²) = 993,600 in.-lb.

Bending moment—dead load $(M_{DL}) = (M_{TL})\frac{w_{DL}}{w_{TL}} =$

(993,600)$\frac{436}{736}$ = 588,600 in.-lb.

Bending moment—wind load $(M_{WL}) = (1.5)(w_{WL})(h^2) =$
(1.5)(300)(50²) = 1,125,000 in.—lb.
$M_{DL} + M_{WL} = 588,600 + 1,125,000 = 1,713,600$ in.—lb.

(2) Section modulus (S) required (total load) =

$\frac{M_{TL}}{(k_2)(F_b)} = \frac{993,600}{(0.90)(2400)} = 460$ in.³

Section Modulus (S) required (DL+WL) = $\frac{M_{DL} + M_{WL}}{(k_3)(F_b)} =$

$\frac{1,713,600}{(1.13)(2400)} = 632$ in.³

(3) Moment of inertia (I) required = $\frac{(M_{TL})(L)(k_I)}{24,000}$
(based on allowable deflection of l/120)

$\frac{(993,600)(60)(1.94)}{24,000} = 4,819$ in.⁴

From Section Properties table, for a 1½" lamination thickness, select the section having the least area with a section modulus and a moment of inertia that are equal to, or greater than, those computed; and having a depth to width ratio of less than 5 to 1 (for laterally unsupported condition). Select a 6¾"x24" section with A=162 in.², S=648 in.³, and I=7,776 in.⁴.

COLUMN DESIGN

Glued laminated columns offer the same advantages as other laminated timber elements; i.e., higher allowable stresses, improved appearance and the ability to fabricate variable or curved sections.

Simple Rectangular Columns

Formulas for wood columns assume pin-end conditions, but they may also be applied to square-end conditions. For simple, rectangular sawn or glued laminated timber columns, the ratios of the unsupported length between points of lateral support, ℓ, in each vertical plane of the column to the dimension of the column, d, in that plane are determined. The larger of these two ratios is the "slenderness ratio," ℓ/d, and may not exceed 50.

The maximum design value for a simple rectangular column, F_c', expressed in pounds per square inch of cross-sectional area, is determined from the following formulas:

(a) Short columns—those having an ℓ/d ratio of 11 or less:
$$F_c' = F_c$$

(b) Intermediate columns — those having an ℓ/d ratio greater than 11 but less than K, where $K = 0.67\sqrt{E/F_c}$:
$$F_c' = F_c\left[1 - \tfrac{1}{3}\left(\frac{\ell/d}{K}\right)^4\right]$$

(c) Long columns — those having an ℓ/d ratio of K or greater, but not exceeding 50:
$$F_c' = \frac{0.30E}{(\ell/d)^2}$$

where F_c is the allowable compression parallel to grain stress value in psi, adjusted for service conditions, duration of load and other applicable modifications; and E is the allowable modulus of elasticity value in psi, adjusted for service conditions and other applicable modifications. The E value is not subject to duration of load modifications. The F_c' value as determined from these formulas is not subject to further modification for service conditions or duration of load.

Round Columns

The design load for a column of round cross section will be the same as that for a square column of the same cross-sectional area.

Tapered Columns

The dimension, d, in each vertical plane of a column of rectangular cross section, tapered at one or both ends, is the sum of the minimum dimension in that plane plus one-third the difference between the minimum and maximum dimensions in that plane.

Spaced Columns

Spaced columns consist of two or more individual members with their longitudinal axes parallel, separated at the ends and at the midpoint by blocking, and joined at the ends by fastenings capable of developing the required shear resistance.

Complete design information for simple, round, tapered and spaced columns may be found in the 1977 edition of the "National Design Specification for Wood Construction," by the National Forest Products Association, 1619 Massachusetts Avenue, N.W., Washington, D.C. 20036.

RECTANGULAR COLUMN

TAPERED COLUMN

SPACED COLUMN

PANELIZED ROOF SYSTEMS
ai assembly, installation

Fork lift installs main glulam load carrying member.

On-site crew assembles larger preframed panels from 4′ x 8′ units.

Large preframed starter panel set into place.

Forklift placing 8′ x 30′ preframed panel.

Key beam is set for three span cantilever system.

A very cost efficient construction method for the fast erection of roofs for large industrial/commercial buildings involves the utilization of glulam beams, preframed plywood panels, and lumber.

Combining the desirable qualities of economy, availability, speed of erection and overall building aesthetics, the panelized roof system has proven to be a very effective solution to the demand for a technologically advanced roof erection process.

GRIDS

Keys to the panelized system are glulam beams and girders. Main beams support solid sawn or glulam purlins which, in turn, carry preframed plywood panels. This results in an efficient option for the design of large buildings, plus a versatile approach to interior support placement (see typical grid systems on pages 25-27). This efficiency is based on the effective use of cantilever beam systems (see table on pages 14-15).

4x8 PANEL SYSTEM

A 4x8 foot plywood sheet nailed to 2x4 inch or 2x6 inch stiffeners is the basic unit of the preframed panel. The stiffeners are 16 or 24 inches on center, as indicated on the Preframed Panel table on page 27. These preframed panels can be designed to act as structural diaphragms to resist lateral forces induced by wind and earthquake. An Underwriters Laboratories Class 90 wind-uplift resistance rating has been established for the panelized roof system. The individual preframed panels, with attached metal hangers, are nailed to the in-place purlin system in accordance with engineered nailing schedules.

LARGER PANEL SYSTEMS

Even greater erection speed can be gained by the use of larger panels. With the basic 4x8 units, ground crews form larger panels — for example 8x20 or 8x30 feet — with the purlins attached. After these sections have been fabricated, they are lifted into place by a forklift. Erection time is greatly decreased through the use of this system.

Forklift lifting stack of 4' x 8' panels

Crew places preframed 4' x 8' panel on purlins.

Exposed glulam beams and heavy decking contribute to
the relaxing atmosphere in this retail store. Cost efficient system
requires no dropped ceilings.

Glulam beams and purlins are used with the panelized roof
system in this fully sprinkled warehouse. Long spans permit easy
movement of materials.

Heavy timber tongue-and-groove decking is used in this
installation, which enhances the diaphragm action of the system.
Heavy decking also increases spans.

Steel U-plate is welded to the top of the pipe column to
support the glulam beam in this two-span cantilever roof.
Sprinkler system is easily suspended from the purlins.

Roof systems for this restaurant area features glulam beams,
together with exposed decking that contains outlets for sound
and light, as well as HVAC system. Even the table tops are
compatible with the overall wood theme.

Heavy plywood panels used with the glulam members produce
an effective heavy timber rated structure. Wider purlin spacing is
also gained with the thicker plywood. Meets ICBO Research
Recommendation #1007 specifications.

Long, clear spans can be gained with glulam beams in
a cantilever design for efficient space utilization without
column interruption. Lighting equipment and related
items are easily installed.

COST EFFICIENT ROOF SYSTEM

When evaluating different construction materials and methods, the final cost determination must be made on an installed
basis. This means that material delivery schedules and erection time must be assigned dollar values.

Time lost or saved directly affects the total construction bud-
get. This is where the cost efficiency of the glulam roof system
dominates.

All components are laminated and prefabricated to exact
specifications. There is a minimum of on-site labor involved,
other than actual erection. This installation, requiring only
conventional hand tools and a forklift, is economical, fast and
efficient.

The system is also very adaptable, being suitable for many
types of commercial/industrial applications.

Glulam roof systems — the cost efficient answer.

Suspended beam in a cantilever beam system uses a
saddle type connection to transfer loading to the supporting
beams. A bent strap type connector is used for the purlins.

Large glulam beams are supported on strong glulam columns
in this warehouse. Lateral purlin brace has been added to the
column U-plate connections. Bent strap type connections
are used for the purlins.

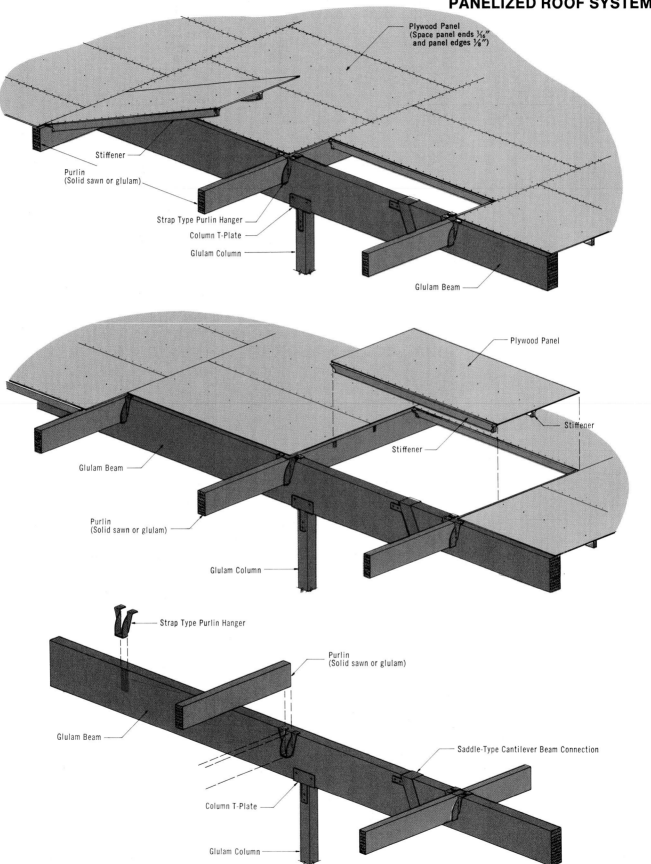

Plywood Panel
(Space panel ends 1/16"
and panel edges 1/8")

Stiffener

Purlin
(Solid sawn or glulam)

Strap Type Purlin Hanger

Column T-Plate

Glulam Column

Glulam Beam

Plywood Panel

Stiffener

Glulam Beam

Stiffener

Stiffener

Purlin
(Solid sawn or glulam)

Glulam Column

Strap Type Purlin Hanger

Purlin
(Solid sawn or glulam)

Glulam Beam

Saddle-Type Cantilever Beam Connection

Column T-Plate

Glulam Column

NOTE: Hinge connections and metal hangers specified must be in accordance with applicable building code regulations.

PANELIZED ROOF GRID SYSTEMS

ts technical support

The selection of an economical grid system for a building utilizing the panelized roof system depends upon efficient placement of intermediate column supports to optimize the strength and span capabilities of the glulam beams in the primary framing system. Structural glued laminated timber members can be manufactured to virtually any length, with shipping and handling presenting the major limitations to final size. Glulam spans considered most economical for the panelized roof system range from 30 to 80 feet. Longer or shorter spans are also possible depending upon the particular design situation.

When possible, consideration should be given to the use of long span glulam members designed as a cantilevered beam or girder system. Cantilever beam systems permit longer spans or larger loads for a given member size than do simple span systems, provided member size is not governed by compression perpendicular to grain at supports or by horizontal shear.

The selection of an efficient column grid system is facilitated by the determination of an efficiency factor. Two separate factors are calculated; one for the ratio of the board footage of glulam used in the primary framing system to the square feet of space enclosed under roof cover; and the other for the board footage of material (solid sawn or glulam) used in the secondary framing (purlin) system to the square feet of covered area. The lower these ratios, the more efficient the system.

The example below illustrates the calculation of the efficiency factors for a selected building size and primary and secondary framing system. The dead load used in this example is 10 psf (excluding the weight of the beam) with a live load of 20 psf.

Glulam and purlin sizes and corresponding efficiency factors are given in each layout for two different live loads. (NOTE: Black type refers to one LL factor, with red type for the other. See footnotes for complete explanation.) Member sizes shown are governed by either bending or shear. Solid sawn purlin sizes are based on the use of a No. 1 Douglas fir grade. In all cases, the data is subject to specific design requirements of local codes or special conditions; including applicable deflection requirements. A minimum roof slope of ¼'' per foot should be provided in addition to camber to minimize water ponding. The example shown are illustrative only and a complete design check should be made by competent engineering personnel.

Design aids which will assist in the determination of glulam beam or girder sizes for various column grid systems include the cantilever beam table on pages 14-15 and the simple span beam table on pages 12-13 of this brochure. Simple span beam sizes can also be determined by using the AITC Glulam Beam Calculator — a slide chart which can be used for preliminary sizing of simple span beams. Questions about the panelized roof system can be directed to the AITC technical staff by calling toll free (800) 525-1625. Alaska, Colorado and Hawaii residents, call (303) 761-3212.

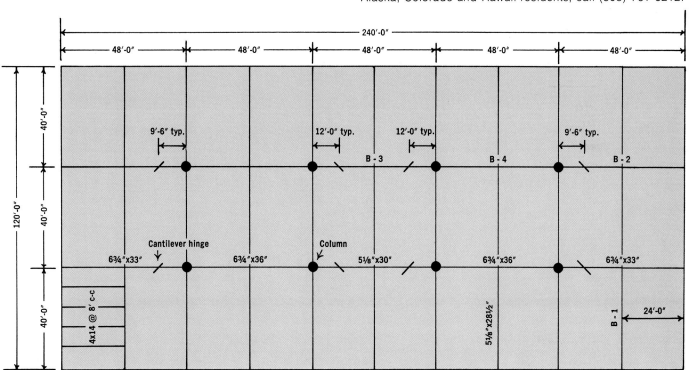

CALCULATION OF EFFICIENCY FACTORS

B-1's ; fbm = 760 fbm/beam × 27 beams = 20520 fbm
B-2's ; fbm = 1129 fbm/beam × 4 beams = 4517 fbm
B-3's ; fbm = 480 fbm/beam × 2 beams = 960 fbm
B-4's ; fbm = 2224 fbm/beam × 4 beams = 8896 fbm
Total = 34893 fbm

Area enclosed = 28,800 sq. ft.
fbm glulam/sq. ft. = 34,893/28800 = 1.21

Solid sawn purlins; fbm = 112 fbm/purlin × 120 purlins = 13440

fbm solid sawn/sq. ft. = 13440/28800 = 0.47

Assumed design criteria and allowable stresses used in the calculation of the bending member sizes shown for the examples on pages 26-27 are:
 Member sizes governed by either bending or shear.
 Full balanced or unbalanced live load, whichever controls.
 Dead load does not include weight of glulam.
 Bending stress, F_b = 2,400 psi.
 Shear stress, F_v = 165 psi.
 Compression perpendicular to grain stress, $F_{c\perp}$ = 385 psi.
 Modulus of elasticity, E = 1,800,000 psi.
 Duration of load factor: 1.25 for 12 psf live loads; and 1.15 for 20 and 30 psf live loads.

STRUCTURAL GLUED LAMINATED TIMBER
FOR INFORMATION CALL 800/525-1625

COMPARISON OF EFFICIENCY OF COLUMN GRIDS FOR

ts technical support

LL = 12 or 30 psf
20 x 40 COLUMN GRID

Red color is for 30 & 20 psf LL.

LL = 12 or 20 psf
48 x 40 COLUMN GRID

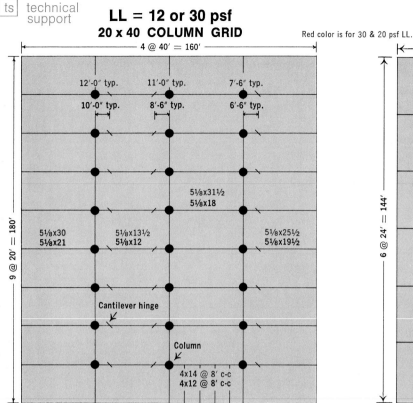

DL = 10psf 10 psf   LL = 12 psf 30 psf
fbm glulam/sq. ft. = 0.55 0.83
fbm solid sawn/sq. ft. = 0.47 0.55

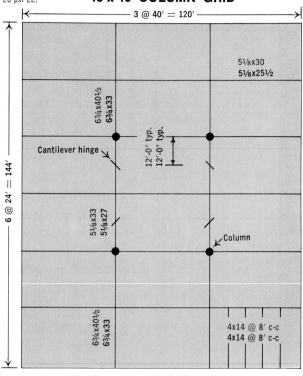

DL = 10 psf 10 psf   LL = 12 psf 20 psf
fbm glulam/sq. ft = 1.05 1.26
fbm solid sawn/sq. ft. = 0.47 0.47

30 x 40 COLUMN GRID

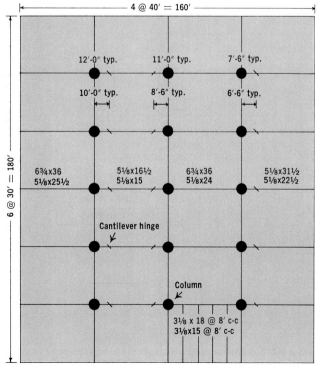

DL = 10 psf 10 psf   LL = 12 psf 30 psf
fbm glulam/sq. ft. = 1.22 1.71
fbm solid sawn/sq. ft. = 0 0

See Notes and example on page 25 for further details.

48 x 60 COLUMN GRID

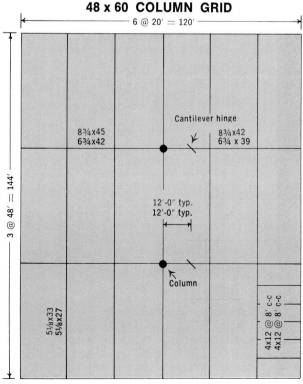

DL = 10 psf 10 psf   LL = 12 psf 20 psf
fbm glulam/sq. ft. = 1.25 1.59
fbm solid sawn/sq. ft. = 0.42 0.42

COMPARISON OF EFFICIENCY OF COLUMN GRIDS FOR LL = 12 or 20 psf

48 x 50 COLUMN GRID Red color is for 20 psf LL. 40 x 40 COLUMN GRID

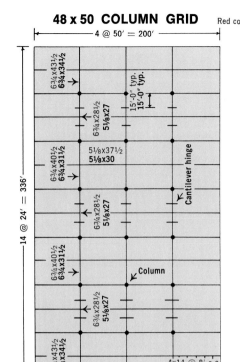

DL = 10 psf 10 psf LL = 12 psf 20 psf
fbm glulam/sq. ft. = 1.18 1.50
fbm solid sawn/sq. ft. = 0.47 0.47

See Notes and example on page 25 for further details.

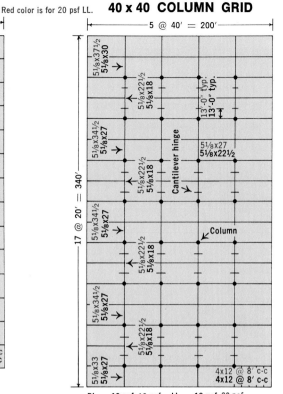

DL = 10 psf 10 psf LL = 12 psf 20 psf
fbm glulam/sq. ft. = 1.05 1.28
fbm solid sawn/sq. ft. = 0.40 0.40

TABLE 1 PREFRAMED PANEL STIFFENER LOADS

CENTER-TO-CENTER PURLIN SPACING②, FT.	STIFFENER SIZE AND SPACING	MAXIMUM ALLOWABLE ROOF LIVE LOAD, PSF ①								
		SELECT STRUCTURAL③			NO. 1③			NO. 2③		
		STRESS ④			STRESS ④			STRESS ④		
		1.00	1.15	1.25	1.00	1.15	1.25	1.00	1.15	1.25
8	2 x 4 @ 16″	52	61	67	43	51	56	33	39	43
	2 x 4 @ 24″	31	37	42	25	31	34	18	23	25
	2 x 6 @ 16″	120	140	153	101	118	129	82	96	105
	2 x 6 @ 24″	77	90	99	64	75	83	52	61	67

NOTES:
① Load values are limited by bending stress. Dead load of 10 psf is assumed. Where building code deflection requirements apply, these load values must be checked. A minimum roof slope of ¼″ per foot should be provided in addition to camber to minimize water ponding.
② Actual span of stiffeners taken as 3½″ less than center-to-center spacing of purlins.
③ Section properties and grades are in accordance with Product Standard PS 20 for lumber. Stresses are those appropriate for the grade, species, and joist spacing, as given in the "National Design Specification" of the National Forest Products Association. Loads are valid for Douglas fir, larch, or KD Southern pine.
④ Loads limited by stress are based on three conditions of duration of load: Normal (1.00); 2 months, such as for snow (1.15); and 7 days (1.25).

TABLE 2 PLYWOOD WITH FACE GRAIN PARALLEL TO SUPPORTS — ALLOWABLE LIVE LOADS FOR ROOF SHEATHING①②

SURFACE	NUMBER AND LENGTH OF SPANS	STRUCTURAL I		GRADES OTHER THAN STRUCTURAL I	
		IDENTIFICATION INDEX AND THICKNESS, INCHES	MAXIMUM ALLOWABLE UNIFORM LIVE LOAD③ PSF	IDENTIFICATION INDEX AND THICKNESS, INCHES	MAXIMUM ALLOWABLE UNIFORM LIVE LOAD③ PSF
Unsanded	Three @ 16″	32/16 — ½″ ④ 32/16 — ½″ ⑤	115 75	24/0 — ½″ ④ 32/16 — ½″ ④	65 70
	Two @ 24″	32/16 — ½″ ⑤ 32/16 — ½″ ④ 42/20 — ⅝″ 48/24 — ¾″	25 40 80 110	32/16 — ½″ ④ ⑥ 32/16 — ⅝″ ④ 42/20 — ⅝″ ④ 42/20 — ¾″ 48/24 — ¾″ 48/24 — ⅞″	25 45 45 50 50 120

NOTES:
① Load values are based on the use of American Plywood Association grade-trade-marked plywood.
② All panel edges supported, as by Plyclips, solid blocking, or framing.
③ Live load is applied load, like snow (1.15 duration of load factor). Dead load is weight of plywood and roofing; 5 psf dead load assumed. Deflection limitations: Span/180 for total load; Span/240 for live load only. Loads valid only for number of spans shown.
④ Five-ply construction only.
⑤ Four-ply construction.
⑥ Solid blocking recommended.

Melody Fair Theater, Tonawanda, New York
Architects: Biggie-Shaflucas, Buffalo, New York

Oak Harbor High School Fieldhouse, Oak Harbor, Washington.
Architects: Botesch & Nash, Everett, Washington.

Normandy High School, Parma, Ohio   Architect: Lipaj, Woyar & Tomsik, Cleveland, Ohio

PREFRAMED ROOF PANELS

ts technical support

Forklift places stack of 4' x 8' panels on roof

PLYWOOD ROOF DIAPHRAGMS

Because of its high strength, plywood sheathing is used in structures that must resist lateral loads, such as those imposed by wind or earthquake. Plywood diaphragms can be designed to carry shears as high as 820 pounds per linear foot.

In diaphragm-roof design, connections and fastenings between roof, walls and foundation are critical in transferring loads to the building foundation and the ground. The steps necessary to design a diaphragm are relatively few:

1. Calculate loads applied to diaphragm.
2. Calculate diaphragm shears.
3. Determine plywood panel layouts.
4. Find plywood nailing schedule from table below.
5. Determine required chord size.
6. Check deflection.
7. Check anchorages at edges, particularly hold-downs at bases of shear walls.

For more information on diaphragm design, contact the American Plywood Association, 1119 A Street, Tacoma, Washington 98401. Phone: (206) 272-2283.

RECOMMENDED SHEAR IN POUNDS PER FOOT FOR HORIZONTAL PLYWOOD DIAPHRAGMS WITH FRAMING OF DOUGLAS FIR, LARCH OR SOUTHERN PINE FOR WIND OR SEISMIC LOADING. (Plywood and framing assumed already designed for perpendicular loads)

Plywood Grade (c)	Common Nail Size	Minimum Nail Penetration in Framing (in.)	Minimum Nominal Plywood Thickness (in.)	Minimum Nominal Width of Framing member (in.)	BLOCKED DIAPHRAGM				UNBLOCKED DIAPHRAGMS	
					Nail Spacing (in.) at Diaphragm Boundaries (All Cases), at Continuous Panel Edges Parallel to Load (Cases 3 & 4), and at All Panel Edges (Cases 5 & 6) (a).				Nails Spaced 6" Maximum at Supported Edges (a)	
					6	4	2½	2	Case 1, Where There Are Neither Unblocked Edges Nor Continuous Panel Joints Parallel to Load	All Other Configurations (Cases 2, 3, 4, 5 & 6)
					Nail Spacing (in.) at Other Plywood Panel Edges (Cases 1, 2, 3 & 4)					
					6	6	4	3		
STRUCTURAL I C-D INT-APA or STRUCTURAL I C-C EXT-APA	6d	1¼	⁵⁄₁₆	2	185	250	375	420	165	125
				3	210	280	420	475	185	140
	8d	1½	³⁄₈	2	270	360	530	600	240	180
				3	300	400	600	675	265	200
	10d	1⅝	½	2	320	425	640 (b)	730 (b)	285	215
				3	360	480	720	820	320	240
C-D INT-APA C-C EXT-APA STRUCTURAL II C-D INT-APA STRUCTURAL II C-C EXT-APA and other APA grades except Species Group 5	6d	1¼	⁵⁄₁₆	2	170	225	335	380	150	110
				3	190	250	380	430	170	125
			³⁄₈	2	185	250	375	420	165	125
				3	210	280	420	475	185	140
	8d	1½	³⁄₈	2	240	320	480	545	215	160
				3	270	360	540	610	240	180
			½	2	270	360	530	600	240	180
				3	300	400	600	675	265	200
	10d	1⅝	½	2	290	385	575 (b)	655 (b)	255	190
				3	325	430	650	735	290	215
			⅝	2	320	425	640 (b)	730 (b)	285	215
				3	360	480	720	820	320	240

(a) Space nails 12 in. on center along intermediate framing members.
(b) Reduce tabulated allowable shears 10 percent when boundary members provide less than 3-inch nominal nailing surface.
(c) All recommendations based on the use of American Plywood Association grade-trademarked plywood.

NOTES:
Design for diaphragm stresses depends on direction of continuous panel joints with reference to load, not on direction of long dimensions of plywood sheet. Continuous framing may be in either direction for blocked diaphragms. See "Plywood Diaphragm Construction" and other publications available from the American Plywood Association, 1119 A Street, Tacoma, Wash. 98401.

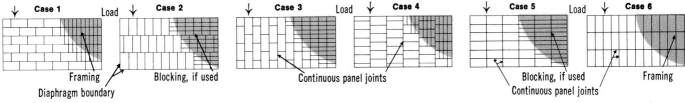

STRUCTURAL GLUED LAMINATED TIMBER
FOR INFORMATION CALL 800/525-1625

TRUSSES
ua uses, applications

Shavings Storage Building, Columbia Falls, Montana.

United California Bank, Palm Springs, California.
Architects: Black, Pagliuso, Kikuchi and O'Dowd,
Palos Verdes, California.

Twining Park Pavilion, Washington, D.C.
Architect: Keyes-Letheridge-Condon, Washington, D.C.

"U" VALUES

Economical thermal insulating methods are becoming increasingly important as heating and cooling energy increases in cost, and as diminishing energy supply results in more stringent insulating standards. Wood roof decks can be insulated through a variety of effective techniques. Thermal conductivities ("U" values) which can be achieved by some of them are compared in tables on these pages.

Installation of insulation to the underside of a plywood deck allows built-up roofing to be hot-mopped directly to the deck. This permits the plywood deck to be designed for a Class 90—fully wind resistive roof system as listed in the U. L. Building Materials List for a similar construction. It is recognized favorably in extended coverage (wind) insurance rates. Contact American Plywood Association, Tacoma, Washington, for further details. Phone: (206) 272-2283.

"U" VALUES OF PLYWOOD ROOF DECKS

NO INSULATION	Winter	Summer
3/8" BU roof — outside air; 1/2" plywood; inside air; 2 x 4 (Typical)	0.578	0.472

REFLECTIVE INSULATION*	No. of Air Spaces	Winter	Summer
*Foil sheets assumed reflective both sides except exposed bottom.	1	0.268	0.096
	2	0.186	0.067
	3	0.114	0.064
Venting may be required for high humidity conditions.			

RIGID INSULATION		Winter	Summer
Fiberboard or expanded perlite (k = 0.36)	1 in.	0.222	0.204
	1½ in.	0.169	0.159
Molded bead polystyrene or fiberglass (k = 0.25)	1 in.	0.175	0.163
	1½ in.	0.129	0.123
Expanded polystyrene (k = 0.20)	1 in.	0.149	0.140
	1½ in.	0.108	0.104
Polyurethane (k = 0.14)	1 in.	0.113	0.108

FLEXIBLE INSULATION	Winter	Summer
R7 with dead air space	0.104	0.098
R11 with no air space	0.079	0.076
R11 with dead air space (2x6 subpurlins required)	0.073	0.070
R19 with no air space	0.048	0.047
Venting may be required for high humidity conditions.		

"U" VALUES OF HEAVY TIMBER DECK SYSTEMS

Type of Deck	None		Type of Rigid Insulation				
			Polystyrene or fiberglass (k = 0.25)		Polystyrene (k = 0.20)		Polyurethane (k = 0.14)
			1 in. thick	1½ in. thick	1 in. thick	1½ in. thick	1 in. thick
	Winter	Summer	Winter Conditions ①				
1⅛ in. thick plywood	0.40	0.34	0.15	0.12	0.13	0.10	0.10
2 in. nom. wood deck (1½ in. actual)	0.33	0.30	0.14	0.11	0.12	0.10	0.10
3 in. nom. wood deck (2½ in. actual)	0.24	0.22	0.12	0.10	0.11	0.08	0.09
4 in. nom. wood deck (3½ in. actual)	0.18	0.17	0.10	0.09	0.10	0.08	0.08

RIGID INSULATION BOARD 3/8" BU ROOF
DECK
GLULAM BEAM

① U values for summer conditions are not included since, in each case, they are no more than 0.01 smaller than the U values for winter conditions.

Hagadone Newspapers Office Building, Coeur d' Alene, Idaho. Architect: R. G. Nelson, Coeur d' Alene, Idaho.

Bazaar at the Crossing Shopping Center, Indianapolis, Indiana. Architects: Wright, Porteous and Lowe, Inc. Indianapolis, Indiana.

Beacon Bay Office Building, Newport Beach, California. Architects: Albert C. Martin and Associates, Los Angeles, California.

GLULAM CONVERSION TABLES
ts technical support

STEEL SECTION ③ ④	EQUIVALENT GLULAM SECTION ②
M 7 x 5.5	3⅛ x 7½
M 8 x 6.5	3⅛ x 9
MC 10 x 8.4	3⅛ x 10½
M 10 x 9	3⅛ x 12
MC 12 x 10.6	3⅛ x 13½
W 10 x 11.5	3⅛ x 13½
M 12 x 11.8	3⅛ x 15
W 12 x 14	3⅛ x 16½
W 12 x 16.5	5⅛ x 15
M 14 x 17.2	5⅛ x 13½
W 12 x 19	5⅛ x 15
C 12 x 20.7	5⅛ x 15
W 12 x 22	5⅛ x 16½

STEEL SECTION ③ ④	EQUIVALENT GLULAM SECTION ②
W 14 x 22	5⅛ x 18
W 14 x 26	5⅛ x 19½
W 16 x 26	5⅛ x 21
W 14 x 30	5⅛ x 21
W 16 x 31	5⅛ x 24
W 14 x 34	5⅛ x 24
W 18 x 35	5⅛ x 25½
W 18 x 40	6¾ x 24
W 21 x 44	6¾ x 27
W 18 x 50	6¾ x 28½
W 21 x 49	6¾ x 28½
W 18 x 55	6¾ x 30
W 24 x 55	6¾ x 31½

SOLID SAWN SECTION ⑤	EQUIVALENT GLULAM SECTION ②
3 x 8	3⅛ x 6
3 x 10	3⅛ x 7½
3 x 12	3⅛ x 9
3 x 14	3⅛ x 10½
3 x 16	3⅛ x 12
4 x 10	3⅛ x 9
4 x 12	3⅛ x 10½
4 x 14	3⅛ x 12
4 x 16	3⅛ x 15
6 x 10	3⅛ x 10½ or 5⅛ x 9
6 x 12	3⅛ x 13½ or 5⅛ x 10½
6 x 14	3⅛ x 15 or 5⅛ x 12
6 x 16	5⅛ x 13½

NOTES:

① Section sizes are based on bending resistance. These sizes should be checked for shear, deflection and lateral stability.

② Glulam sizes based on the use of either a 20 F or 24 F bending combination.

$$S'_G = \frac{M}{F_b C_L}$$

where F_b = allowable bending stress

C_L = duration of load factor taken as 1.15 for 2 month duration of load as for snow

and $S'_G = S_G C_F$

where S_G = section modulus for glulam member

C_F = size factor

③ Steel sizes are selected as the most economical section from Allowable Stress Design Selection Table, pages 2-7 through 2-12 of AISC Manual of Steel Construction, 1970. In determining glulam sizes equivalent to a selected steel section, a 24F bending combination was used.

④ Steel sizes based on:

$F_y = 36,000$ psi (unless lower value specified to comply with compact shape criteria for steel section design).

$F_b = 0.66 F_y$

$$S_{st} = \frac{M}{0.66 F_y}$$

where S_{st} = elastic section modulus for steel bending member.

⑤ Solid sawn sizes based on the use of either a No. 1 or select structural grade of Douglas fir-larch having the following allowable bending stresses:

Size Classification	No. 1	Select Structural
2″ - 4″ thick	1,500 psi	1,800 psi
6″ and wider Beams and Stringers	1,350 psi	1,600 psi

$$\therefore \; S'_{ss} = \frac{M}{F_b C_L}$$

and $S'_{ss} = S_{ss} C_F$

where S_{ss} = section modulus for solid sawn members

C_F = size factor

In determining glulam sizes equivalent to a selected solid sawn section the 24 F bending combination corresponds to the use of the Select Structural grade and the 20 F combination corresponds to the No. 1 grade.

HEAVY TIMBER ROOF SYSTEMS

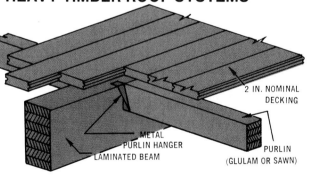

Two-inch Wood Decking on a Laminated Beam and Purlin System. Two-inch nominal thickness wood decking with an economical span range of 6 to 12 feet, is nailed directly to glulam or sawn wood roof purlins, typically on 8 foot centers. Purlins are connected to the main laminated timber beams by metal purlin hangers.

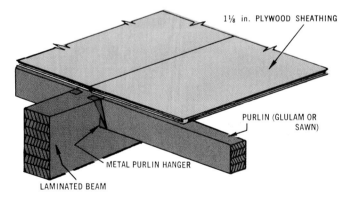

One and one-eighth-inch Plywood. Tongue-and-groove 1⅛ in. thick (2.4.1) plywood is nailed directly to the main laminated beams which are at least 4 inches, nominal, in width. Maximum spacing of the supporting beams is 48 inches, and plywood face grain runs perpendicular to the supports. Commonly designed as structural diaphragms to resist lateral forces.

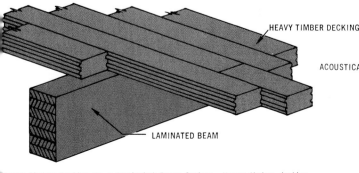

Heavy Timber Decking on a Laminated Beam System. Heavy timber decking, either laminated or solid 3 or 4 inch nominal thickness, is nailed directly to the main laminated beams. The economical span range for the heavy timber decking is 8 to 20 feet, depending upon the thickness and loading conditions.

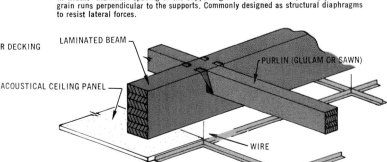

Suspended Ceiling System. Suspended ceilings, consisting of a grid ceiling framework, supported by hanger clips or wires hung from the primary structural members, can easily be installed on a laminated beam system. The grid framework will normally have main runners on 48 inch centers and cross tees on 24 inch centers to permit installation of 2 x 4 acoustical panels or lighting fixtures. The suspended ceiling system provides concealed space for installation of ductwork or piping.

DECKING SYSTEMS

Timber decking forms an important part of the building system utilizing glued laminated timber beams or arches. It not only serves as a structural component, but forms a beautiful exposed surface as well. Information on both laminated and solid decking is given herein. Decking is available in a variety of surfaces including smooth, saw textured, grooved, striated or wire-brushed, and may be prefinished in a wide choice of stains.

Timber decking is most economical when standard random length assortments can be utilized in a controlled random layup continuous over three or more equal spans.

In this arrangement, the distance between end joints in adjacent courses must be at least 4 feet for 3- and 4-inch decking and 2 feet for laminated and 2-inch solid decking. Joints within 6 inches of being in line each way must be separated by at least two intervening courses. Each piece must rest on at least one support. Other span arrangements, including simple span and two-span continuous, can also be used.

LAMINATED DECKING

Glued laminated timber decking is manufactured from three or more individual kiln-dried laminations into single decking members with tongue-and-groove patterns. Laminated decking is available in several thicknesses and in different appearance grades. More detailed information may be obtained from laminated decking manufacturers and suppliers. Laminated roof decking is to be laid with pattern faces down and exposed on the underside. Each course should be nailed to each support with two 20d common nails for 2¼ in. (30d for hem-fir and ponderosa pine); 30d for 2⅞ in.; 40d for 3 in.; 50d for 3²¹⁄₃₂ in.; and 60d for 3¾ in. deck thicknesses. Each course should also be slant nailed to the tongue of the adjacent course using 8d common nails for 2¼ in.; and 16d for

2⅞ in. and greater deck thicknesses. These nails should be spaced 30 inches apart with one nail not over 12 inches from the end of each piece. Nails in adjacent rows should be staggered 15 inches.

SOLID DECKING

Solid timber decking is tongue-and-groove, kiln-dried material available in two grades and in various species. Select quality grade is recommended for construction where good strength and fine appearance are desired. Commercial quality grade is used for purposes served by the higher grade, but where appearance and strength requirements are less critical.

Nominal 3 x 6 in. and 4 x 6 in. solid heavy timber decking sizes have a double tongue-and-groove. The moisture content should be 19% maximum. Solid heavy timber roof decking is to be installed with tongues up on sloped or pitched roofs, and outward in the direction of laying on flat roofs. It is to be laid with the pattern faces down and exposed on the underside. Each piece should be toenailed at each support with one 40d nail and face nailed with one 6-inch spike. Courses are to be spiked to each other with 8-inch spikes, at intervals not to exceed 30 inches, through pre-drilled edge holes and with one spike at a distance not exceeding 10 inches from each end of each piece.

Nominal 2 x 6 solid timber decking has a single tongue-and-groove. The moisture content should be 15% maximum. Solid 2-inch nominal thickness decking should be installed in the same manner as heavy timber decking. Each piece should be toenailed at each support with one 16d nail and face nailed with one 16d nail. Detailed information on solid timber decking is given in "Standard for Tongue-and-Groove Heavy Timber Roof Decking," AITC 112.

TABLE 1: DECKING SPECIES DATA

Species	Modulus of Elasticity, E, psi	Actual Size, in.	Weight, psf	Coverage Factor ①② bd. ft./sq. ft.
LAMINATED TIMBER DECKING ③				
Douglas Fir/ larch and Southern pine④	1,800,000	3²¹⁄₃₂ x 5⅜ 2⅞ x 5⅜ 2³⁄₁₆ x 5⅜	10.5 8.1 6.5	5.58 3.35 3.35
Hem-fir	1,750,000	3¾ x 5⅜ 3 x 5⅜ 2¼ x 5⅜	9.7 7.7 5.8	5.58 4.46 3.35
Idaho white pine and Inland white fir	1,500,000	3²¹⁄₃₂ x 5⅜ 2⅞ x 5⅜ 2³⁄₁₆ x 5⅜	9.5 7.3 5.0	5.58 3.35 3.35
Ponderosa pine	1,250,000	3¾ x 7⅛ 3 x 7⅛ 2¼ x 7⅛	8.8 7.0 5.2	5.61 4.49 3.37
Inland Red Cedar	1,200,000	3²¹⁄₃₂ x 5⅜ 2⅞ x 5⅜ 2³⁄₁₆ x 5⅜	7.5 5.8 4.5	5.58 3.35 3.35

Species and Quality Grade	Modulus of Elasticity, E, psi	Size, in. Nominal	Size, in. Actual	Weight, psf	Coverage Factor ① bd. ft./sq. ft.
SOLID HEAVY TIMBER DECKING					
Douglas fir/ larch — Select Commercial	1,800,000 1,700,000	4 x 6 3 x 6 2 x 6	3½ x 5¼ 2½ x 5¼ 1½ x 5⅜	10.1 7.2 4.3	4.57 3.43 2.40
Hem-fir — Select Commercial	1,500,000 1,400,000	4 x 6 3 x 6 2 x 6	3½ x 5¼ 2½ x 5¼ 1½ x 5⅜	8.0 5.7 3.4	4.57 3.43 2.40
Southern pine — Select Commercial	1,600,000 1,600,000	4 x 6 3 x 6 2 x 6	3½ x 5¼ 2½ x 5¼ 1½ x 5⅜	10.8 7.7 4.6	4.57 3.43 2.40
Western Cedar — Select Commercial	1,100,000 1,000,000	4 x 6 3 x 6 2 x 6	3½ x 5¼ 2½ x 5¼ 1½ x 5⅜	7.3 5.2 3.1	4.57 3.43 2.40

② For 8″ nominal widths (7⅛″ net), coverage factors are: 3¾″ and 3²¹⁄₃₂″— 5.61; 3″—4.49; 2⅞″ and 2¼″—3.37.

③ Laminated decking sizes may vary between manufacturers. The designer should check with the supplier to determine actual sizes and load-carrying capacities.

④ Actual size for Southern pine is 2¼″ x 5⅜″.

① To estimate board feet of decking required, multiply square feet of area to be covered by the coverage factor. Add for jobsite trimming and waste for irregular areas.

ALLOWABLE UNIFORMLY DISTRIBUTED TOTAL ROOF LOAD LIMITED BY DEFLECTION

TABLE 2: LAMINATED TIMBER DECKING—CONTROLLED RANDOM LAYUP ①②③

Each cell value is shown as l/180 (top) / l/240 (bottom).

Species	Actual Size, in.	8	9	10	11	12	13	14	15	16	17	18	19	20
Douglas fir/larch and Southern pine⑤	3 21/32 x 5 3/8							160/120	130/97	107/80	89/67	75/56	64/48	55/41
	2 7/8 x 5 3/8					124/93	98/73	78/59	63/48	53/40	44/33			
	2 3/16 x 5 3/8	181/136	127/96	93/70	70/52	54/40	42/32	33/25	28/20	22/17				
Hem-fir	3 3/4 x 5 3/8								133/100	109/82	91/68	77/57	65/49	56/42
	3 x 5 3/8			172	129	133/100	104/78	84/63	68/51	56/42	46/35	39/29		
	2 1/4 x 5 3/8	142	133/100	97/72	73/54	56/42	44/33	35/26	28/21					
Idaho white pine and Inland white fir	3 21/32 x 5 3/8							133/104	108/81	89/67	74/56	63/47	53/40	46/34
	2 7/8 x 5 3/8					104/77	82/61	65/49	53/40	44/33	37/28			
	2 3/16 x 5 3/8	113	106/80	77/58	59/44	45/33	35/26	28/21	23/17	19/14				
Ponderosa pine	3 3/4 x 7 1/8					192/144	151/113	120/90	98/74	81/61	68/51	57/43	48/36	41/31
	3 x 7 1/8					95/71	75/56	60/45	49/37	40/30	33	28		
	2 1/4 x 7 1/8	101	95/71	69/52	52/39	40/30	31/23	25	20					
Inland Red Cedar	3 21/32 x 5 3/8							106/79	86/64	71/53	59/45	50/38	43/32	37/27
	2 7/8 x 5 3/8					83/62	65/49	52/39	42/32	35/26	29/22			
	2 3/16 x 5 3/8	121/90	85/63	62/46	46/35	36/27	28/21	22/17	18/14	15/11				

TABLE 3: SOLID HEAVY TIMBER DECKING—CONTROLLED RANDOM LAYUP ①④

Each cell value is shown as l/180 (top) / l/240 (bottom).

Species and Quality Grade	Actual Size, in.	8	9	10	11	12	13	14	15	16	17	18	19	20
Douglas fir/Larch—Select	3 1/2 x 5 1/4					200/150	157/118	126/94	102/77	84/63	70/53	59/44	50/38	43/32
	2 1/2 x 5 1/4		173/129	126/94	94/71	73/55	57/43	46/34	37/28	31/23	26/19	22/16	18/14	16/12
	1 1/2 x 5	46/34	32/24	23/18	18/13	14/10								
Douglas fir/Larch—Commercial	3 1/2 x 5 1/4					189/142	148/111	119/89	97/72	80/60	66/50	56/42	48/36	41/31
	2 1/2 x 5 1/4		163/122	119/89	89/67	69/52	54/41	43/32	35/26	29/22	24/18	20/15	17/13	15/11
	1 1/2 x 5	43/32	30/23	22/17	17/12	13/10								
Southern pine—Select and Commercial	3 1/2 x 5 1/4					178/133	140/105	112/84	91/68	75/56	62/47	53/39	45/34	38/29
	2 1/2 x 5 1/4		153/115	112/84	84/63	65/49	51/38	41/31	33/25	27/20	23/17	19/14	16/12	14/10
	1 1/2 x 5	41/30	28/21	21/16	16/12	12/9								
Hem-fir—Select	3 1/2 x 5 1/4					166/125	131/98	105/79	85/64	70/53	59/44	49/37	42/31	36/27
	2 1/2 x 5 1/4		144/108	105/79	79/59	61/46	48/36	38/29	31/23	26/19	21/16	18/13	15/11	13/10
	1 1/2 x 5	38/29	27/20	20/15	15/11	11/8								
Hem-fir—Commercial	3 1/2 x 5 1/4					155/117	122/92	98/73	80/60	66/49	55/41	46/35	39/29	34/25
	2 1/2 x 5 1/4	191/143	134/101	98/73	73/55	57/42	45/33	36/27	29/22	24/18	20/15	17/13	14/11	12/9
	1 1/2 x 5	36/27	25/19	18/14	14/10	10/8								
Western Cedar—Select	3 1/2 x 5 1/4			158	158/119	122/92	96/72	77/58	63/47	52/39	43/32	36/27	31/23	26/20
	2 1/2 x 5 1/4	150/113	105/79	77/58	58/43	44/33	35/26	28/21	23/17	19/14	16/12	13/10	11/8	10/8
	1 1/2 x 5	28/21	20/15	14/11	11/8									
Western Cedar—Commercial	3 1/2 x 5 1/4		197	192/144	144/108	111/83	87/65	70/52	57/43	47/35	39/29	33/25	28/21	24/18
	2 1/2 x 5 1/4	136/102	96/72	70/52	52/39	40/30	32/24	25/19	21/16	17/13	14/11	12/9	10/8	
	1 1/2 x 5	25/19	18/13	13/10	10									

① Allowable uniformly distributed total roof load in pounds per square foot of roof surface for flat roofs, consisting of live load and dead load, including weight of deck (see Table 1). These roof loads do not exceed bending loads allowable under recognized bending formulas. Loads are for dry condition of use.

② All load values assume installation conforming to manufacturer's recommendations.

③ Load values are based on manufacturer's recommendations. In all cases, data is subject to special requirements of local building codes.

④ To determine allowable loads for 2 5/8 in. net thickness, multiply tabulated loads for 2 1/2 in. deck by 1.16. To determine allowable loads for 1 5/8 in. net thickness, multiply tabulated load for 1 1/2 in. deck by 1.27.

⑤ Actual size for Southern pine is 2 1/4" x 5 3/8". To calculate total loads for Southern pine for this size, multiply the listed value by 1.075.

BEAM CONNECTIONS

op overall product, in place

Separate tension ties for use in earthquake zones where required to tie beams together.

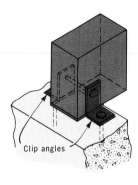

Supported member

CANTILEVER BEAM CONNECTION WITH TENSION TIE — Vertical reaction of supported member carried by side plates and transferred to both members by bearing plates in perpendicular to grain bearing. Saddle rotation due to eccentric loading is resisted by tabs at top and bottom. Separate tension tie resists separation force developed between beams.

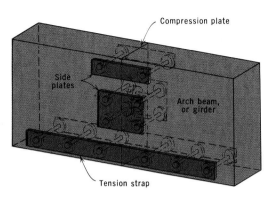

MOMENT SPLICE. Compression stress is taken in bearing on the wood through a steel compression plate. Tension is taken across the splice by means of steel straps and shear plates. Side plates and straps are used to hold sides and tops of members in position. Shear is taken by shear plates in end grain. Bolts and shear plates are used as design and construction considerations require.

Clip angles

BEAM ANCHORAGE DETAIL. For anchorages which resist both uplift and horizontal forces. May have one or more anchor bolts in masonry and one or more bolts with or without shear plates through beam. One-half inch minimum clearance or impervious moisture barrier on all wall contact surfaces, ends, sides, and tops (if masonry exists above beam end).

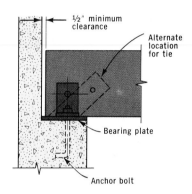

SIMPLE BEAM ANCHORAGE CLEARANCE DETAIL. For beams with depths 24 in. and less. Resists uplift and small horizontal forces. Bearing plate or moisture barrier recommended.

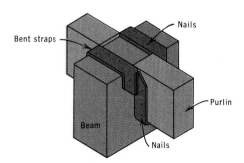

WELDED AND BENT STRAP TYPE PURLIN HANGER. For moderate and heavy loads. Provides uniform fit where good appearance is desired. Purlins must be raised above top of beam to allow sheathing to clear straps.

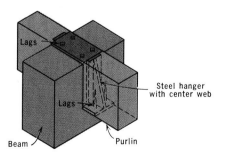

PARTIALLY CONCEALED TYPE PURLIN HANGER. For moderate loads. Base may be let in flush with bottom of purlins.

36

COLUMN CONNECTIONS

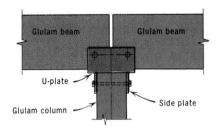

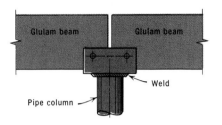

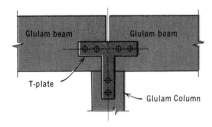

BEAMS TO GLULAM COLUMN U-PLATE. Steel U-plate passes under abutting glulam beams and is welded to steel plates bolted to glulam column.

BEAMS TO PIPE COLUMN.

BEAMS TO GLULAM COLUMN T-PLATE. Steel T-plate is bolted to abutting glulam beams and to glulam column. Loose bearing plate may be used where column cross-sectional area is insufficient to provide bearing for beams in compression perpendicular to grain.

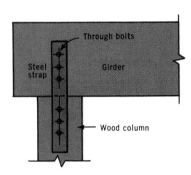

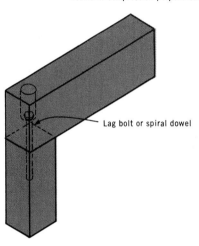

GIRDER TO GLULAM COLUMN. Provides for uplift. Metal bearing plate may be used where column cross-sectional area is insufficient to provide bearing for girder in compression perpendicular to grain.

CONCEALED TYPE GIRDER TO GLULAM COLUMN

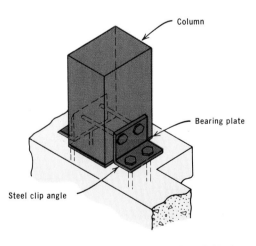

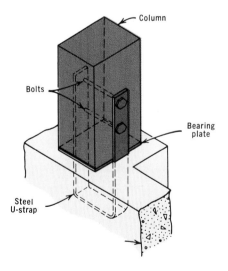

CLIP ANGLE ANCHORAGE TO CONCRETE BASE. Recommended for industrial buildings and warehouses to resist both horizontal forces and uplift. Bearing plate or moisture barrier is recommended.

U-STRAP ANCHORAGE TO CONCRETE BASE. Recommended for industrial buildings and warehouses to resist both horizontal forces and uplift. Bearing plate or moisture barrier is recommended. May be used with shear plates.

STRUCTURAL GLUED LAMINATED TIMBER
FOR INFORMATION CALL 800/525-1625

ARCH CONNECTIONS
op overall product, in place

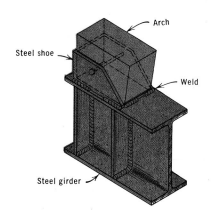

ARCH ANCHORAGE TO STEEL GIRDER. Vertical uplift load and thrust are taken through the weld.

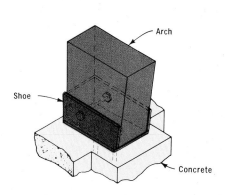

ARCH SHOE WITH CONCEALED ANCHOR BOLTS. Daps are provided in arch base for anchor bolt heads. Thrust is taken by the anchor bolts in shear into concrete.

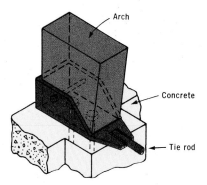

TIE ROD TO ARCH SHOE. Thrust due to vertical load is taken directly by the tie rod welded to arch shoe. This detail is intended for use with a raised floor. Concrete should not be placed around arch base.

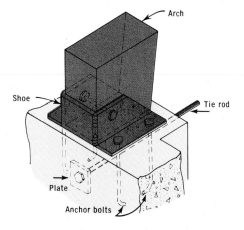

TIE ROD IN CONCRETE. Thrust is taken by anchor bolts in shear into concrete foundation and tie rod.

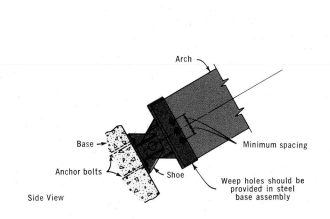

Side View

TRUE HINGE ANCHORAGE FOR ARCHES. Recommended for arches where true hinge action is desired. Bridge pin welded to arch shoe. Pipe bearings bolted to base plate.

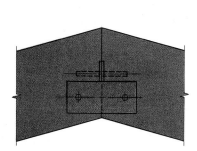

ARCH PEAK. Shear plates back-to-back centered on a dowel are used with a tie plate and through bolts. When appearance is important, a bent plate may be dapped into top of arch and secured with lags.

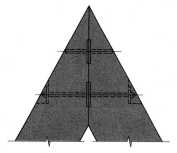

ARCH PEAK. When the vertical shear is too great for one pair of shear plates, or when deep sections would require extra shear plates for alignment, additional pairs of shear plates centered on dowels or through bolts may be used.

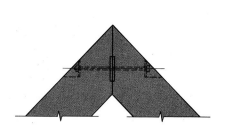

ARCH PEAK. This connection transfers both vertical and horizontal forces. It consists of two shear plates back-to-back and a through bolt or threaded rod with washers counterbored into the arch.

38

OTHER CONNECTION DETAILS

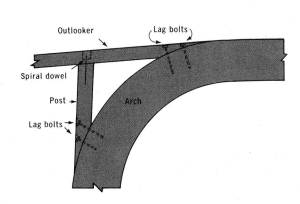

OUTLOOKER CONNECTION TO CURVED ARCH.

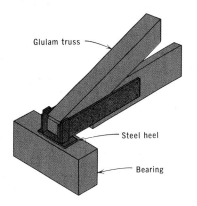

TRUSS HEEL CONNECTION. If substantial cross grain shrinkage is anticipated, double steel straps may be used in place of single strap.

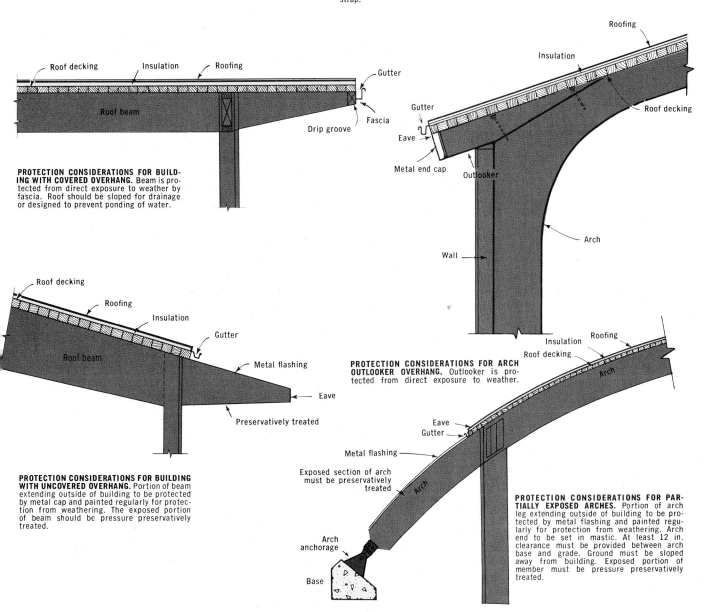

PROTECTION CONSIDERATIONS FOR BUILDING WITH COVERED OVERHANG. Beam is protected from direct exposure to weather by fascia. Roof should be sloped for drainage or designed to prevent ponding of water.

PROTECTION CONSIDERATIONS FOR BUILDING WITH UNCOVERED OVERHANG. Portion of beam extending outside of building to be protected by metal cap and painted regularly for protection from weathering. The exposed portion of beam should be pressure preservatively treated.

PROTECTION CONSIDERATIONS FOR ARCH OUTLOOKER OVERHANG. Outlooker is protected from direct exposure to weather.

PROTECTION CONSIDERATIONS FOR PARTIALLY EXPOSED ARCHES. Portion of arch leg extending outside of building to be protected by metal flashing and painted regularly for protection from weathering. Arch end to be set in mastic. At least 12 in. clearance must be provided between arch base and grade. Ground must be sloped away from building. Exposed portion of member must be pressure preservatively treated.

STRUCTURAL GLUED LAMINATED TIMBER
FOR INFORMATION CALL 800/525-1625

AITC'S quality inspection mark indicates conformance to PS 56-73.

QUALITY CONTROL AND INSPECTION
[cc] code acceptability, certification

It is your professional responsibility to insure your client that the structural glued laminated timber used is of a consistent and dependable quality. The best way to accomplish this is to specify quality inspected materials.

As a service to the construction industry, AITC provides a quality control and inspection system based on two references: Voluntary Product Standard PS 56-73 for Structural Glued Laminated Timber, and the Inspection Manual, AITC 200.

The AITC program consists of three elements:

1. **Licensing of manufacturers.** AITC licenses qualified laminators whose personnel, procedures and facilities have complied with the requirements of PS 56-73.

2. **Quality control maintenance.** Each licensee agrees to accept responsibility of maintaining a quality control sys-

tem which is in compliance with PS 56-73 and AITC standards.

3. **Periodic plant inspection.** AITC's Inspection Bureau, a nationwide team of qualified inspectors, conducts frequent, unannounced inspection and verification checks of laminators' in-plant quality control system, procedures and production.

DESIGN AIDS
[ts] technical support

AITC provides a service to assist designers, specifiers and users of glulam systems. Questions about glulam systems can be directed to the AITC technical staff by calling toll free (800) 525-1625. Alaska, Colorado and Hawaii residents call (303) 761-3212. The technical staff will be available to answer your questions about glulam construction.

AITC has developed a number of design aids to assist in the proper design of glulam structures. A complete list is available from AITC upon request.

PUBLICATIONS
[ts] technical support

Timber Construction Manual. Technical information on timber design and construction. John Wiley & Sons, Inc., publisher. $17.50.

Spec-Data Sheet (on structural glued laminated timber). Specification information in the Construction Specifications Institute format.

Glulam Bridge Systems Plans and Details. Design plans for glulam panel deck bridge systems.

Glulam Systems for Recreational Structures. Conceptual design information on major recreational facilities.

What About Fire? Information on fire performance of glulam in heavy timber construction.

Assistance in the proper application of glulam and additional information are available from either AITC or the following AITC Active Members:

ABLE FABRICATORS, INC.
P.O. Box 5274
Spokane, Washington 99201
(509) 326-0427

AMERICAN FOREST PRODUCTS CORPORATION
Timber-Lam
Vredenburg, Alabama 36481
(205) 337-4323

ANTHONY FOREST PRODUCTS CO.
Laminating Division
P. O. Box 1877
El Dorado, Arkansas 71730
(501) 862-5594

BOHEMIA, INC.
P.O. Box 1819
Eugene, Oregon 97401
(503) 342-6262

BOISE CASCADE CORPORATION
P. O. Box 200
Boise, Idaho 83701
(208) 384-7151

CHAMPION BUILDING PRODUCTS
Beam Plant
P. O. Box 1208
Salmon, Idaho 83467
(208) 756-3530

DUCO-LAM, INC.
P. O. Box 297
Drain, Oregon 97435
(503) 836-2191

KOPPERS COMPANY, INC.
Forest Products Division
Koppers Building
Pittsburgh, Pennsylvania 15219
(412) 391-3300
    Laminating plant locations:
    Magnolia, Arkansas
    Morrisville, North Carolina

LAMINATED TIMBERS, INC.
P. O. Box 470
London, Kentucky 40741
(606) 864-5134

LAMINATED WOOD PRODUCTS CO.
P. O. Box "L"
Ontario, Oregon 97914
(503) 889-5357

MID-WEST LUMBER COMPANY
P. O. Box 82009
Lincoln, Nebraska 68501
(402) 475-5102

MISSISSIPPI LAMINATORS
P. O. Box 405
Shubuta, Mississippi 39360
(601) 687-4371

MOD-LAM PRODUCTS
3909 So. 8000 West
Magna, Utah 84044
(801) 250-7453

POTLATCH CORPORATION
P.O. Box 5414
Spokane, Washington 99205
(509) 455-4260

RIDDLE LAMINATORS
P.O. Box 66
Riddle, Oregon 97469
(503) 874-2234

ROSBORO GLU-LAM PRODUCTS
P.O. Box 63
Springfield, Oregon 97477
(503) 746-8411

SENTINEL STRUCTURES, INC.
477 S. Peck Avenue
Peshtigo, Wisconsin 54157
(715) 582-4544

SOUTHERN LAMINATORS, INC.
P.O. Box 1062
Denham Springs, Louisiana 70726
(504) 664-3359

STANDARD STRUCTURES, INC.
P. O. Box K
Santa Rosa, California 95402
(707) 544-2982
    Laminating plant locations:
    Santa Rosa, California
    Fresno, California

STRUCTURAL WOOD SYSTEMS, INC.
P. O. Box 250
Greenville, Alabama 36037
(205) 382-3118

STRUCTURAL WOOD SYSTEMS OF MISSOURI, INC.
P. O. Box 87
El Dorado Springs, Missouri 64744
(417) 876-2541

TIMBERWELD MANUFACTURING
P. O. Box 1535
Billings, Montana 59103
(406) 252-7119

TIMFAB, INC.
P. O. Box 7
Clackamas, Oregon 97015
(503) 656-1668

UNADILLA LAMINATED PRODUCTS
Unadilla, New York 13849
(607) 369-9341

WEYERHAEUSER COMPANY
Tacoma, Washington 98401
(206) 924-2345
    Laminating plant locations:
    Albert Lea, Minnesota
    Cottage Grove, Oregon

WOOD FABRICATORS, INC.
Iron Horse Park
North Billerica, Massachusetts 01862
(617) 663-6511

WOODLAM, INC.
1476 Thorne Road
Tacoma, Washington 98421
(206) 383-4488

 THE AMERICAN INSTITUTE OF TIMBER CONSTRUCTION

333 West Hampden Avenue • Englewood, Colorado 80110 • Telephone 303/761-3212

Wood Moulding and Millwork

WOOD MOULDING AND
MILLWORK PRODUCERS

 ®

Wood Mouldings

WOOD MOULDING STANDARD PATTERNS

The moulding patterns illustrate those generally available in the United States. Additional patterns of local preference are also manufactured. Contact your local source of supply if special patterns are required.

WHERE TO BUY

Wood Mouldings are available from retail lumber dealers, building material distributors, and millwork jobbers.

SPECIES AND PRODUCTS

The species available will vary depending on local preferences, and may include western pines, Douglas fir, white fir, and lauan.

Pine mouldings are also available in many areas in specified length, finger-jointed for use in applications where the surface will be covered with an opaque finish.

Prefinished mouldings are available in natural toned finishes, vinyl wrapped or grain printed.

FOR ADDITIONAL INFORMATION

A complete wood moulding pattern catalog and standards for inside jambs and exterior frames are available at $1.50 per set.

For additional product information, write to Wood Moulding and Millwork Producers, P.O. Box 25278, Portland, Oregon, 97225, Dept. WB-77.

Moulding patterns not illustrated actual size.

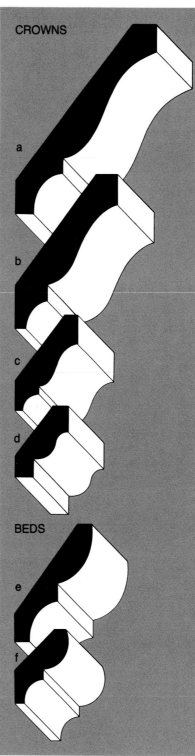

CROWNS

a
b
c
d

BEDS

e
f

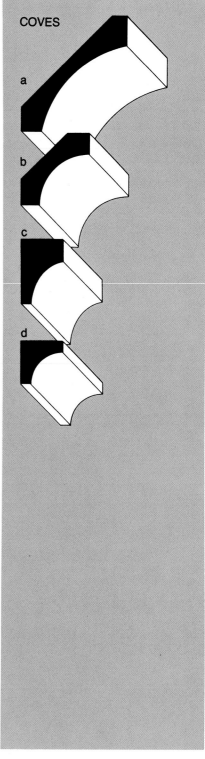

COVES

a
b
c
d

CROWNS
a—WM 47 $^{11}/_{16}$ x 4$^{5}/_{8}$
b—WM 49 $^{11}/_{16}$ x 3$^{5}/_{8}$
c—WM 54 $^{9}/_{16}$ x 2$^{1}/_{4}$
d—WM 60 $^{9}/_{16}$ x 1$^{3}/_{4}$

BEDS
e—WM 70 $^{9}/_{16}$ x 2$^{3}/_{4}$
f—WM 74 $^{9}/_{16}$ x 1$^{3}/_{4}$

COVES
a—WM 82 $^{9}/_{16}$ x 2$^{3}/_{4}$
b—WM 85 $^{9}/_{16}$ x 1$^{3}/_{4}$
c—WM 90 $^{3}/_{4}$ x 1$^{1}/_{8}$
d—WM 93 $^{3}/_{4}$ x $^{3}/_{4}$

QUARTER ROUNDS
a—WM 104 $^{11}/_{16}$ x 1$^3/_8$
b—WM 105 $^3/_4$ x $^3/_4$
c—WM 106 $^{11}/_{16}$ x $^{11}/_{16}$
d—WM 108 $^1/_2$ x $^1/_2$
e—WM 110 $^1/_4$ x $^1/_4$
HALF ROUNDS
f—WM 123 $^5/_{16}$ x $^5/_8$
g—WM 124 $^1/_4$ x $^1/_2$

BASE CAPS
a—WM 163 $^{11}/_{16}$ x 1$^3/_8$
b—WM 164 $^{11}/_{16}$ x 1$^1/_8$
c—WM 167 $^{11}/_{16}$ x 1$^1/_8$
BRICK MOULDS
d—WM 175 1$^1/_{16}$ x 2
e—WM 180 1$^1/_4$ x 2

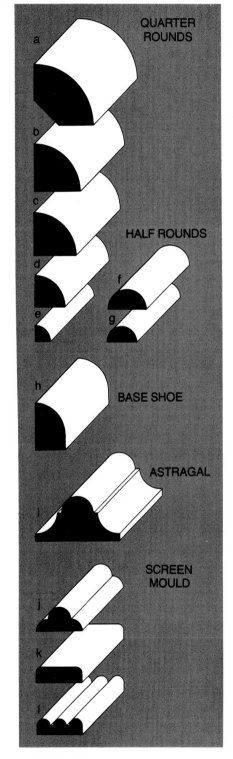

QUARTER ROUNDS

HALF ROUNDS

BASE SHOE

ASTRAGAL

SCREEN MOULD

BASE CAPS

BRICK MOULDS

PANEL MOULDINGS

DRIP CAPS

Photo: Alderman Studios for Sherwin-Williams

Photo: Alderman Studios for American of Martinsville

BASE SHOE
h—WM 126 $^1/_2$ x $^3/_4$
ASTRAGAL
i—WM 134 $^{11}/_{16}$ x 1$^3/_8$
SCREEN MOULD
j—WM 137 $^3/_8$ x $^3/_4$
k—WM 142 $^1/_4$ x $^3/_4$
l—WM 144 $^1/_4$ x $^3/_4$

PANEL MOULDINGS
f—WM 182 $^{11}/_{16}$ x 1$^5/_8$
g—WM 183 $^9/_{16}$ x 1$^1/_8$
DRIP CAPS
h—WM 188 1$^1/_{16}$ x 1$^5/_8$
i—WM 197 $^{11}/_{16}$ x 1$^5/_8$

CORNER GUARDS
a—WM 200 ¾ x ¾
b—WM 202 1⅛ x 1⅛
c—WM 203 ¾ x ¾
d—WM 205 1⅛ x 1⅛
e—WM 206 ¾ x ¾

HAND RAILS
a—WM 230 1½ x 1¹¹/₁₆
b—WM 231 1½ x 1¹¹/₁₆
c—WM 240 1¼ x 2¼

Photo: Hedrick-Blessing for Sherwin-Williams

Photo: Vincent Lisanti

CORNER GUARDS

a

b

c

d

e

SHINGLE/PANEL MOULDING

f

BATTENS

g

h

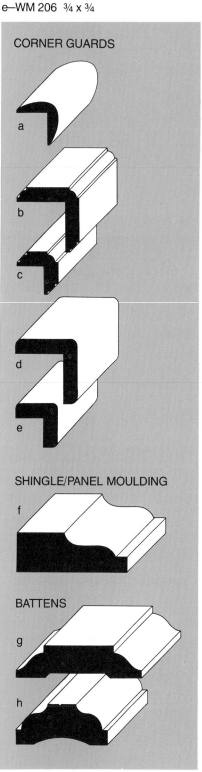

HAND RAILS

a

b

c

ROUNDS

d

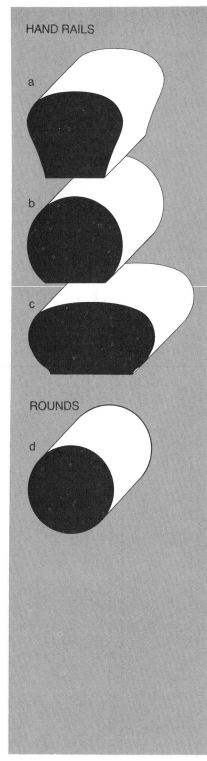

SHINGLE/PANEL MOULDING
f—WM 209 ¹¹/₁₆ x 2

BATTENS
g—WM 224 ⁹/₁₆ x 2¼
h—WM 229 ¹¹/₁₆ x 1⅝

ROUNDS
d—WM 233 1⁵/₁₆

SQUARES
a—WM 238 1¹/₁₆ x 1¹/₁₆
SCREEN/S4S STOCK
b—WM 246 ³/₄ x 2³/₄
c—WM 248 ³/₄ x 1³/₄
d—WM 250 ³/₄ x 1½

PICTURE MOULDING
a—WM 273 ¹¹/₁₆ x 1³/₄
WAINSCOT/PLY CAP MOULDINGS
b—WM 292 ⁹/₁₆ x 1⅛
c—WM 295 ½ x 1¼
d—WM 296 ³/₄ x ³/₄

SQUARES

SCREEN/
S4S STOCK

LATTICE

PICTURE MOULDING

WAINSCOT/PLY CAP
MOULDINGS

CHAIR RAILS

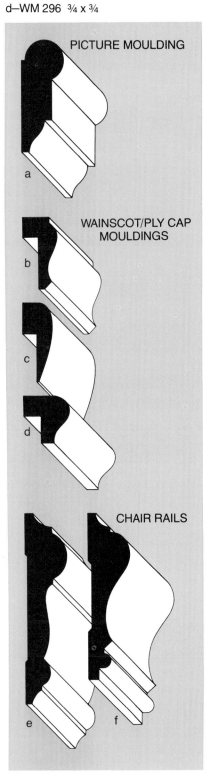

Designer: Gordon D. Smyth

Designer: Gordon D. Smyth

LATTICE
e—WM 265 ⁹/₃₂ x 1³/₄
f—WM 267 ⁹/₃₂ x 1⅜

CHAIR RAILS
e—WM 297 ¹¹/₁₆ x 3
f—WM 390 ¹¹/₁₆ x 2⅝

RANCH CASING
a—WM 306 $^{11}/_{16}$ x 2¼
b—WM 315 $^{11}/_{16}$ x 2½
c—WM 316 $^{11}/_{16}$ x 2¼
d—WM 324 $^{11}/_{16}$ x 2¼
e—WM 327 $^{11}/_{16}$ x 2¼
f—WM 329 $^{11}/_{16}$ x 2¼
g—WM 448 $^{11}/_{16}$ x 3½

TRADITIONAL CASING
a—WM 351 $^{11}/_{16}$ x 2½
b—WM 356 $^{11}/_{16}$ x 2¼
c—WM 361 $^{11}/_{16}$ x 2½
d—WM 366 $^{11}/_{16}$ x 2¼
e—WM 371 $^{11}/_{16}$ x 2½
f—WM 376 $^{11}/_{16}$ x 2¼
g—WM 440 $^{11}/_{16}$ x 2½

Photo: Max Eckert

Designer: Gordon D. Smyth

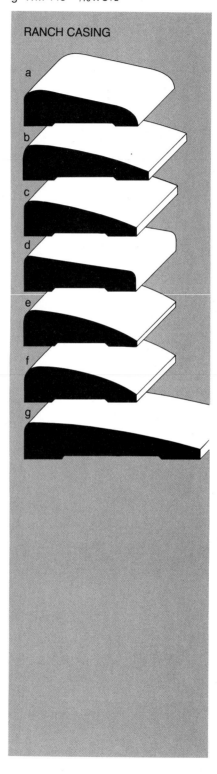

RANCH CASING

a
b
c
d
e
f
g

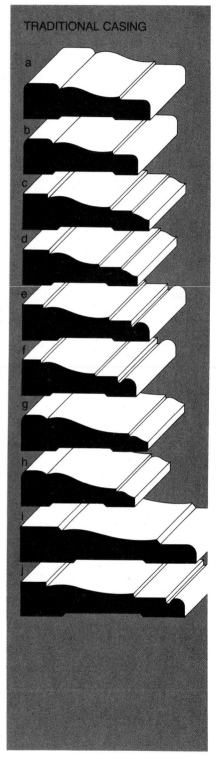

TRADITIONAL CASING

a
b
c
d
e
f
g
h
i
j

h—WM 442 $^{11}/_{16}$ x 2¼
i—WM 444 $^{11}/_{16}$ x 3½
j—WM 445 $^{11}/_{16}$ x 3¼

ROUND EDGE CASING
a—WM 433 $\frac{9}{16}$ x $3\frac{1}{4}$
b—WM 472 $\frac{9}{16}$ x $2\frac{1}{2}$
c—WM 492 $\frac{7}{16}$ x $2\frac{1}{2}$

RANCH STOPS
a—WM 816 $\frac{7}{16}$ x $1\frac{3}{8}$
b—WM 846 $\frac{7}{16}$ x $1\frac{3}{8}$

ROUND EDGE STOPS
c—WM 876 $\frac{7}{16}$ x $1\frac{3}{8}$

TRADITIONAL STOPS
d—WM 906 $\frac{7}{16}$ x $1\frac{3}{8}$
e—WM 936 $\frac{7}{16}$ x $1\frac{3}{8}$

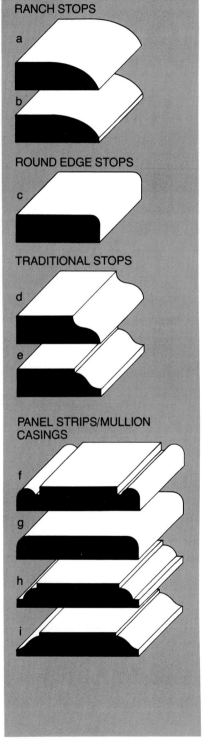

Designer: Gordon D. Smyth

Photo: House Beautiful

TRADITIONAL BASE
d—WM 618 $\frac{9}{16}$ x $5\frac{1}{4}$
e—WM 620 $\frac{9}{16}$ x $4\frac{1}{4}$
f—WM 623 $\frac{9}{16}$ x $3\frac{1}{4}$
g—WM 662 $\frac{9}{16}$ x $3\frac{1}{2}$
h—WM 663 $\frac{9}{16}$ x $3\frac{1}{4}$

RANCH BASE
i—WM 713 $\frac{9}{16}$ x $3\frac{1}{4}$

PANEL STRIPS/MULLION CASINGS
f—WM 957 $\frac{3}{8}$ x $1\frac{3}{4}$
g—WM 973 $\frac{3}{8}$ x $1\frac{3}{4}$
h—WM 978 $\frac{3}{8}$ x $1\frac{3}{4}$
i—WM 983 $\frac{3}{8}$ x $1\frac{3}{4}$

Door Jambs

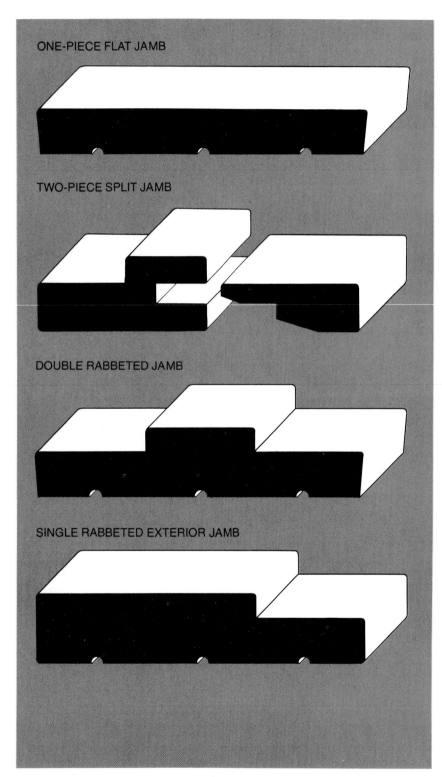

ONE-PIECE FLAT JAMB

TWO-PIECE SPLIT JAMB

DOUBLE RABBETED JAMB

SINGLE RABBETED EXTERIOR JAMB

Designer: Gordon D. Smyth

Photo: Alderman Studios for Sherwin-Williams

ONE-PIECE FLAT JAMB $^{11}/_{16}$ x $3^9/_{16}$, $4^9/_{16}$, 5¼, Beveled $^1/_{32}$ each edge
TWO-PIECE SPLIT JAMB Main member 1⅛ x 2¾, Extender member $^{11}/_{16}$ x 2¼
DOUBLE RABBETED JAMB 1⅛ x $3^9/_{16}$, $4^9/_{16}$, 5¼, Beveled $^1/_{32}$ each edge
SINGLE RABBETED EXTERIOR JAMB 1¼ x $4^9/_{16}$, 5¼

awpi

AMERICAN WOOD
PRESERVERS INSTITUTE
1651 OLD MEADOW ROAD
MCLEAN, VIRGINIA 22101

BASIC

Pressure-Treated Wood–
Unlimited Versatility in Design

DT Document

This booklet was developed to provide architects, engineers and other interested parties with:
- a brief review of the major wood products produced by the pressure-treating industry.
- appropriate specifications for these products.
- a means to secure prompt answers to questions about pressure-treated wood and its applications.

MR Manufacturer

The American Wood Preservers Institute is a not-for-profit association dedicated to disseminating information about the proper use of pressure-treated wood, and to providing essential technical services. Its activities are supported by numerous companies in the industry. Members of the institute represent about two-thirds of the industry's capacity to pressure-treat wood products.

AWPI's home office is at:
1651 Old Meadow Rd.
McLean, Va. 22101

For addresses and telephone numbers of field offices, call Sweet's "Buyline" toll-free (800) 255-6880.

In this brochure, the following acronyms are used:
AWPA
    American Wood-Preservers' Association
AWPB
    American Wood Preservers Bureau
AWPI
    American Wood Preservers Institute

Table of Contents

Pressure-treated wood offering protection against decay, termites and other wood destroyers

Our treasury of trees

Trees enrich our lives in innumerable ways. They beautify the landscape. They form enchanted forests for nature lovers, and homes for game and wildlife.

As a prolific managed natural resource, trees provide lumber for our homes, buildings and furniture; paper for newspapers, books and packaging; sugar and syrup to sweeten our meals. They are automatic cellulose fiber factories, energized by the sun, to give us ingredients for the manufacture of paints, lacquers, photographic film, cellophane, and rayon.

America is blessed with some of the world's most abundant forests. About one-third of the entire nation is wooded and much of this acreage has been harvested, used at least once, then grown back. Some forests have been regrown as many as five times in the past 350 years.

A renewable resource

Trees reproduce themselves. But in the forest, wood is subject to decay-producing fungi, wood-destroying insects, vagaries of weather and wild animals. As a result, many trees are returned to the soil as nutrients. Overgrowth and undergrowth, fire and lightning also take their toll.

Today, foresters are able to grow more wood on less land than nature can. This involves harvesting the trees at the optimum time, establishing new trees as rapidly as possible, fertilizing and thinning the growing stand to insure most rapid growth of the best trees, and controlling natural enemies such as fire, disease and insects.

Two-thirds of America's forestlands are commercial forests capable of growing trees for eventual harvest; one-third is noncommercial, either unproductive or restricted to a single use such as wilderness or parklands.

Wood for the thousands of products most Americans use in their daily lives comes from the nearly 500 million acres of our commercial forests. Sixty percent of these forests are owned by individuals; 28 percent by federal, state or local governments; and 13 percent by the forest industry. As a result of intensive forestry practices, industry-owned lands are twice as productive.

Pressure-treatment is true conservation, too

The same biological degraders that can destroy wood in the forest also can threaten its serviceability as lumber. Decay fungi, living plants that depend on wood fiber for a food supply, must have moisture to live. Anytime the moisture content of wood exceeds its fiber-saturation point (over 30%), and assuming favorable temperature and adequate oxygen, it becomes susceptible to fungi attack. As the wood fibers are decayed, the lumber loses its strength. By the time such damage becomes visible, it is too late to save the wood.

Termites, the most common wood-eating insects, live on the cellulose content of wood. In temperate zones, they are soil-dwellers that attack wood from below. Some termites live above ground and attack untreated wood wherever it is used.

By impregnating wood with preservative chemicals that render the

fiber useless as food for fungi or insects, industry produces a building material that will remain sound indefinitely. Through pressure-treatment, wood becomes an economical material for more and more uses, reducing the drain on exhaustible metals and minerals used to produce other building products.

Wood is the most versatile building material

The workability of wood has made it a favored material of construction. It can be used to frame the simplest structure, or be shaped into many diverse forms. Its many species, grades, patterns, and colors make it ideal for a variety of textures and architectural effects. The skill of carpenters and cabinetmakers, working with sophisticated power tools, permits its fabrication with speed and economy. Its ready availability as poles, planks, beams, shakes, shingles, plywood and laminated units also adds to its economical use, and offers architects and engineers practically unlimited scope for the application of their ideas.

The ratio of strength to stiffness is much higher for timber than for iron or steel and even substantially higher than for cast iron or concrete. Wooden structural members also have a greater shock resistance than steel or cast iron members. This strength and resilience accounts for the unusual structural durability of wood structural members.

Proven performance

Boardwalks, marinas, churches, schools, beach and mountain homes built with pressure-treated lumber decades ago show no loss of structural integrity from decay or termite attack, even those built in hot, humid climates.

The same holds true of farm structures, commercial buildings and industrial installations erected many years ago that used pressure-treated lumber in critical areas.

The economies and value inherent in such long service life are apparent and have led to the use of pressure-treated lumber and plywood for ever-growing applications in recreational and park structures, building foundations and swimming pools.

Pressure-treated wood meets fire safety requirements

Wood has another enemy more fearsome than fungi or termites. Fire is its most destructive foe. But pressure-treated wood that is highly fire retardant is readily available.

Impregnated with special chemical formulations, fire-retardant treated wood reacts automatically when attacked by flames. At temperatures below the normal ignition point of untreated wood, the salts release noncombustible gases and water vapor from the wood. These effects retard combustion. The treatment also causes the wood surface to insulate itself with a hard layer of carbon char during direct exposure to flame. Fire-retardant treated wood retains its structural strength during a fire longer than unprotected steel, retards the spread of flame, and gives firemen added time and safety to combat a fire.

Fire-retardant lumber, plywood, shakes and shingles are not only valuable assets to a home, they are preferred materials in the safety-conscious construction of schools, churches, restaurants, shopping centers or buildings housing public gatherings.

DR Design Requirements
Determine the Preservative

There are two broad classes of pressure/protective treatments:

(1) preservative treatment for protection against decay, wood-destroying insects and marine organisms,

(2) fire-retardant treatment.

Those in category (1), fall into three broad groups: creosote, oilborne, and waterborne.

Creosote: Creosote and creosote/coal-tar solutions.

Oilborne: Pentachlorophenol; copper-8-quinolinolate; and tributyl-tin oxide.

Waterborne: Acid copper chromate (ACC), Ammoniacal copper arsenate (ACA), Chromated copper arsenate (CCA), Chromated zinc chloride (CZC), and Fluor chrome arsenate phenol (FACP).

Fire-retardant treatments are required to have a performance rating in structural lumber (AWPA Standard C20) and plywood (Standard C27):

Material shall have no **greater** flame spread than 25 when tested in accord with ASTM E 84 and when the test is extended to 30 minutes duration it shall have no greater flame spread than equivalent of 25 and no evidence of significant progressive combustion.

Applications Unlimited

With the near perfection of wood-treating technology and the emergence of clean, leach-free preservatives and fire-retardants, architects and engineers are finding broader uses for pressure-treated wood in each new project they work on. This is but a partial list of applications:

arenas	glulam beams
boardwalks	grandstands
bridges	guard rails
cabanas	gutters
cabins	lighting standards
canneries	marinas
car decking	patios
columns	piles
cooling towers	poles
cribbing	porches
crossarms	railroad ties
culverts	roofs
docks	shelters
fascia	stadium seats
flooring	sunning benches
foundations	towers
furniture	trestles
furring	warehouses

▲ (Top, left)
Long Pier
Madeira Beach, Florida

▲ (Top, right)
Dana Point Marina
Dana Point, California

◄ (Far, left)
Railroad Bridge
Western U. S.

▼ (Bottom, left)
Ideal Toy Corp.
Newark, New Jersey
Designer: Engineers, Inc.

◄ Beach House
New Jersey

▼ Marina
Barnegat Bay, New Jersey

▼ Bulkhead construction
Inland Waterway, New Jersey

PROVEN PERFORMANCE AND PERMANENCE
Pressure-Treated Timber Piles for foundations, bridges, trestles, marine structures

PP Product Presentation

Pressure-treated piles are timbers that have been treated by pressure impregnation with proven chemical preservatives to protect them from wood destroyers and soil chemicals and thus provide a long-term foundation for the structures they support. Because the structures that rest on pressure-treated timber piles are unique in themselves, and the environment in which they are required to serve varies so widely, the architect and engineer are advised to carefully examine the American Wood-Preservers'Association specifications for the three major applications of this product: foundation piles, land and fresh water, and marine piles.

UA Uses, Applications

Pressure-treated timber piles are used for apartments, commercial and industrial buildings, trestles, highway bridges, docks, piers, terminals, marinas, bulkheads and beach homes.

OP Overall Product in Place

Service Life

Timber piling has supported loads for centuries. Even untreated timber piling used below the permanent water table in Europe has supported calculated design loads of over 60 tons for hundreds of years. *Pressure-treated* timber piling in the U.S. has a documented service life of over 85 years, with no record of failure.

Permanence

Pressure-creosoted timber piles were among the first used (1890) in foundations for permanent structures where pile heads project above the ground water line, or where future subsidence of the water table may expose the piles to alternate wetting and drying. One only has to review the older uses of untreated lumber piling and their untimely failure to see the merits and permanence inherent in pressure-treated piling.

Durability

Pressure-treated timber piles are chemically protected from the ravages of bacteria, decay fungi, termites, and other wood destroying insects. They have demonstrated superior serviceability in a wide range of exposures. For homes along waterways, for commercial buildings built on land prone to wide variances in the water table, for grain elevators in high alkali soil areas, for acid-laced soil around chemical plants, and for landfills . . . for these and other applications, pressure-treated timber piles have an unmatched record of performance.

Proven Load Carrying Capabilities

Actual loads tests on timber foundation piles have been carried successfully to 235 tons.

Most building codes recognize the superior strength of timber piles in their allowable stress. ICBO allows design stresses in compression parallel to the grain (which is how load is carried) of 1200 psi. AASHTO* Bridge specifications allow 1200 psi for timber piles.

Proven Economy

Pressure-treated piles permit soils engineers and designers to pass along a variety of cost-savings opportunities not offered by other materials. Their first cost is lower than other materials. They can be driven faster. They can be cut off and ready for the footing cap immediately. For well over half a century this has meant significant savings in all types of structures, from arenas and coliseums, to bridges, storage tanks and rapid transit facilities.

AI Assembly, Installation

Modern equipment for driving, preboring and jetting is widely used by major pile driving contractors. As a consequence, timber piles can be driven anywhere a displacement pile can be used. When hard driving is anticipated (and Douglas fir is the species being driven), steel strapped piles may be specified.

TS Technical Support

Specifications

Once the allowable stresses and size piling required to carry the load have been determined, the specifier can detail the information required to assure delivery of the proper piling:
1. Physical properties (ASTM D 25).
2. Minimum allowable stresses.
3. Nominal butt *or* tip circumferences *(not both)*.
4. Lengths.
5. Pressure treatment (AWPA C3).

ASTM D 25, *Standard for Specification of Round Timber Piles,* clearly defines the acceptable properties. It also provides two tables of sizes—

*American Association of State Highway and Transportation Officials.

one for friction piles, one for end-bearing piles. The diameters and lengths required can then be determined through normal engineering design processes.

AWPA C3, *Piles—Standard for Preservative Treatment by Pressure Processes,* delineates the acceptable preservatives and the various conditioning and treatment requirements for foundation piles, land and fresh water piles, and marine piles.

Limitations

A special note about specifying preservative treatment for *marine piles.* Here is one instance where the specifier should spell out which of the three preservative treatments are required, based on the following:

• For areas where Teredo (shipworm) and pholad attack are known or expected and where *Limnoria tripunctata* attack is not expected, specify creosote and/or creosote/coal tar solution.

• For areas where *Limnoria tripunctata* and pholad attack are known or expected, specify dual treatment (waterborne salts *and* creosote).

• For areas where *Limnoria tripunctata* attack is known or expected and where pholads are absent, specify either dual treatment or waterborne salts preservatives.

Quality Mark, Certification

In addition to specifying conformance to AWPA C3, the designer may require that each pile bears the appropriate American Wood Preservers Bureau quality mark.

The AWPB mark certifies conformance to the AWPA standards. The mark, in the form of a distinctive brand on a monel-metal tag, can be applied only to piling that have been treated under controlled conditions subject to quality control inspection. Quality marked marine piling automatically conform to AWPA standards for treatment as follows:

MP-1 = C3, dual treatment
MP-2 = C3, creosote
MP-4 = C3, waterborne salts.

CC Code Acceptability

Pressure-treated timber piles are accepted by all major building codes.

AC Availability, Cost

Pressure-treated piles are readily available in most states.

A new directory with complete information on types of preservatives, products available, and all AWPI member companies is available from the office listed on the back cover, or call Sweet's "Buy-line" (800) 255-6880.

◄ Nu-Southern Dyeing and
Finishing Co., Inc.
Henderson, North Carolina
Consulting Engineer:
Man H. Kwong

► Lake Barkley Lodge
Cadiz, Kentucky
Designer:
Edward Durrell Stone, FAIA
Architect:
Lee Potter Smith & Assoc., AIA

► NAHB Research Foundation House
Lexington Park, Maryland

► Waterfront Village
Hawaii Kai, Hawaii
Architect: David G. Stringer

TRULY VERSATILE DESIGN MATERIALS

Pressure-Treated Lumber, Timber and Plywood offer specifiers economy, performance, and long service life

PP Product Presentation

When you consider the fifty-plus-year service life of crossties and utility poles in rugged outdoor, in-ground exposure, it is easy to understand how the products on these pages can be made more durable than the structures in which they are used.

Designers and specifiers can utilize a variety of preservatives, listed on page three, to impart permanent chemical protection against decay, termites and other wood destroyers.

Pressure-treated lumber and plywood need no maintenance and may be left unfinished in both interior and exterior applications.

UA Uses, Applications

Pressure-treated wood has virtually unlimited uses and applications. The variety of available preservative treatments—each with its own special characteristics — gives specifiers a solution to any application where decay, wood-destroying insects, and chemical or corrosive atmospheres are a problem.

The adaptability of treated forest products, in combination with the many species of wood, leads to structural and decorative uses in virtually every market. Residential, industrial, commercial, institutional, municipal, marine and utility applications are merely broad headings for a warp and woof of uses that criss-cross applications, types of structures, and design treatments.

OP Overall Product in Place

Pressure-treated lumber, timber and plywood are used whenever wood is to be placed in the ground; in water; in contact with masonry; or where exposed to wetting or corrosive environments. Treated wood is also recommended for construction in hot, humid climates, or wherever wood would be susceptible to decay organisms or termites.

For above-ground locations, all the American Wood-Preservers' Association-recognized preservatives may be used. For soil or fresh water

contact, creosote, pentachlorophenol and waterborne salts solutions are recommended. Waterborne preservatives are used in house foundations and light frame construction. Creosote or non-leaching waterborne preservatives should be used for installations in tidal waters. When proximity to foodstuffs is a consideration, only copper-8-quinolinolate is currently approved by AWPA standards and the FDA.

AI Assembly, Installation

Pressure-treated lumber, timber and plywood are as easy to install as untreated wood products. Special cuts and bolt holes should be effected before treatment, especially when heavy timbers are involved. When on-site fabrication is required, all cuts and holes should be liberally swabbed with a concentrated solution of the preservative in accordance with AWPA Standard M4.

CS Coatings, Surfacings

Creosote and penta in heavy oils do not require painting and have the advantage of enhancing the weathering characteristic of wood used for bulkheads and other severe exposure conditions. These preservatives prevent moisture absorption, thereby greatly reducing progressive checking and splitting. Penta in LPG and light solvents can be painted, but

"paintable" should be incorporated in the specification. For indoor architectural applications, the waterborne preservatives have been most frequently specified because of their clean, odorless, paintable characteristics.

TS Technical Support

Testing and Inspection

Systematic testing and sampling is performed by several independent agencies under the standards and procedures of the American Wood Preservers Bureau. All treaters operating under the Bureau's quality control program are authorized to use the AWPB quality mark on their pressure-treated wood products.

Treatment in accordance with AWPB standards has no effect on the strength values of wood; the design values for untreated wood are to be used as outlined in the National Forest Products Association's "National Design Specifications for Stress Grade Lumber and Its Fastenings."

Specifications

The American Wood Preservers Institute (AWPI) recommends the following basic approach to specifying pressure-treated lumber, timber and plywood:

All (lumber) (timber) (plywood) designated pressure-treated on the drawings shall conform to AWPA standard C2-___(above ground) (soil contact). In addition, waterborne salts treated wood shall bear the AWPB quality mark designation (LP-2) (LP-22) (FDN).

The above sample specification applies where only one type of pressure-treated wood or plywood is required. The specifier must provide similar paragraphs where more than one type is to be specified.

This sample specification provides a broad specification under which all treatable species and all currently acceptable preservatives may be furnished.

Although AWPI recommends writing a broad-based specification to encourage competitive bidding and to enhance availability and delivery, certain product lines may be less suitable than others for various uses. Therefore, the above specification must be modified wherever the specifier wishes to place additional limitations on the material that may be furnished. Such information may include grade marks and/or stress ratings for lumber and plywood, acceptable species, and preservatives.

AWPB Standards

The American Wood Preservers Bureau has issued quality control standards for all lumber and plywood. They are designed to provide users with properly pressure-treated wood products. The AWPB quality mark on each piece of pressure-treated lumber and plywood is evidence of treatment in accordance with AWPA standards. AWPB standards cover lumber, timber, plywood, and marine piles.

AC Availability, Cost

Pressure-treated lumber, timber and plywood is available in all 50 states. When not stocked by local lumber dealers, users normally can obtain pressure-treated lumber and plywood from AWPI member companies on short notice. A directory to these companies, their addresses, the preservatives they use and products they treat is available from your nearest AWPI office listed on the back cover; or telephone Sweets "Buyline" (800) 255-6880.

The cost of preservative treatment is negligible compared with the expense of one replacement or repair job.

CC Code Acceptability

Pressure-treated wood is recognized by all of the model building codes throughout the United States. Pressure-treated wood is also approved by the Federal Housing Administration and other regulatory agencies concerned with the permanency of construction.

▲ South Seas Restaurant
Nimitz Highway, Honolulu, Hawaii
Architect: Wimberly, Whisenand, Allison,
Tong & Goo Architects, Ltd.

▼ (Bottom, left)
"Heaven on the Bayou" House & Sun Decks
Gulf Shores, Alabama
Architect: Ellis White-Spunner

▶ (Top, right)
Lighting Standard
Inverrary Country Club
Ft. Lauderdale, Florida

▼ (Bottom, center)
Summer Home
Westbrook, Connecticut
Architect: Richard Owen Abbott, AIA

▶ (Center)
Pier Approach
Redondo Beach, California
Architect: Corwin H. Eberting, Jr.

▶ (Bottom, right)
Sign Posts
Eastern U. S. turnpike

BROADER VISTAS
FOR OLD RELIABLES
Pressure-Treated Poles and Posts solve challenging design problems

PP Product Presentation

The performance and extended service life of poles and posts used in transmission and distribution lines and pole frame buildings have been widely documented by utility companies and farmers across the land. More often than not, the poles and posts outlast the lines they are first used in . . . and are frequently reused at a new location.

This kind of performance and the design economies offered by pole buildings and the rich, natural beauty of round and square-sawn posts, have prompted pioneering and innovative architects to use these materials for a wide range of functional structures.

UA Uses, Applications

Stemming from nearly half a century of proven performance on farms, building poles are being used for warehouses, bulk storage buildings, materials handling equipment storage, automotive dealerships, and ski chalets. In the past fifteen years, the broad application of pole-type construction has blanketed the home building market with design innovations up to and including townhouses.

OP Overall Product in Place

Pressure-treated poles and posts can help provide dramatic design solutions to building problems on hillsides, along waterfronts, in fact anywhere there's a desire to maintain the natural setting.

Labor and Material Savings

Savings in construction labor can also be substantial. Site preparation is less involved and, therefore, less costly than methods involving bulldozing and excavating. And pole frame construction is much lower in cost.

Flexibility

Expensive footings and costly foundations are eliminated. Walls and partitions are nonloadbearing. This combination of factors means that designers have maximum utility in the use of interior space. Remodeling and adding-on are simple. Even prefabricated modules are readily accepted by a pole framework.

Strength, Security

As documented by the USDA, pole-frame houses and buildings exhibit exceptional resistance to storms, hurricane force winds, earth shocks and tremors.

CS Coatings, Surfacings

Poles treated with creosote or penta in heavy oil are widely used for pole-platform construction where painting is not required. Waterborne salts-treated poles are dry, paintable, and free of objectionable odor. They are the normal choice where painting or staining is a prime consideration and where poles will be exposed within the building. Penta in LPG or light solvent can also be the specified treatment when painting is required. However, the specification should indicate "paintable."

TS Technical Support
Grading and Strength Factors

Pole grading and strength are given by the American National Standards Institute in its publication, "Specifications and Dimensions for Wood Poles." It gives the dimensions for poles of Douglas fir and Southern pine. This bulletin (ANSI Standard 05.1) also gives specifications and dimensions for all of the common varieties of timber used for poles, together with the manufacturing and handling requirements.

Specifications

All of the specification information needed to be assured of the performance required by *building poles* will be covered when you specify American Wood-Preservers' Association Standard C23, "Round Poles and Posts used in Building Construction — Preservative Treatment by Pressure Processes."

Although there are several types of preservative treatments, each of which has uses in pole-frame construction, cleanliness, paintability, color, and odor may affect the selection for a particular project. Cost and local availability are other considerations.

AWPA Standard C2 covers square sawn posts.

AC Availability, Cost

Pressure-treated poles and posts are readily available in most states.

A new directory with complete information on types of preservatives, products available, and all AWPI member companies is available from the office listed on the back cover, or call Sweet's "Buy-line" (800) 255-6880 for current listings.

FIRE PROTECTION AND BEAUTY

Fire-Retardant Treated Wood offers added safety, design latitude, insurance savings

PP Product Presentation

Fire-retardant treated wood (FRTW) identifies lumber, plywood, shakes and shingles that have been pressure treated and fire tested in accordance with appropriate standards to reduce their combustibility, flammability, and rate of heat release.

UA Uses, Applications

Fire-retardant treated wood is commonly used in fire resistive and noncombustible construction for studs, plates and blocking in non-bearing partitions, for trusses and rafters including connecting members (purlins) and decking; for furring strips and for studs, plates and blocking in exterior non-bearing walls.

Exterior fire-retardant treatment, when tested by any duly accredited laboratory under the rain test standard (ASTM D 2898) and so labeled, is used for Class B and Class C wood shingles and shakes. It may also be used under the rating schedules of the Insurance Services Offices (ISO) in wood frame exterior walls without a penalty being imposed.

Another use for exterior grade fire-retardant treated lumber and plywood is for decorative purposes on buildings where exterior facings are required to be noncombustible.

OP Overall Product in Place

Fire Safety

UL labeled fire-retardant treated wood has a surface flammability of 25 or less; its rate of heat release is decreased during exposure to fire and there is no evidence of progressive combustion. Without a fuel source fire retardant wood will not burn. Under fire conditions it can support design loads over long periods of time and in many cases longer than unprotected steel, giving firefighters added time to fight the fire and perhaps save lives.

Until recently, handsplit shakes and shingles were often not permitted on roofs of any buildings within fire limits. Wood preservers can now deliver shakes and shingles anywhere in the U.S. that are rated as Class "B" or "C." Western red cedar shakes and shingles can be

assigned the important Class "B" rating when they are incorporated in a roof covering system having the proper underlayment.

Fire-retardant treated shakes and shingles have two added safety features: they reduce the probability of ignition by firebrands from other sources, and they themselves will not produce firebrands dangerous to surrounding combustibles.

Extra Protection

Some of the chemicals used to make wood fire-retardant also impart a resistance to decay and insect attack. However, this added value should not be a prime consideration when FRTW is specified.

Lower Insurance Rates

UL approval places fire-retardant treated wood in the 0-25 Class, similar to non-combustible materials. That qualifies it for greatly decreased insurance rates than those prevailing with the use of untreated wood. Lower rate recognition varies from state to state, so consultation with local authorities is recommended.

Strength

With respect to design values, the allowable unit stresses and fastener loads are reduced 10 percent for lumber pressure-impregnated with fire-retardant chemicals. For further information see the National Forest Product Association's "National Design Specifications for Stress Grade Lumber and Its Fastenings" (NDS), Sections 202-C, 202-D, and 400-C.

AI Assembly, Installation

Preparation is the same as for untreated wood except that saw blades should be carbide-tipped. Fire-retardant treated wood should have a moisture content of 19% or less at the time of installation.

Precautions

Interior grade fire-retardant treated wood should not be stored outside unless set on skids and thoroughly covered. When installed it should not be exposed to exterior weather elements. Each piece of lumber or plywood must bear an appropriate label

▲ Big Daddy's Lounge
Ft. Lauderdale, Florida
Architect: Dan C. Duckham

▲ Laguna Beach County Library
Laguna Beach, California
Architect: Fred Briggs

▶ Landmark of Raleigh Apartments
Raleigh, North Carolina
Architect:
Brundage, Cohen, Kroskin & Assoc.

▶ Snapfinger Woods
Atlanta, Georgia
Designer: Callister & Payne

▶ Foothill High School
Pleasanton, California
Architect:
Corwin Booth & Associated Architects

▼ Congregation Or VeShalom
Atlanta, Georgia
Architect:
Epstein and Hirsh, Architects, Inc.

such as that of UL in order to certify fire resistivity outlined in the prescribed standards and required by building codes.

Laminated beams, plywood and any other laminated components must use waterproof glues if they are to be pressure treated *after* assembly.

CS Coatings, Surfacings

Pressure-treatment for fire retardance does not change the color of lumber, plywood, shakes or shingles to any marked degree. A whitish powder sometimes appears on the surface. Normal manufacturer precautions should be followed before paint, varnish or sealer is applied. For architectural finishes the surface should be lightly sanded before applying the first or prime coat.

TS Technical Support

Testing and Inspection

Systematic testing is performed under the testing and re-inspection programs of such agencies as Underwriters' Laboratories, Inc. (UL) in accordance with applicable standards. Other agencies having approval/re-inspection services may be accepted by some codes. Each piece of fire-retardant treated wood must be identified by an appropriate label.

Specifications

Fire-Retardant Treated Wood shall be pressure treated with fire-retardant chemicals in accordance with AWPA recommended practice C20, *Structural Lumber—Fire-Retardant Treatment by Pressure Processes,* or C27, *Plywood—Fire-Retardant Treatment by Pressure Processes,* and have a flame spread rating not higher than equivalent of 25 with no evidence of significant progressive combustion when tested for 30 minutes' duration under the Standard Test Method for Fire Hazard Classification of Building Materials, UL 723, NFPA 255, ASTM E 84. Fire-retardant treated lumber and plywood shall be labeled and tested by an approved testing agency showing the performance rating thereof.

After treatment, all plywood and lumber, 2″ nominal or less, shall be dried to a moisture content of 19% or less (designers may want to specify a lower moisture content for fire-retardant treated wood to be used for millwork, cabinets, office paneling and other special uses).

Except where exterior-grade treatment complying with rain testing is specified, fire-retardant treated wood shall not be used where it will be exposed directly to the weather.

AC Availability, Cost

Fire-retardant treated wood is readily available in all 50 states. You can receive a product directory of AWPI member companies from the AWPI office listed on the back cover, or telephone Sweet's "Buyline" (800) 255-6880 for current listings.

Costs vary according to species, quantity, grade and transportation requirements, but are readily obtainable from treating plants, building supply companies or retail lumber dealers. Fire-retardant wood is higher priced than untreated lumber, but since insurance rating bureaus give it preferential treatment, this savings should be considered when costing a system or structure.

CC Code Acceptability

An approved label identifies fire-retardant treated wood that is eligible for use under building code requirements.

Fire-retardant treated wood is recognized and permitted for use in all four model building codes and most city, county and state codes throughout the United States.

OM Operation, Maintenance

Fire-retardant treated wood does not lose its fire-retardant qualities. Interior grade FRTW used under dry conditions, such as in most covered structures, and not exposed to the weather and high humidity, will retain its effectiveness for a long time. Tests of fire-retardant treated wood doors in the Old Belmont Hotel in New York after 25 years of service show no deterioration of the chemicals nor reduction in surface flammability.

American Wood Preservers Institute

The American Wood Preservers Institute is the technical/promotional arm of the wood treating industry. It originated as a service bureau of AWPA but, for over 50 years, has been an independently functioning organization. Its membership consists of the primary treating companies and manufacturers of preservatives in the United States. AWPI neither writes nor publishes product standards at this time. But, it should be your primary source for technical data, design recommendations, and recommended specifications.

About Specifications

Although standards relating to specific products are cited on the preceding pages, a brief explanation of specifications is in order.

Because of the plethora of standards created over the years by various agencies and organizations, the architect and engineer are advised to follow a simple rule of thumb:

1. Use AWPA standards as the basic reference to specify pressure-treated wood.

2. Use federal, military, or AASHTO specifications only when you are required to do so by government agencies.

3. Specify that waterborne-salts-treated lumber and plywood shall also bear one of the AWPB quality marks. (Also, you may wish to specify the proper AWPB mark for marine piling.)

There is one thing that makes AWPA standards the first choice: Virtually all standards that are widely used and accepted within the treating industry and by government agencies are based directly upon AWPA standards. Usually, other standards either copy AWPA requirements or include them by reference.

Additional Information

Most questions about treated wood, its selection, use, and specifications, are answered in one or more of the many publications available from AWPI. A comprehensive publications list is updated and published bi-monthly, in *A/E Concepts*, our magazine of design ideas and data about pressure-treated wood.

If you are an architect or engineer and would like to receive *A/E Concepts* free of charge, please contact our headquarters office.

To enable us to serve you best, use a current publications list. We respond to letter inquiries to the best of our ability, but frequently people see, then request, older publications that are now out of print, or items that we cannot supply except at modest cost. You can obtain a current list and order form:

• From AWPI offices.

• From our headquarters office whose address is listed below.

For current addresses and telephone numbers, telephone Sweet's "Buyline" toll-free 800-255-6880.

We can serve you better and faster when you request specific information on our form.

Questions? ☎ Call AWPI toll-free, prompt answer service **800-336-0148**

awpi

AMERICAN WOOD
PRESERVERS INSTITUTE
1651 OLD MEADOW ROAD
MCLEAN, VIRGINIA 22101

Litho in U.S.A.

The APA Series

Construction

Plywood Wall Systems

18872

American Plywood Association

February 1978

7

CLADDING SIDING

Plywood

Introduction

Plywood. Tough enough for corner bracing or shear walls and good looking enough to adorn the most striking buildings and structures going up around the country. Virtually unmatched as a versatile, economical building material, softwood plywood's credentials are well established in the realm of structural wall systems.

Problem solving plywood applications are seen in nearly every aspect of wall construction. Plywood wall sheathing has been acknowledged for decades as a basic workhorse in the building trade. And plywood siding . . . it's appearing more and more on beautiful exteriors and interiors . . . with or without separate sheathing. Numerous designs exist for plywood in fire rated wall systems, and wood's sound absorbancy makes plywood a natural in wall designs for noise control. Plywood walls offer excellent protection from air infiltration and are easy to insulate—wall designs meeting or exceeding HUD-MPS insulation requirements using plywood and conventional insulation materials are used in all parts of the country.

This American Plywood Association publication provides a kind of mini-handbook on plywood wall systems. You will find design data and applications information for all major APA® plywood wall systems. A number of special wall systems are also covered and a separate section presents details and data on such important topics as insulation and energy saving walls, fire rated walls, and walls designed for noise control.

Whatever your wall system needs may be, look to plywood. It has a corner on the best answers.

NOTE: For information on plywood types, groups, grades, Identification Indexes, and method of ordering, refer to APA's **Plywood Specification and Grade Guide,** C20.

TABLE 1
Guide to Grades for Plywood Walls

Use These Terms When You Specify Plywood	Description and Most Common Uses	Typical Grade-trademarks	Face	Inner Plies	Back	Most Common Thicknesses (inch)				
Interior Type										
C-D INT-APA	**Sheathing.** Most often manufactured with exterior glue; but may have interior glue. Specify exterior glue for best durability in long construction delays and for treated wood foundations.	C-D 32/16 INTERIOR APA EXTERIOR GLUE	C	D	D	5/16	3/8	1/2	5/8	3/4
STRUCTURAL I C-D INT-APA and STRUCTURAL II C-D INT-APA	**High load shear walls, box beams, stressed-skin panels, etc.** Where plywood strength properties are of maximum importance. Made only with exterior glue. See (a) for species group requirements. More commonly available in STRUCTURAL I. Check local supply.	STRUCTURAL I C-D 24/0 INTERIOR APA EXTERIOR GLUE	C	D	D	5/16	3/8	1/2	5/8	3/4
C-D PLUGGED (a) INT-APA	**Built-ins, wall and ceiling tile backing** Touch-sanded.	C-D PLUGGED GROUP 2 INTERIOR APA	C plugged	D	D	5/16	3/8	1/2	5/8	3/4
DECORATIVE PANELS—APA	**Interior paneling.** Rough sawn, brushed, grooved, striated, or specially textured faces. For paneling interior accent walls, built-ins, displays, and exhibits. Check with manufacturer or distributor for specific product names.	DECORATIVE · BD · G1 · INT·APA· PS 1·74	C or btr.	D	D	5/16	3/8	1/2	5/8	
A-D INT-APA	**Interior walls.** Sanded panel for paint finishes, wallpaper or other wall coverings or coatings.	A-D GROUP 1 INTERIOR APA	A	D	D	1/4	3/8	1/2	5/8	3/4
Exterior Type										
A-C EXT-APA (a)	**Soffits and fences.** Exterior use where appearance of only one side is important, including substrate for high performance exterior coatings. Not recommended for siding under conventional paint or stain finishes. Sanded.	A-C GROUP 1 EXTERIOR APA	A	C	C	1/4	3/8	1/2	5/8	3/4
C-C EXT-APA	**Siding on service and farm buildings, sheathing for wood foundations, etc.** Unsanded	C-C 42/20 EXTERIOR APA	C	C	C	5/16	3/8	1/2	5/8	3/4
STRUCTURAL I C-C EXT-APA and STRUCTURAL II C-C EXT-APA	**Engineered applications** where plywood strength properties are of maximum importance and where full Exterior panels are required. Unsanded. See (a) for species group requirements. More commonly available in STRUCTURAL I. Check local supply.	STRUCTURAL I C-C 32/16 EXTERIOR APA	C	C	C	5/16	3/8	1/2	5/8	3/4
MDO EXT-APA (a)(b)	**Siding and interior paneling, accent panels, soffits, fascia.** Medium Density Overlaid with resin fiber overlay one or both panel faces. Ideal base for paint finishes.	303 SIDING O/L MDO GROUP 2 24 oc SPAN EXTERIOR APA	B	B or C	C	5/16	3/8	1/2	5/8	3/4
303 SIDING (b) EXT-APA	**Siding and interior paneling.** Textured plywood panels for siding, fencing, etc. Special surface treatment such as V-groove, channel groove, striated, brushed, rough-sawn, coarse sanded. Recommended for stain finishes.	303 SIDING 6-W GROUP 4 16 oc SPAN EXTERIOR APA	(c)	C	C		3/8	1/2	5/8	
T 1-11 EXT-APA (b)	**Siding and interior paneling.** Special 303 panel having grooves 1/4" deep, 3/8" wide, spaced 4" or 8" o.c. Other spacing optional. Edges shiplapped. Available unsanded, textured, and MDO.	303 SIDING O/C T 1-11 GROUP 2 24 oc SPAN EXTERIOR APA	C or btr.	C	C				5/8	

(a) Can be manufactured in STRUCTURAL I (all plies limited to Group 1 species) and STRUCTURAL II (all plies limited to Group 1, 2, or 3 species).
(b) Stud spacing for siding direct-to-studs is shown on grade stamp.
(c) C or better for 5 plies; C-plugged or better for 3 plies.

APA Plywood Siding for Exteriors and Interiors

PRODUCT INFORMATION

**Patterns & Grades of APA 303®
Siding.** APA 303 Sidings include a wide variety of surface textures and patterns, most of them developed for optimum performance with stain finishes. Typical surface patterns are illustrated on the following pages. Actual dimensions of groove spacing, width and depth may vary with the manufacturer. Where the characteristics of a particular wood species are desired, specify by grade and species preference.

APA plywood siding products are also available in a variety of face grades corresponding to categories of repair and appearance characteristics. Depending on species, type of repair, finishing, etc., premium appearance products may be found in all grades. Each grade* is denoted by code within the 303 siding product designation.

There are four basic APA plywood siding classifications:

Class	Patches
303-0	none
303-6	maximum 6
303-18	maximum 18
303-NL	no limit

Within the 303-0 class, three grades are defined:

303-0/C**	clear
303-0/L	overlaid
303-0/R	rustic (permits open knotholes, etc.)

Within the other classes, grades are further designated:

- W   wood repairs only
(e.g. 303-6-W)

- S   synthetic repairs only
(e.g. 303-6-S)

-S/W   wood and synthetic repairs
(e.g. 303-6-S/W)

*Limitations on grade characteristics are based on 4 ft. x 8 ft. panel size. Limits on other sizes vary in proportion.
**Check local availability.

Thus, with APA 303 siding products it is easy to select and specify the siding grade appropriate for any project in terms of finished appearance sought. Repair limitations for standard APA 303 plywood siding face grades are summarized in Table 2.

Siding panels with the identification "16 oc" on the grade stamp may be applied vertically direct to studs spaced 16 inches on center in APA Sturd-I-Wall construction. Panels marked "24 oc" may be applied vertically direct to studs spaced up to 24 inches on center. All 303 panel sidings may be applied horizontally direct to studs spaced 16 or 24 inches on center.

Texture 1-11® plywood siding is a special 303 panel manufactured with 3/8-inch-wide parallel grooves and shiplapped edges. Texture 1-11 is available unsanded or with a variety of surface treatments generally in thicknesses of 19/32 and 5/8 inch.

Medium Density Overlaid Plywood.
For paint finishes, MDO plywood is strongly recommended. MDO has a special resin-treated wood fiber surface permanently bonded to the panel under heat and pressure, making it an excellent base for paint. It is available with a smooth, grooved or texture-embossed surface and in both panel and lap siding.

The most common APA plywood siding panel dimensions are 4 x 8 feet though siding panels also are available in 9- and 10-foot lengths; lap sidings to 16 feet. Some manufacturers scarf-glue panels to lengths longer than 10 feet.

Plywood siding is easy to use, covers fast and requires no special tools or skills. Painted or stained, plywood's dimensioned panels are a key to efficient and economical construction.

TABLE 2
Repair Limitations in APA 303 Siding Face Grades

Grade	Type of Patch	
	Wood	**Synthetic**
303 - O/C	Not permitted	Not permitted
303 - O/L	Not applicable for overlays	
303 - O/R	Not permitted	Not permitted
303 - 6 - W	Limit 6	Not permitted
303 - 6 - S	Not permitted	Limit 6
303 - 6 - S/W	Limit 6—any combination	
303 - 18 - W	Limit 18	Not permitted
303 - 18 - S	Not permitted	Limit 18
303 - 18 - S/W	Limit 18—any combination	
303 - NL - W	No limit	Not permitted
303 - NL - S	Not permitted	No limit
303 - NL - S/W	No limit - any combination	

All panels except 303 - O/R allow restricted minor repairs such as shims. These and such other face appearance characteristics as knots, knotholes, splits, etc. are limited by both size and number in accordance with panel grades, 303 - O/C being most restrictive and 303 - NL being least. Multiple repairs are permitted only on 303 - 18 and 303 - NL panels. See *303 Series Specialty Siding Manufacturing Specification*, Form B840, available from the American Plywood Association for a comprehensive description of 303 siding face grades. Patch size is restricted on all panel grades.

KERFED ROUGH-SAWN
303 Siding

Rough-sawn surface with narrow grooves providing a distinctive effect. Long edges shiplapped for continuous pattern. Grooves are typically 4'' o.c. Also available with grooves in multiples of 2'' o.c. Generally available in 11/32'', 3/8'', 1/2'', 19/32'', 5/8'' and 3/4'' thicknesses.

BRUSHED
303 Siding

Brushed or relief-grain surfaces accent the natural grain pattern to create striking textured surfaces. Generally available in 11/32", 3/8", 1/2", 19/32", 5/8" and 3/4" thicknesses. Available in redwood, Douglas fir, cedar, and other species.

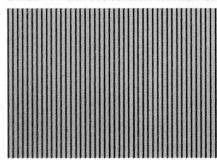

APA TEXTURE 1-11
303 Siding

Panel with shiplapped edges and parallel grooves 1/4'' deep, 3/8'' wide; grooves 4'' or 8'' o.c. are standard. Other spacings sometimes available are 2'', 6'' and 12'' o.c., check local availability. T 1-11 is generally available in 19/32'' and 5/8'' thicknesses. Also available with scratch-sanded, overlaid, rough-sawn, brushed and other surfaces. Available in Douglas fir, cedar, redwood, southern pine, lauan, other species. At left, unsanded T 1-11; at right rough-sawn surface.

ROUGH-SAWN
303 Siding

Exterior plywood siding with a slight, rough sawn texture running across panel. Available without grooves, or with grooves of various styles; in lap sidings, as well as in panel form. Generally available in 11/32'', 3/8'', 1/2'', 19/32'', 5/8'' and 3/4'' thicknesses. Rough-sawn also available in reverse board-and-batten (5/8'' thick), channel groove (3/8'' thick), and V-groove (1/2'' or 5/8'' thick). Available in Douglas fir, redwood, cedar, southern pine, lauan, other species.

FINE-LINE
303 Siding

Fine grooves cut into the surface to provide a distinctive striped effect. The grooving reduces surface checking and provides additional durability of finish. Generally available in 11/32'', 3/8'', 1/2'', 19/32'', 5/8'' and 3/4'' thicknesses. Available factory-primed. Shallow grooves about 1/4'' o.c., 1/32'' wide. Also available combined with Texture 1-11, channel grooving spaced 4" or 8" o.c. and with reverse board-and batten. Available in several species.

CHANNEL GROOVE
303 Siding

Shallow grooves typically 1/16″ deep, 3/8″ wide, cut into faces of 3/8″ thick panels, 4″ or 8″ o.c. Other groove spacings available. Shiplapped for continuous patterns. Generally available in surface patterns and textures similar to Texture 1-11 and in 11/32″, 3/8″ and 1/2″ thicknesses. Available in redwood, Douglas fir, cedar, lauan, southern pine and other species.

REVERSE BOARD-AND-BATTEN
303 Siding

Deep, wide grooves cut into brushed, rough-sawn, coarse sanded or other textured surfaces. Grooves about 1/4″ deep, 1″ to 1-1/2″ wide, spaced 8″, 12″ or 16″ o.c. with panel thickness of 19/32″, 5/8″ and 3/4″. Provides deep, sharp shadow lines. Long edges shiplapped for continuous pattern. Available in redwood, cedar, Douglas fir, lauan, southern pine and other species.

MEDIUM DENSITY OVERLAID

Available without grooving; with V-grooves (spaced 6″ or 8″ o.c. usually standard); or in T 1-11 or reverse board-and-batten grooving as illustrated at left. MDO panel siding available in 11/32″, 3/8″, 1/2″, 19/32″ and 5/8″ thicknesses; also in mill precut widths for horizontal-lap siding (sizes: 12″ or 16″ width, 3/8″ thickness; lengths to 16′ on order). MDO available factory-primed. MDO siding is overlaid on one side and available with texture embossed surfaces.

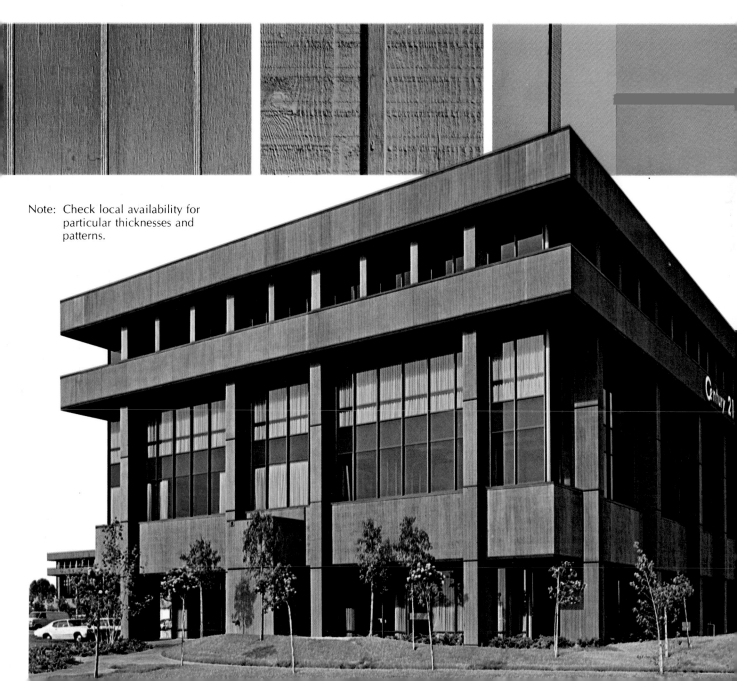

Note: Check local availability for particular thicknesses and patterns.

Plywood Siding for Exteriors

The information in Fig. 1 and Table 3 applies to construction of walls built with plywood siding over sheathing. This traditional method remains in general use, though many builders around the country prefer the APA Sturd-I-Wall single layer system described on pages 10 and 11. APA Sturd-I-Wall plywood construction cuts materials and labor costs while continuing to meet or exceed thermal and structural performance requirements.

Based on established construction technology and practice, both systems are backed by years of successful field experience. Both are accepted by HUD-MPS, the model codes and many local codes. And with either system, let-in bracing and, usually, building paper requirements are eliminated.

FIGURE 1
Plywood Panel Siding

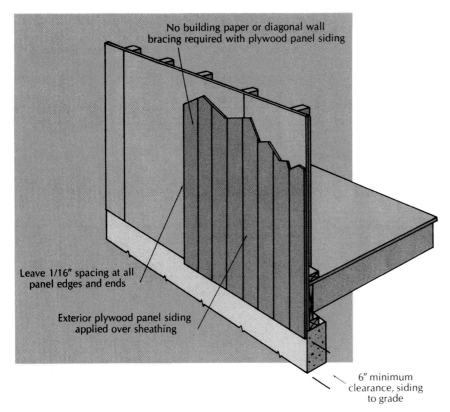

No building paper or diagonal wall bracing required with plywood panel siding

Leave 1/16" spacing at all panel edges and ends

Exterior plywood panel siding applied over sheathing

6" minimum clearance, siding to grade

Siding joints may occur away from studs with nailable plywood or lumber sheathing.

Caulk vertical joints or treat plywood edges with water repellent unless edges are shiplapped or battened. Nails through battens must penetrate studs at least 1'', or through nailable lumber or plywood sheathing.

Nailable plywood or lumber sheathing includes:

1. Nominal 1" boards with studs 16" or 24" o.c.
2. 1/2" 4 or 5 ply plywood, face grain either parallel or perpendicular to studs 16" or 24" o.c.
3. 3/8"* or 1/2" 3 ply plywood, face grain perpendicular to studs 24" o.c.; or with face grain either parallel or perpendicular to studs 16" o.c.
4. 5/16"* plywood, face grain perpendicular to studs 16" o.c.

*Check local building code.

PLYWOOD SIDING OVER SHEATHING.

Plywood siding grade and thickness recommendations given here are for all species.

Install plywood panel siding vertically or horizontally leaving 1/16-inch space at all ends and edges. A good way to assure correct spacing between panels is to drive 4d galvanized finishing (0.072-inch shank) or casing (0.080-inch shank) nails into studs alongside and flush with shiplap joint. Two to three nails along the length of the panel will be sufficient. When adjacent panel is installed, approximate spacing of 1/16 inch is automatic. Siding joints may occur away from studs with approved nailable sheathing (see definition below Figure 1.) Use nonstaining box, siding or casing nails: 6d for panels 1/2 inch thick or less and 8d for thicker panels. Use next larger nail size when sheathing (other than plywood or lumber) is thicker than 1/2 inch. Space nails 6 inches apart along panel edges and 12 inches along intermediate supports.

Provide 6-inch minimum clearance between plywood and finish grade.

TABLE 3
Exterior Plywood Siding Over Nailable Plywood or Lumber Sheathing
For plywood siding over other types of sheathing, see Sturd-I-Wall recommendations.

Plywood Siding			Maximum Spacing (in.) of Vertical Rows of Nails		Nail Size (Use nonstaining box, siding or casing nails)	Nail Spacing (in.)	
	Description (All species groups)	Nominal Thickness (in.)	Face Grain Vertical	Face Grain Horizontal		Panel Edges	Intermediate
Panel Siding	MDO EXT-APA	11/32, 3/8	16	24	6d for panels 1/2" thick or less; 8d for thicker panels.	6	12
		1/2 & thicker	24	24			
	303-16 o.c. Siding EXT-APA	5/16 & thicker	16	24			
	303-24 o.c. Siding EXT-APA	7/16 & thicker	24	24			
Lap Siding	MDO EXT-APA	11/32, 3/8	—	24	6d for siding 3/8" thick or less; 8d for thicker siding.	4" @ vertical butt joints; 6" along bottom edge.	8" (if siding wider than 12".)
		1/2 & thicker	—	24			
	303-16 o.c. Siding EXT-APA	5/16, 11/32, 3/8	—	24			
	303-16 o.c. Siding EXT-APA 303-24 o.c. Siding EXT-APA	7/16 & thicker	—	24			

EXTERIOR PLYWOOD SOFFITS

With open soffit design, a nice finishing touch is the use of APA plywood siding, face down, for the bottom row of roof sheathing panels. This is especially effective when the siding pattern used for soffits ties in with that used for the exterior wall siding. Or where a design calls for closed soffits, an APA Exterior plywood can usually save time. It simplifies soffit construction and presents a smooth, attractive surface easy to paint or stain. In any soffit design, Exterior type plywood should be used wherever the underside of the roof deck or soffit is exposed to the weather.

Load-span capability (open soffits). The minimum recommendations given in Table 4A were developed assuming uniformly distributed loads. Except as noted, allowable loads are at least 40 psf live load, plus 5 psf dead load (weight of plywood plus finish roofing); 1-1/8-inch panels of Group 2, 3, or 4 support 35 psf live load.

Plywood should be continuous over two or more spans, face grain *across* supports. Under these conditions, the deflection under full live load will not exceed 1/240 of span. When using spans of 32 or 48 inches in open soffit construction, be sure to provide adequate blocking, tongue-and-groove edges, or other edge support such as Plyclips.

Special conditions, such as concentrated heavy loads, may require constructions in excess of these minimums but maximum spans should not be exceeded regardless of design live load.

Some special panels manufactured by APA member mills may have greater load-span capacities than the minimums listed here.

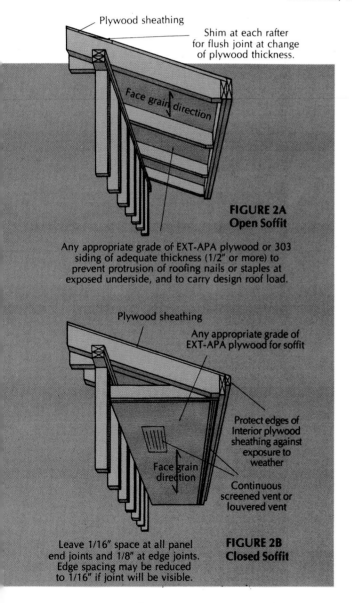

Plywood sheathing
Shim at each rafter for flush joint at change of plywood thickness.

Face grain direction

**FIGURE 2A
Open Soffit**

Any appropriate grade of EXT-APA plywood or 303 siding of adequate thickness (1/2" or more) to prevent protrusion of roofing nails or staples at exposed underside, and to carry design roof load.

Plywood sheathing

Any appropriate grade of EXT-APA plywood for soffit

Protect edges of interior plywood sheathing against exposure to weather

Face grain direction

Continuous screened vent or louvered vent

Leave 1/16" space at all panel end joints and 1/8" at edge joints. Edge spacing may be reduced to 1/16" if joint will be visible.

**FIGURE 2B
Closed Soffit**

TABLE 4A
Plywood for Open Soffit or for combined decking-ceiling
(Face grain across support)

Max. Span (inches)	Panel Description (Minimum Recommendations)	Species Group
16	7/16" APA 303 Siding	1, 2, 3, 4
	1/2" APA (c)	1, 2, 3, 4
24	1/2" APA (c)	1, 2, 3
	19/32" APA 303 Siding (including T1-11)	1
	5/8" APA 303 Siding (including T1-11)	1, 2, 3, 4
	5/8" APA (c)	1, 2, 3, 4
	3/4" APA 303 Siding	1, 2, 3, 4
32(a)	5/8" APA (c)	1
	3/4" APA 303 Siding	1
	3/4" APA (c)	1, 2, 3, 4
48(a)	1 1/8" APA Textured (b)	1, 2, 3, 4

(a) Provide adequate blocking, tongue-and-groove edges or other suitable edge supports such as Plyclips.
(b) 1 1/8" panels, of Group 2, 3 or 4 species will support 35 psf live load plus 5 psf dead load.
(c) Applies to sanded, touch-sanded and unsanded grades.

TABLE 4B
Plywood for Closed Soffit (Face grain across supports)

Nominal Plywood Thickness	Group	Maximum Span (inches), all edges supported
5/16" APA 303 Siding 3/8" APA (a)		24
7/16" APA 303 Siding 1/2" APA (a)	All Species Groups	32
19/32" or 5/8" APA 303 Siding 19/32" or 5/8" APA (a)		48

(a) Applies to sanded, touch-sanded and unsanded grades.

Plywood for Interiors

Installation. For closed soffits, use nonstaining box or casing nails: 6d for 5/16-inch, 3/8-inch and 7/16-inch panels and 8d for 5/8-inch panels. Space nails 6 inches at panel edges and 12 inches along intermediate supports.

For open soffits, use 6d common smooth, ring-shank or spiral-thread nails for plywood panels 1/2 inch thick or less; 8d for panels from 5/8 inch to 1 inch thick. Use 8d ring-shank or spiral-thread, or 10d common smooth-shank nails for 1-1/8-inch textured panels. Space nails 6 inches at panel edges and 12 inches along intermediate supports, except that where spans are 48 inches, space nails 6 inches at all supports.

APA grade-trademarked plywood siding helps create warm, luxurious interiors.

Accent panels or full wall paneling. Either way, an elegant touch . . . especially when tied in with the exterior siding design.

Whether part of the original design or applied as part of a remodeling/renovation project, APA plywood siding panels or Decorative or sanded panels are easy and quick to apply and offer a range of styles and textures to fit any decor.

Installation. Support spacing recommendations given here apply to all species groups.

Leave 1/32-inch space at panel ends and edges. Use casing or finishing nails. Size recommendations are given in the Fasteners table. Space nails at 6 inches o.c. along panel edges and 12 inches along intermediate supports.

TABLE 5.
Fasteners

Plywood Thickness (inch)	Nail size (casing or finishing)
1/4	4d
5/16	6d
3/8	6d
1/2	6d
5/8	8d
3/4	8d
Texture 1-11	8d

When using any of the grooved panelings, one may nail through grooves to the stud, where they line up.

TABLE 6
Interior Plywood Paneling Spans

Nominal Plywood Thickness (inch)	Maximum Support Spacing (inches)
1/4	16(a)
5/16	16(b)
3/8	24
1/2	24
5/8	24

(a) Can be 20 inches if face grain of paneling is across studs
(b) Can be 24 inches if face grain of paneling is across studs

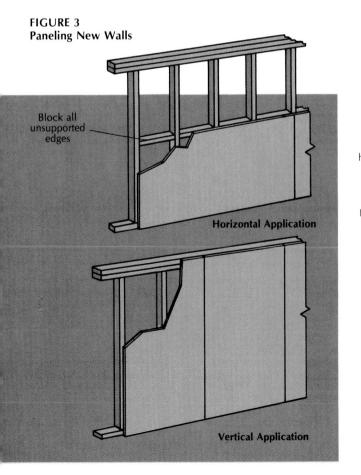

FIGURE 3
Paneling New Walls

Block all unsupported edges

Horizontal Application

Vertical Application

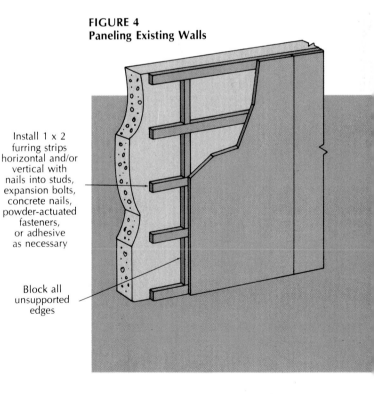

FIGURE 4
Paneling Existing Walls

Install 1 x 2 furring strips horizontal and/or vertical with nails into studs, expansion bolts, concrete nails, powder-actuated fasteners, or adhesive as necessary

Block all unsupported edges

APA Sturd-I-Wall Building System

Plywood combines the natural warmth and toughness of real wood with the engineered properties of a manufactured product. Cross-laminated design puts the along-the-grain strength properties of wood to work in two dimensions. It produces a siding panel recognized by the model codes and most local codes for use as a single-layer sheathing/siding material.

Utilizing APA grade-trademarked plywood siding, this building system is known as APA Sturd-I-Wall and is being enthusiastically adopted by quality builders all across the country. The system provides substantial cost savings while producing strong, handsome structures that sell easily

and deliver what the homebuyer wants: years of comfort, efficiency, low maintenance, and basic security against the elements. In short, pleasureful home living.

ENERGY CONSERVATION WITH APA STURD-I-WALL

Energy conservation is an important consideration to builder and buyer alike.

Using standard R-11 batt type insulation with typical Sturd-I-Wall construction gives a U-value of 0.08; the use of R-13 gives U=0.07. These

common assemblies satisfy, respectively, the HUD-MPS insulation requirements for one- and two-family and multi-family residential construction, and most other common codes and insulation requirements (see "Energy Saving Wall Systems," page 17).

APA STURD-I-WALL CONSTRUCTION

Siding grades and span recommendations given here apply to all species groups. Any plywood panel siding may be applied direct-to-studs according to the provisions of Table 7.

Install plywood siding panels vertically or horizontally leaving 1/16-inch space at all end and edge joints. A good way to assure correct spacing between panels is to drive 4d galvanized finishing (0.072-inch shank) or casing (0.080-inch shank) nails into studs alongside and flush with shiplap joint. Two to three nails along the length of the panel will be sufficient. When adjacent panel is installed, approximate spacing of 1/16 inch is automatic. APA 303 plywood siding bearing the designation *24 oc* may be applied vertically direct to studs 24 inches on center. Panels designated *16 oc* may be used vertically over studs spaced 16 inches on center. All panel siding shown in the table may be used direct to studs 16 or 24 inches on center when applied horizontally. All edges should be backed with framing or blocking but no corner bracing is required with plywood panel siding.

Use nonstaining, noncorrosive box, siding, or casing nails: 6d for plywood 1/2 inch thick or less and 8d for thicker panels. Nail spacing should be 6 inches at panel edges and 12 inches along intermediate supports.

When APA Sturd-I-Wall is used for multi-story buildings, horizontal joints may require more than the normally required end spacing to accommodate framing shrinkage, especially if green lumber joists are used.

Provide 6-inch minimum clearance between plywood and finish grade unless plywood has been pressure-preservative-treated.

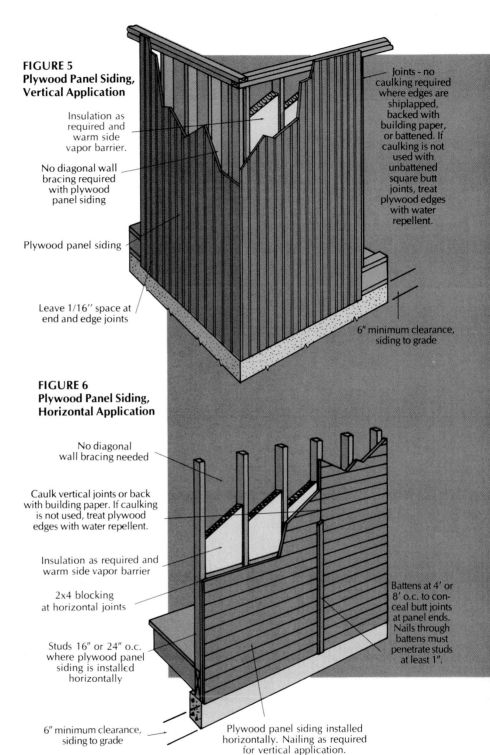

FIGURE 5
Plywood Panel Siding, Vertical Application

Insulation as required and warm side vapor barrier.

No diagonal wall bracing required with plywood panel siding

Plywood panel siding

Leave 1/16" space at end and edge joints

Joints - no caulking required where edges are shiplapped, backed with building paper, or battened. If caulking is not used with unbattened square butt joints, treat plywood edges with water repellent.

6" minimum clearance, siding to grade

FIGURE 6
Plywood Panel Siding, Horizontal Application

No diagonal wall bracing needed

Caulk vertical joints or back with building paper. If caulking is not used, treat plywood edges with water repellent.

Insulation as required and warm side vapor barrier

2x4 blocking at horizontal joints

Studs 16" or 24" o.c. where plywood panel siding is installed horizontally

6" minimum clearance, siding to grade

Plywood panel siding installed horizontally. Nailing as required for vertical application.

Battens at 4' or 8' o.c. to conceal butt joints at panel ends. Nails through battens must penetrate studs at least 1".

TABLE 7
APA Sturd-I-Wall Construction
Recommendations Also Apply Over Sheathing Other Than Plywood or Lumber.

Plywood Panel Siding Description (All species groups)	Nominal Thickness (in.)	Max. Stud Spacing (in.)		Nail Size (Use nonstaining box, siding or casing nails)	Nail Spacing (in.)	
		Face Grain Vertical	Face Grain Horizontal		Panel Edges	Intermediate
MDO EXT-APA	11/32 & 3/8	16	24	6d for panels 1/2" thick or less;		
	1/2 & thicker	24	24			
303-16 o.c. Siding EXT-APA	5/16 & thicker	16	24	8d for thicker panels.*	6	12
303-24 o.c. Siding EXT-APA	7/16 & thicker	24	24			

*If applied over sheathing thicker than 1/2 inch, use next regular nail size

11

Plywood Wall Sheathing

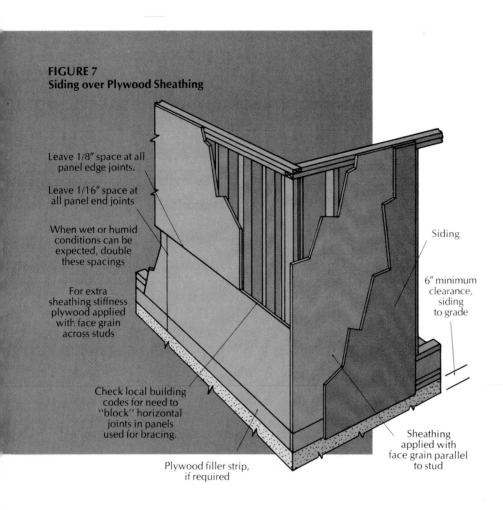

FIGURE 7
Siding over Plywood Sheathing

Leave 1/8" space at all panel edge joints.

Leave 1/16" space at all panel end joints

When wet or humid conditions can be expected, double these spacings

For extra sheathing stiffness plywood applied with face grain across studs

Check local building codes for need to "block" horizontal joints in panels used for bracing.

Plywood filler strip, if required

Siding

6" minimum clearance, siding to grade

Sheathing applied with face grain parallel to stud

Plywood wall sheathing covers large areas rapidly and gives tremendous strength and rigidity to the structures it encloses.

Panels may be installed either vertically or horizontally, although horizontal application is recommended when sidings such as shingles are to be nailed directly to the sheathing. In general, horizontal application delivers greater stiffness under loads perpendicular to the surface; vertical application provides greater racking resistance. (Racking resistance with horizontal application is equal to that of vertical application if horizontal joints are blocked.)

With plywood sheathing, let-in corner bracing and diagonal wall bracing can be omitted because the plywood itself delivers ample resistance to racking in low- and medium-rise buildings. And no building paper is required with plywood sheathing.

Installation. Plywood recommendations for specific stud spacings given here assume panels continuous over two or more spans.

Use common smooth, annular, or spiral-thread nails, or use galvanized box nails, or T-nails of the same diameter as common nails (e.g. 8d box nail diameter equals 6d common — 0.113 inch). For 5/16-inch, 3/8-inch, or 1/2-inch plywood sheathing, use 6d nails spaced 6 inches along panel edges and 12 inches along intermediate supports. Staples may be used, but with closer spacing (see Table 8B). Note: engineered shear walls may require closer fastener spacing (see under **"Plywood Shear Walls"**, page 14.)

TABLE 8A
Plywood Wall Sheathing (a) (b)
(Plywood continuous over 2 or more spans)

Panel Identification Index	Panel Thickness (inch) & Construction	Maximum Stud Spacing (inches) Exterior Covering Nailed to:		Nail Size (c)	Nail Spacing (inches) (c)	
		Stud	Sheathing		Panel Edges (when over framing)	Intermediate (each stud)
12/0, 16/0, 20/0	5/16	16	16(d)	6d	6	12
16/0, 20/0, 24/0, 32/16	3/8 & 1/2 3 ply	24	16 24(d)	6d	6	12
24/0, 32/16	1/2 4 & 5 ply	24	24	6d	6	12

(a) When plywood sheathing is used, building paper and diagonal wall bracing can be omitted.
(b) In dry conditions space panel edges ⅛", panel ends 1/16". In wet or humid conditions double spacing.
(c) Common smooth, annular, spiral-thread, or galvanized box, or T-nails of the same diameter as common nails (0.113" dia. for 6d) may be used. Staples also permitted at reduced spacing. See Table 8B.
(d) Apply plywood with face grain across studs.

TABLE 8B
Recommended Minimum Stapling Schedule for Plywood
Wall Sheathing (Without Diagonal Bracing)

Plywood Thickness (inch)	Staple Leg Length (inches)	Spacing Around Entire Perimeter of Sheet (inches)	Spacing at Intermediate Members (inches)
5/16	1-1/4	4	8
3/8	1-3/8	4	8
1/2	1-1/2	4	8

PLYWOOD SHEATHING FOR CORNER BRACING.

When fiberboard sheathing is used, plywood corner panels of the same thickness can eliminate costly let-in bracing. Plywood's superior racking resistance delivers the needed strength.

When 1/2-inch corner bracing panels are used, they do the job if nailed with the same size and spacing of nails used for the fiberboard (1-1/2-inch galvanized roofing nails at 4 inches around panel edges and 8 inches over intermediate studs, or equivalent).

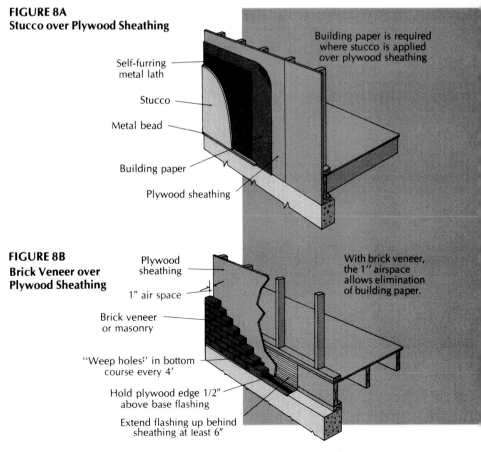

FIGURE 8A
Stucco over Plywood Sheathing

Self-furring metal lath

Stucco

Metal bead

Building paper

Plywood sheathing

Building paper is required where stucco is applied over plywood sheathing

FIGURE 8B
Brick Veneer over Plywood Sheathing

Plywood sheathing

1" air space

Brick veneer or masonry

"Weep holes" in bottom course every 4'

Hold plywood edge 1/2" above base flashing

Extend flashing up behind sheathing at least 6"

With brick veneer, the 1" airspace allows elimination of building paper.

13

Plywood Shear Walls

Plywood's tremendous racking resistance and excellent nailing characteristics make it ideal for structures that require engineered shear walls to transmit lateral loads. Either plywood sheathing or siding can be used in shear wall design. The data presented here give maximum shears for walls with plywood sheathing, plywood siding installed direct to studs (APA Sturd-I-Wall), and for plywood applied over gypsumboard in fire-rated walls.

Typical layout for shear walls

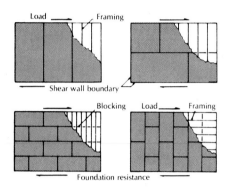

To design a shear wall, follow these steps.

1. Determine the unit shear transferred by the roof diaphragm to the wall. This generally will be one-fourth the area of the adjacent wall, multiplied by the wind load, divided by the length of the shear wall being designed (subtract length of large doors).
2. Determine the required nailing schedule from Table 9. Check anchor bolts in sill plate for shear.
3. Check wall framing on each end of shear wall and design foundation anchor if required (see example, this section).

For additional information on plywood shear wall or diaphragm design, see **Plywood Diaphragm Construction**, U310, published by the American Plywood Association, or contact your regional APA field office or the Technical Services Division of the Association in Tacoma, Washington.

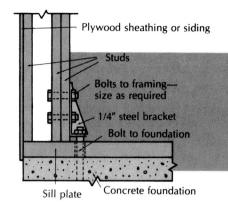

FIGURE 9
Shear Wall Foundation Anchor

High shear-wall overturning moments may be transferred by a fabricated steel bracket such as this. Regular foundation bolts are all that is required in many cases. Additional strength is furnished by the corner plywood panel acting as a nailed gusset plate.

TABLE 9
Recommended Shear in Pounds Per Foot for Plywood Shear Walls with Framing of Douglas Fir, Larch, or Southern Pine (a,b)
Wind or Seismic Loading

Plywood Grade	Minimum Nominal Plywood Thickness (in.)	Minimum Nail Penetration in Framing (in.)	Plywood Applied Direct to Framing					Plywood Applied Over 1/2" Gypsum Sheathing				
			Nail Size (common or galvanized box)	Nail Spacing at Plywood Panel Edges (in.)				Nail Size (common or galvanized box)	Nail Spacing at Plywood Panel Edges (in.)			
				6	4	2½	2		6	4	2½	2
STRUCTURAL I C-D INT-APA, or STRUCTURAL I C-C EXT-APA	5/16 or 1/4(c)	1-1/4	6d	200	300	450	510	8d	200	300	450	510
	3/8	1-1/2	8d	230(d)	360(d)	530(d)	610(d)	10d	280	430	640(e)	730(e)
	1/2	1-5/8	10d	340	510	770(e)	870(e)	—	—	—	—	—
C-D INT-APA C-C EXT-APA STRUCTURAL II C-D INT-APA STRUCTURAL II C-C EXT-APA APA panel siding (f) and other APA grades except species Group 5.	5/16 or 1/4(c)	1-1/4	6d	180	270	400	450	8d	180	270	400	450
	3/8	1-1/2	8d	220(d)	320(d)	470(d)	530(d)	10d	260	380	570(e)	640(e)
	1/2	1-5/8	10d	310	460	690(e)	770(e)	—	—	—	—	—
APA panel siding (f) except Species Group 5	5/16(c)	1-1/4	Nail Size (galvanized casing) 6d	140	210	320	360	Nail Size (galvanized casing) 8d	140	210	320	360
	3/8	1-1/2	8d	130(d)	200(d)	300(d)	340(d)	10d	160	240	360	410

(a) For framing of other species: (1) Find species group of lumber in the NFPA Nat'l Design Spec. (2) (a) For common or galvanized box nails, find shear value from table for nail size, and for STRUCTURAL I plywood (regardless of actual grade). (b) For galvanized casing nails, take shear value directly from table. (3) Multiply this value by 0.82 for Lumber Group III or 0.65 for Lumber Group IV.

(b) All panel edges backed with 2-inch nominal or wider framing. Plywood installed either horizontally or vertically. Space nails 6" o.c. along intermediate members for 3/8" plywood with face grain parallel to studs spaced 24" o.c. For other conditions and plywood thicknesses, space nails 12" o.c. on intermediate supports.

(c) 3/8" or 303-16 o.c. is minimum recommended when applied direct to framing as exterior siding.

(d) Shears may be increased 20% provided (1) studs are spaced a maximum of 16" o.c., or (2) plywood is applied with face grain across studs, or (3) plywood is 1/2" or greater in thickness.

(e) Reduce tabulated shears 10% when boundary members provide less than 3-inch nominal nailing surface.

(f) 303-16 o.c. plywood may be 5/16", 3/8" or thicker. Thickness at point of nailing on panel edges governs shear values.

Special Plywood Wall Systems

Plywood is well known for its many attributes and advantages in the design and construction of major wall systems. But its problem solving capabilities certainly don't end there. Plywood is an integral part of the All-Weather Wood Foundation system; it is used to build structurally glued stressed-skin wall panels as well as lumber and plywood box beams. And it can be used over metal wall framing systems.

ENGINEERED 24-INCH FRAMING

Engineered 24 is another money-saving, quality building system. One that makes good sense and offers such advantages that it has made staunch advocates of the many builders and contractors who are now using it. And the word is spreading.

The concept underlying this practical and sensible system is the 24-inch framing module. Floor, wall, and roof framing all set 24 inches on center—structurally, a series of in-line frames using lumber and plywood to best advantage.

Either siding-over-sheathing construction or APA Sturd-I-Wall can be used with the Engineered 24 system.

The 24-inch wood framing module provides for efficient utilization of materials and simpler, more rapid construction procedures. For more information on the Engineered 24 system contact the American Plywood Association in Tacoma, Washington, or contact any field office, for a copy of **Engineered 24" Framing and Plywood: A Building System**, Form B420.

ALL-WEATHER WOOD FOUNDATION WALLS

The All-Weather Wood Foundation. Innovative. Sensible. A truly significant development in foundation system design. It costs less to build, installation is fast (as little as two to three hours on a prepared site), and it's easier to finish inside.

A smart choice in any location, its advantages are a special bonus in climates where foundation work normally stops in freezing or rainy weather. Or in areas where masonry or concrete is in short supply or high in cost. The AWWF can be constructed nearly anywhere, under all but the most severe weather conditions. Hence no expensive schedule delays for seasonal weather or waiting for concrete delivery.

Approved for HUD mortgage insurance programs, the AWWF has been accepted by the major model building code agencies, is rapidly gaining acceptance in state and local building codes and has wide acceptance by lending institutions and private insurers of mortgage loans.

Basically a conventional frame construction, the AWWF is a very practical construction approach. All parts of the supporting structure for the building are included in the foundation system. It's applicable to all types of low-rise, light-frame construction, including nonresidential buildings.

For complete design and construction information on the AWWF system, see the following APA publications.

The All-Weather Wood Foundation: Why, What and How, Form A400.

AWWF: A Builder's Checklist, Form B405

PLYWOOD OVER METAL FRAMING

Plywood is compatible with metal framing systems. Modern mechanical and adhesive fastening methods make plywood application to metal framing easy, whether used for wall sheathing, siding, or interior paneling. Some reasons for plywood's increasing use with metal framing systems are:

- ☐ **Workability** - plywood is easy to work, using conventional tools and labor.
- ☐ **Availability** - plywood is readily available in every area of the country.
- ☐ **Shear values** - plywood develops high shear values for shear walls and diaphragms.
- ☐ **Fire ratings** - FRT (Fire-Retardant-Treated) plywood usually has the same or better insurance rating as unprotected metal siding or decking.
- ☐ **Insulation properties** - eliminates vapor condensation properties associated with metal and concrete surfaces.
- ☐ **Lightweight** - plywood is amazingly lightweight in relation to its strength properties.

For more complete information see APA's **Plywood Over Metal Framing**, Form A330.

PLYWOOD-AND-LUMBER BOX BEAMS AND HEADERS

APA grade-trademarked plywood-and-lumber box beams are an excellent solution where roof load or span requirements are too great for commonly available dimension lumber or timbers. An inexpensive alternative to steel or glulam wood beams, plywood-and-lumber beams offer several advantages.

☐ excellent stiffness and strength properties
☐ lightweight
☐ no shrinkage, warping, or twisting
☐ materials readily available
☐ fast and easy to fabricate
☐ quick and simple to install

Many builders familiar with nailed plywood-and-lumber beams are using them in place of solid-sawn wood lintels. They offer all the advantages above plus they fabricate to residential wall thicknesses and they're easy to insulate.

For design and fabrication information on plywood-and-lumber box beams and headers see the following APA publications.

Nailed Plywood & Lumber Beams, Form Z416
Nailed Plywood & Lumber Lintels, Tech Note A409
Fabrication of Plywood-Lumber Beams, Form V335
Plywood Design Specification, Form Y510
Plywood Design Specification, Supplement 2: Design of Plywood Beams, Form S812

STRESSED-SKIN WALL PANELS

Structurally glued stressed-skin plywood and lumber wall panels are an efficient and effective solution for walls which must bear heavy lateral or vertical loads. Flat panels with plywood skins rigidly glued to spaced lumber stringers act like a series of built up I-beams. The plywood skins take most of the bending stresses as well as performing as sheathing, while the lumber stringers take shear stresses. Suitable for large commercial wall sections or residential construction, prefabricated and insulated stressed-skin plywood panels close in buildings fast—at minimum cost for structural properties delivered.

To function properly it is critical that stressed-skin panels be properly designed and fabricated to assure a continuous, rigid glue bond between plywood and lumber. For design and fabrication information on stressed-skin panels see the following APA publications.

Plywood Design Specification, Form Y510
Plywood Design Specification, Supplement 3: Design of Plywood Stressed-Skin Panels, Form U813
Fabrication of Plywood Stressed-Skin Panels, Form V340

PLYWOOD SANDWICH PANELS

The plywood sandwich panel offers the stiffness and load handling capability of a stressed-skin panel, plus light weight, high insulation values for relatively small thicknesses, and fast, panelized construction.

Panels are shop prefabricated by sandwiching an insulating core material such as polystyrene or polyurethane foam, or a paper honeycomb, between skins of plywood. The process is done in such a way that a structural bond is formed between the core and the skins. Bonds are made through the use of full structural glues or, in the case of some of the foam materials, through direct adhesion of foam to the faces.

With attractive APA plywood siding for the outside skins, plywood sandwich panels make good looking, energy conserving single and multi-family dwellings . . . as well as office complexes, bank branches, supermarkets, jiffy markets, schools, gymnasiums . . .

For design and fabrication information on plywood sandwich panels see the following APA publications.

Plywood Design Specification, Form Y510
Plywood Design Specification, Supplement 4: Design of Plywood Sandwich Panels, Form U814
Fabrication of Plywood Sandwich Panels, Form V309

Energy Efficiency, Fire Ratings and Noise Control

In today's marketplace, builder and designer alike must deal with the important factors of energy conservation, fire ratings, and noise control. Consumers, and in many cases codes, are requiring structures which are more energy efficient, safer, and which give a greater sense of privacy and security.

Numerous plywood wall designs dealing effectively with such problems are in common use.

ENERGY-SAVING WALL SYSTEMS

Energy conservation is a key consideration in today's building design and construction. In hot or cold weather, high resistance to heat flow means less fuel is consumed to maintain a comfortable living environment.

That's why a plywood wall system makes sense. In the first place, large plywood panels, themselves natural insulators, significantly reduce air infiltration—a major cause of heat loss. Add the fact that the plywood-and-wood frame wall is fast and easy to insulate, using conventional insulation materials, and you have a high quality, cost **and** energy-effective wall system—one which meets or exceeds HUD-MPS and most other prevailing insulation requirements in the country.

FIRE-RATED PLYWOOD WALL SYSTEMS

Most of us realize today that there is no such thing as **fireproof** construction. Rather, building systems are rated relative to how **firesafe** they are. Ratings are given on the basis of major safety criteria such as flame spread and fire resistance.

In many cases, ordinary wood-framed plywood construction provides ample fire safety and is completely acceptable. When unusual circumstances require additional protection, the designer's options include **protected** construction and **treated** construction. Check with local authorities for specific requirements in your area.

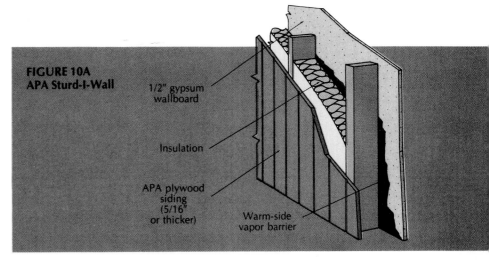

FIGURE 10A APA Sturd-I-Wall
1/2" gypsum wallboard
Insulation
APA plywood siding (5/16" or thicker)
Warm-side vapor barrier

APA Sturd-I-Wall—R11

Meets or exceeds HUD-MPS insulation requirements for one-and two-family dwellings, all regions.

		Resistance*
Outside air	=	0.17
5/16" plywood	=	0.39
R11 insulation	=	11.00
1/2" gypsum wallboard	=	0.45
Inside air	=	0.68
	R =	12.69
	U = 1/R =	0.08

*R values from ASHRAE Guide. Actual thickness and species groups affect plywood insulation values.

APA Sturd-I-Wall—R13

Meets or exceeds HUD-MPS insulation requirements for one- and two-family dwellings and multi-family construction, all regions.

		Resistance*
Outside air	=	0.17
5/16" plywood	=	0.39
R13 insulation	=	13.00
1/2" gypsum wallboard	=	0.45
Inside air	=	0.68
	R =	14.69
	U = 1/R =	0.07

*R values from ASHRAE Guide. Actual thickness and special groups affect plywood insulation values.

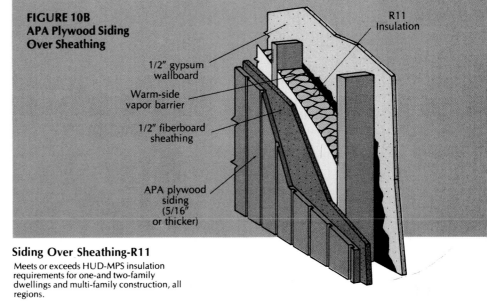

FIGURE 10B APA Plywood Siding Over Sheathing
R11 Insulation
1/2" gypsum wallboard
Warm-side vapor barrier
1/2" fiberboard sheathing
APA plywood siding (5/16" or thicker)

Siding Over Sheathing-R11

Meets or exceeds HUD-MPS insulation requirements for one-and two-family dwellings and multi-family construction, all regions.

		Resistance*
Outside air	=	0.17
5/16" plywood	=	0.39
1/2" fiberboard sheathing	=	1.32
R11 insulation	=	11.00
1/2" gypsum wallboard	=	0.45
Inside air	=	0.68
	R =	14.01
	U = 1/R =	0.07

*R. values from ASHRAE Guide. Actual thickness and species groups affect plywood insulation values.

FIGURE 11
Typical One-Hour
Exterior Wall Construction

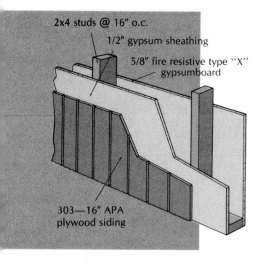

2x4 studs @ 16" o.c.

1/2" gypsum sheathing

5/8" fire resistive type "X" gypsumboard

303—16" APA plywood siding

Protected Walls. Wood and plywood exterior wall systems may earn improved ratings as protected walls. With gypsumboard interior finish and 1/2-inch gypsum sheathing, a one-hour rating can be achieved. See illustration. Note that addition of textured plywood to the exterior of a rated wall will add shear strength and improved appearance without impairing the fire rating.

Interior Walls and Partitions.
Generally accepted building code regulations place a flame spread index limit of 200 on materials used for interior surfaces (in areas other than certain exitways and corridors). Since softwood plywood's rating generally falls within Class III or 76-200, it is well within the range of acceptable materials.

Treated Walls. For special interior areas that do require lower flame spread ratings, fire-retardant-treated (FRT) plywood paneling is acceptable; such panels qualify for the Underwriters' Laboratory label, are capable of a Class I rating and are accepted by codes. Fire-retardant paints, properly applied, may also be used to reduce the flame spread rating to Class I or II and are often recognized by building officials. Certain plywood species and thicknesses may be used to meet Class II requirements without treatment. Contact the American Plywood Association for specific details.

For more complete information on fire ratings see the APA publication **Plywood Construction for Fire Protection**, Form W305.

PLYWOOD WALL SYSTEMS FOR NOISE CONTROL

An increasingly important aspect of building design and construction is the control of unwanted noise. There are two important types of noise for which indexes of control have been established: airborne noise and impact noise.

Airborne noises generated by traffic, voices, television, stereo equipment, etc., penetrate through walls, ceilings, doors and other structural elements. The index of control for airborne noise is the Sound Transmission Rating (STC). STC ratings are given for both wall assemblies and floor- or roof-ceiling assemblies.

Impact sounds are produced by falling objects, footfalls . . . mechanical impacts. These come mainly through floor-ceiling assemblies. The index of control for impact noise is the Impact Insulation Class (IIC).

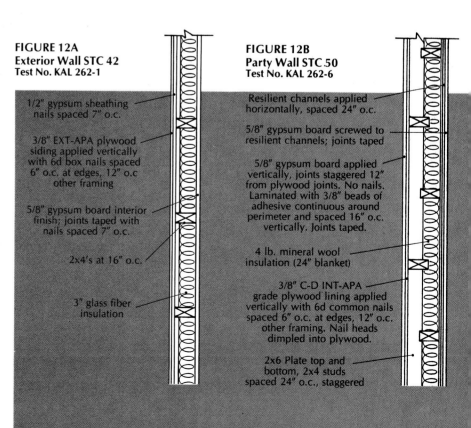

FIGURE 12A
Exterior Wall STC 42
Test No. KAL 262-1

1/2" gypsum sheathing nails spaced 7" o.c.

3/8" EXT-APA plywood siding applied vertically with 6d box nails spaced 6" o.c. at edges, 12" o.c. other framing

5/8" gypsum board interior finish; joints taped with nails spaced 7" o.c.

2x4's at 16" o.c.

3" glass fiber insulation

FIGURE 12B
Party Wall STC 50
Test No. KAL 262-6

Resilient channels applied horizontally, spaced 24" o.c.

5/8" gypsum board screwed to resilient channels; joints taped

5/8" gypsum board applied vertically, joints staggered 12" from plywood joints. No nails. Laminated with 3/8" beads of adhesive continuous around perimeter and spaced 16" o.c. vertically. Joints taped.

4 lb. mineral wool insulation (24" blanket)

3/8" C-D INT-APA grade plywood lining applied vertically with 6d common nails spaced 6" o.c. at edges, 12" o.c. other framing. Nail heads dimpled into plywood.

2x6 Plate top and bottom, 2x4 studs spaced 24" o.c., staggered

Additional Information

For additional information on the use of plywood in walls and wall system designs, contact the American Plywood Association, 1119 A Street, PO Box 2277, Tacoma, Washington 98401, or the nearest APA field office. Single copies of all publications referred to in each section of this book or those listed below are available without charge. Simply write, listing titles and form numbers of publications desired.

Plywood Residential Construction Guide, Y405.
Plywood Commercial/Industrial Construction Guide, Y300.
Joint Details for Exterior Plywood Wall Systems, X330.
Plywood Siding Portfolio, A350.
Plywood for Paneling and Siding, Y345.
Plywood: Its Handling, Storage and Installation, Y880.

APA: THE MARK OF QUALITY

The American Plywood Association's grade-trademarks are used by qualified member mills to identify plywood that has been manufactured to meet the requirements of **U.S. Product Standard PS 1-74 for Construction and Industrial Plywood**. Mills who use the APA marks must participate in the Association's quality inspection and testing program—a program designed to help member manufacturers verify that they are maintaining satisfactory quality.

But the American Plywood Association's services go far beyond testing and inspection. The Association's ongoing programs of research and promotion play important roles in developing and maintaining quality products and in helping users to understand and correctly apply plywood products and systems.

Information covered in this and all APA publications is based upon the use of plywood of known quality. Always insist on plywood bearing the mark of quality—the APA grade-trademark.

The STC rates a structural assembly's ability to reduce airborne noise. Most authorities agree that interior walls in multi-occupancy construction should have an STC rating of at least 45; 50 is considered premium construction.

The illustrations shown here give two examples of plywood wall systems which have been tested for STC ratings. The party wall achieves an STC rating of 50. The exterior wall rating of 42 is generally considered adequate in residential neighborhoods where moderate traffic noise is likely.

Plywood systems to help control noise are detailed more fully in the APA publication, **Plywood Construction for Noise Control**, Form W460.

FINISHING PLYWOOD

For detailed recommendations on finishing and refinishing plywood, see the APA publication, **Stains and Paints On Plywood**, Form B407.

SPECIFICATION GUIDE

Each panel of construction plywood shall meet the requirements of the latest edition of U.S. Product Standard PS 1, and shall be identified with the appropriate grade-trademark of the American Plywood Association. All plywood which has any edge or surface permanently exposed to the weather or moisture conditions shall be Exterior type.*

Panel thickness, grade, and Group or Identification Index shall be equal to or better than that shown on the drawings. Application shall be in accordance with recommendations of the American Plywood Association.

*An exception may be made in the case of plywood used for the All-Weather Wood Foundation, which may be Interior type with exterior glue provided it is pressure-preservative-treated in accordance with the American Wood Preservers Bureau AWPB-FDN Standard.

Our field representatives can help. For additional assistance in specifying plywood, get in touch with your nearest American Plywood Association field service representative. Call or write:

ATLANTA
Paul D. Colbenson
P. O. Box 90550
Atlanta, Georgia 30364
(404) 762-6649

CHICAGO
Vernon D. Haskell
120 East Ogden Avenue
Room 204
Hinsdale, Illinois 60521
(312) 323-5787

DALLAS
A. M. Leggett
10010 Miller Road
Suite 105
Dallas, Texas 75238
(214) 348-0643

LOS ANGELES
Long Beach, California
(213) 439-8616

NEW YORK
Englewood Cliffs, New Jersey
(201) 567-7238

SAN FRANCISCO
Philip L. Benfield
P. O. Box 3536
Fremont, California 94538
(415) 657-5959

WASHINGTON, D.C.
Paul G. Nystrom
4121 Chatelain Road
Room 203
Annandale, Virginia 22003
(703) 750-3993

The plywood use recommendations contained in this brochure are based on the American Plywood Association's continuing program of laboratory testing, product research and comprehensive field experience. However, quality of workmanship and the conditions under which plywood is used vary widely. Because the Association has no control over these elements, it cannot accept responsibility for plywood performance or designs as actually constructed.

Plywood cuts costs. Not quality.

AMERICAN PLYWOOD ASSOCIATION

P. O. Box 2277 / Tacoma, WA 98401

Form No. C30

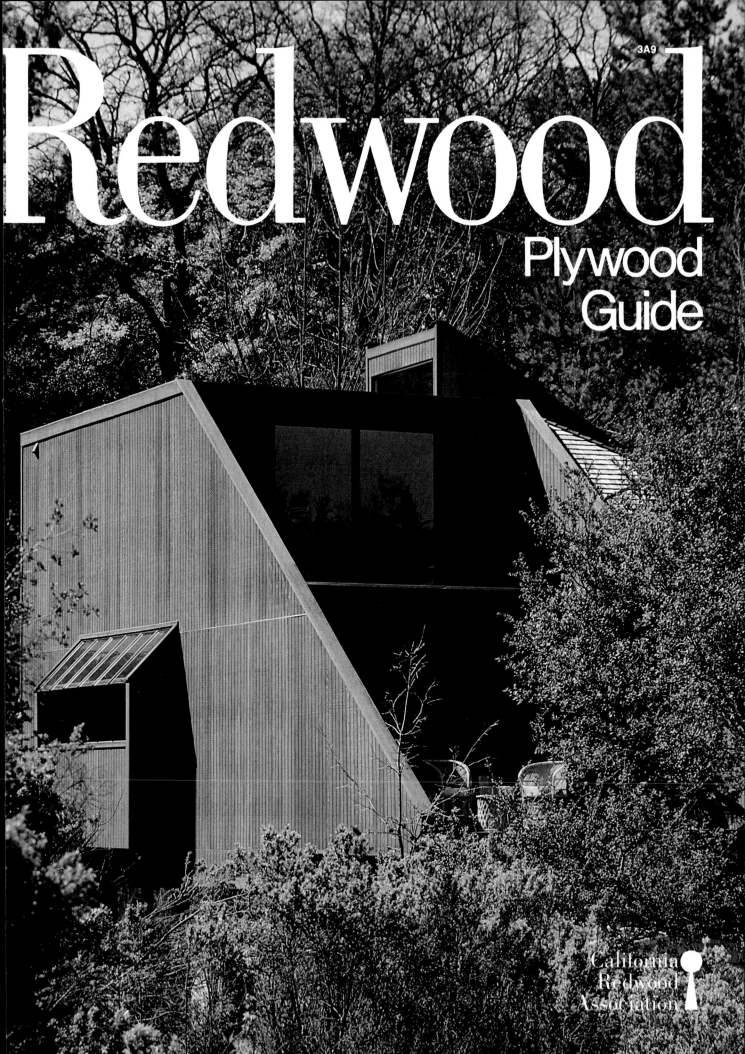

Redwood

Plywood
Guide

3A9

California
Redwood
Association

CRA quality redwood plywood offers all the practical construction efficiencies of plywood combined with the unique physical and aesthetic appeals of redwood.

Redwood is recognized for its natural beauty, durability, dimensional stability, insulating qualities, and ease of finishing. Where panel products are desired, no other species can equal redwood plywood in terms of universal sales appeal and utilitarian advantages.

It is available with clear heartwood face veneers, or face veneers containing sapwood. The heartwood veneers contain natural extractives that are repellent to insects and decay organisms. Assuring the ultimate in dimensional stability, redwood plywood stays in place and keeps its shape. Its abilities to resist the erosive effects of weathering, and to take and hold a wide variety of finishes, are unexcelled.

Redwood plywood may be used for either exterior or interior applications because it is manufactured with waterproof glue. In addition, all standard orders of saw-textured redwood plywood are finished at the mills with water repellent preservative.

Redwood Plywood Texture and Grades

Redwood plywood is manufactured with a saw-textured surface, which yields delicate shadow effects and is suitable for all exterior and interior uses.

Saw-textured plywood* is manufactured in two appearance grades:

The top grade, with a clear, all heartwood face veneer, is identified by the proprietary grade names *"Premium Ruf-Sawn"*[1] and *"Clear Heart Saw-Textured."*[2]

The other grade, with a redwood face veneer which may contain sapwood, is identified by the proprietary grade names *"Custom Ruf-Sawn"*[1] and *"Select Saw-Textured."*[2]*

Note: Redwood plywood produced by CRA member mills meets or exceeds standards set by the American Plywood Association for 303 siding face grades.

Panel Characteristics

Heartwood face veneers are reasonably color matched when of more than one piece in a panel, and have the following characteristics: Knots and knotholes are not allowed. Pin knots allowed up to 3/8 inch. No open splits. Router or sled patches only allowed, reasonably matched for grain and color and limited to edges and ends, except occasional patch allowed in panel face. Shims, reasonably color matched, allowed. Approved synthetic repairs may be used in lieu of wood repairs providing their durability is equal to or exceeds that of wood repairs. This top quality redwood plywood product is factory-coated with a special water repellent.

Sapwood-containing face veneers have the following characteristics: Knots and knotholes not allowed. Synthetic-filled knotholes allowed. Pin knots allowed up to 3/8 inch. No open splits. Router or sled patches only allowed. Wood or synthetic shims allowed. This redwood product is factory-coated with a special water repellent.

Material Composition

CRA quality redwood plywood is classed as Group 3 in accordance with U.S. Product Standard PS 1.

Sizes. Available thicknesses are 3/8 inch and 5/8 inch. Width of grooved panels is 48-3/8 inches, shiplapped on long edges to give a 48-inch face. Ungrooved panels are 48 inches wide and edges are not ship-lapped. All are available in lengths of 8, 9, and 10 feet.

Number of plies. 3/8 inch: 3 plies; 5/8 inch: 5 plies.

Veneer. Face veneers are clear heart redwood or may contain sapwood, depending on the grade (see *Texture and Grades*

section above). Backs are redwood which may contain sapwood in any amount.

Inner plies. Cross banding: redwood or other species at mill option.

Center ply of Inverted Batten: solid redwood in 5-ply panels.

Center ply of other 5-ply grooved panels is redwood.

Type of glue. CRA quality redwood plywood is manufactured with fully waterproof exterior glue.

Method of cutting. Redwood veneer for plywood is obtained by rotary cutting.

Exterior and Interior Uses

Siding. Redwood plywood has gained wide acceptance as a siding in residential and commercial construction—especially where a natural wood appearance is desired for maximum beauty and minimum maintenance.

Panels can be applied directly to studs, thus serving the dual purpose of sheathing and siding. (See *Application,* page 6.)

Because of plywood's ability to prevent racking when properly nailed, diagonal bracing is not required when redwood plywood is applied to one 8-foot section or three 4-foot sections in each wall. Another important labor-saving, material-saving benefit is that building paper is not required with the installation of redwood plywood.

(continued on page 6)

Opposite page

Top left: Art gallery in Minnesota college uses ceiling accents of rough-sawn Clear All Heart redwood plywood grooved 4″ o.c.

Center left: Distinctive beauty of redwood plywood supplements the sleek lines of this contemporary California home design.

Bottom left: Living room accent wall is sapwood-streaked redwood plywood.

Bottom right: Warm natural beauty and texture of redwood plywood with a resawn surface adorns this Massachusetts medical building.

Large photo, top: Dramatic exterior of redwood plywood grooved 8″ o.c.

This page

Top right: Scenic settings benefit from the rustic look of natural redwood plywood.

Center left: Outdoor feeling of landscape architects' offices is interpreted with saw-textured redwood plywood grooved 4″ o.c.

Center right: Distinctive wide redwood plywood soffit on a Minnesota home.

Bottom left: Home on a small site uses natural redwood plywood with contrasting trim.

Other exterior uses. Redwood plywood serves superbly for such applications as garage doors, carport walls, shear walls, ceilings and storage areas, soffits, garden shelters, garden work centers, accent walls, patio dividers, fences and other outdoor structures. For recommended shear values in redwood plywood shear wall construction, refer to American Plywood Association's *Plywood for Walls* insert in Wood Book.

Paneling. Redwood plywood as an interior paneling material is increasing in popularity among architects and interior designers seeking large panels with interesting grains and textures. It offers a third-dimensional surface character unavailable in thin hardwood veneers and manufactured substitutes.

Technical Data

Flame spread. Fire hazard classification tests conducted by Underwriters' Laboratories, Inc., have established a flame-spread rating of 75 for $5/8$-inch untreated redwood plywood, and 95 for $3/8$-inch untreated redwood plywood. These tests qualify the $5/8$-inch material as Class II under the Uniform Building Code and the Basic Building Code, and as Group I under the Southern Standard Building Code and the National Building Code. The $3/8$-inch material qualifies as Class III and Group II respectively under the above two sets of codes.

Fire retardant treatment. Redwood plywood treated with fire retardant qualifies as Class I (0-25) under the above mentioned codes. Only exterior type fire retardant treatments are recommended.

Insulation value. Redwood k=0.83; R ($3/8$")=0.45; R ($5/8$")=0.75.

Acceptances

HUD/FHA and building codes requirements. CRA quality redwood plywood complies with the requirements of the HUD/FHA Minimum Property Standards and UM-64. It also is accepted by all major building codes for application directly to the studs as well as over sheathing. These codes include the Uniform Building Code, the Basic Building Code, and the Southern Standard Building Code.

Standards. Redwood plywood manufactured by CRA member mills conforms to U.S. Product Standard PS 1 and the American Plywood Association's "303 Siding Specifications" when the panels bear the APA's 303 SIDING grade trademark. The face veneers of redwood plywood are exceptionally free of noticeable repairs, knots, and knotholes permitted under the above standards.

Application

When the redwood plywood arrives on the job, it should be placed under cover and off the ground. Plywood stored outdoors and covered can pick up moisture from the ground or from surface water underneath, which can cause finish problems later. To prevent this, the plywood should be covered with a waterproof covering in such a way that air can circulate between panels, and between the covering and the panels.

Nailing. Three-eighths-inch plain or channel-grooved and all $5/8$-inch redwood plywood panels may be nailed directly to studs 16 inches on centers. Ungrooved $5/8$-inch thick panels, and other panels bearing the designation "303-24 o.c.," may be nailed vertically to studs 24 inches o.c. Panels bearing the designation "303-16 o.c." may be nailed horizontally to studs 24 inches o.c. when horizontal joints are blocked. When applied over sheathing (minimum $3/8$-inch thick), studs may be spaced 24 inches o.c. In this case, panel edges should have a solid backing of studs or blocking. Local building code authorities should be checked for local variations.

For exterior joints, at least $1/8$-inch of space should be left between plain panels and $1/16$-inch between grooved panels. If panels are not shiplapped, joints should be caulked or covered with battens. Inside and outside corners should be caulked.

On each exterior panel, nails should be placed at 12-inch intervals first to intermediate members then at 6-inch intervals at the perimeter where nails should be set in $3/8$ inch or more from the panel's edge.

For exterior applications, 6-penny siding nails are recommended for $3/8$-inch panels; 8-penny for $5/8$-inch panels applied directly to studs. Over sheathing use nails that penetrate studs at least 1 inch.

In all exterior applications nails should be driven flush—not set.

Use proper nails. Noncorrosive nails should be used where redwood will be exposed to moisture. Recommended noncorrosive nails are stainless steel, aluminum alloy, or top quality, *hot-dipped* galvanized. Beware of nails with a thin coating of zinc applied by electroplating, mechanical plating, tumbler galvanizing, or poorly controlled hot dipping. Such nails may lose their zinc coating when driven, and cause stain streaks.

For interior applications, use 4- or 6-penny casing or finishing nails that provide at least $3/4$ inch penetration into studs. Nails should be spaced at 8-inch intervals.

Redwood Plywood Profiles

Saw-textured plywood is available in the following standard sizes and patterns (all available in lengths of 8, 9, and 10 feet). All patterns are available in $3/8$-inch thickness on special order, with groove spacings as shown but grooves $1/16$-inch deep. Other special patterns are available on quantity orders. Panels are shiplapped on long edges only.

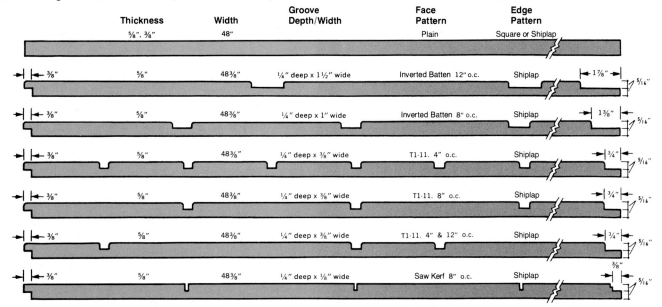

Thickness	Width	Groove Depth/Width	Face Pattern	Edge Pattern
$5/8$", $3/8$"	48"		Plain	Square or Shiplap
$5/8$"	$48 3/8$"	$1/4$" deep x $1 1/2$" wide	Inverted Batten 12" o.c.	Shiplap
$5/8$"	$48 3/8$"	$1/4$" deep x 1" wide	Inverted Batten 8" o.c.	Shiplap
$5/8$"	$48 3/8$"	$1/4$" deep x $3/8$" wide	T1-11. 4" o.c.	Shiplap
$5/8$"	$48 3/8$"	$1/4$" deep x $3/8$" wide	T1-11. 8" o.c.	Shiplap
$5/8$"	$48 3/8$"	$1/4$" deep x $3/8$" wide	T1-11. 4" & 12" o.c.	Shiplap
$5/8$"	$48 3/8$"	$1/4$" deep x $1/8$" wide	Saw Kerf 8" o.c.	Shiplap

1. Plain, all heart.
2. Inverted Batten, grooved 8″ on centers, all heart.
3. Inverted Batten, grooved 12″ o.c., containing sapwood.
4. T1-11 grooving 8″ o.c., containing sapwood.
5. T1-11 grooving 8″ o.c., all heart.
6. Inverted Batten, grooved 12″ o.c., all heart.
7. T1-11 grooving 4″ o.c., all heart.
8. Plain, containing sapwood.

Finish Suggestions

Exterior Finishes

For ease of finishing and for maximum finish durability on exterior applications, the saw-textured surface of redwood plywood is both absorbent and mechanically retentive to finishes.

No finish. Without further finishing of the factory-applied water repellent treated product, the surface will slowly weather to a buckskin tan, then eventually to a tannish gray.

Water repellent. The buckskin tan color can be prolonged by an additional coat of water repellent applied six months to a year after exposure.

Bleaching oil. If a natural driftwood-gray appearance is desired, the normally slow weathering process can be speeded and made uniform by application of a quality bleaching oil. Quick and satisfactory bleach effect can be achieved by adding gray pigmented stain to the bleach or using a bleaching oil containing gray pigmentation. The saw-textured surface is especially receptive to the bleaching treatment.

Stains. There are two basic types of stains; the semitransparent penetrating type, and the heavy bodied type. The semitransparent stains readily penetrate the wood and provide enduring color without obscuring the visibility of the redwood grain. The heavily pigmented stains tend to conceal the grain, but the saw-textured surface remains distinct.

Paints. If paint is used on redwood plywood, as with any redwood, an oil-based primer should be applied before the finish coat to prevent the possibility of extractive bleeding. Top coats, however, should be latex paint.

Low-luster alkyd top coats are not recommended for redwood since they absorb water readily and can lead to painting problems. Shake-and-shingle paints, either oil or alkyd, are not recommended for application on redwood.

Varnishes. The use of varnish or any clear, film-forming finish for exterior applications is definitely not recommended by California Redwood Association. No varnish or film finish yet tested by CRA has withstood the long-range effects of weather erosion. Most begin to deteriorate within a short period and are extremely difficult to refinish.

Interior Finishes

Although designed primarily for exterior application, redwood plywood performs very well indoors. When redwood plywood is used in a closed interior space the plywood should be sealed with one or two coats of an alkyd-resin base penetrating sealer. The sealer finish will prevent vaporizing of the factory-applied water-repellent. In kitchens and bathrooms, two or more coats of sealer are recommended for easy cleaning.

Penetrating sealer can be applied either directly to the wood or over a coat of penetrating stain.

Sample Specification

Example: "Exterior redwood plywood panels shall be saw-textured using clear heartwood, selected face veneers; face pattern: inverted batten with grooves 12" on centers with shiplap edge pattern. Size: $5/8$"thick $\times 48 3/8$" wide $\times 9'$ long. Each panel shall be water repellent finished at the mill and be identified with the APA grade-trademark of the American Plywood Association, and shall meet the requirements of the U.S. Product Standard PS 1."

Related Literature

More information on redwood plywood application is available in the CRA publication *Redwood Plywood Living*. For information on the many uses of redwood lumber see CRA Data Sheet 3A4, *Redwood Exterior Guide*, and Data Sheet 3A7, *Redwood Interior Guide*. For information on uses of the garden grades of redwood, see CRA Data Sheet 3A5, *Redwood Landscape Guide*. These Data Sheets are in the Wood Book. Other design idea booklets are available by writing to the California Redwood Association.

Rustic multi-units of easy-care redwood plywood.

The CRA trademark is your assurance of quality. The California Redwood Association is a nonprofit organization maintained by the principal redwood producers. Its interests extend from the growth and protection of quality timber for the future and the best utilization of current forest crops, to research, and the dissemination of information on the use of redwood.

California
Redwood
Association

One Lombard Street
San Francisco, California 94111
Telephone: (415) 392-7880

Redwood Plywood Sales Offices

Simpson Timber Company
900 Fourth Avenue, Seattle, WA 98164
Telephone: (206) 292-5000

The Pacific Lumber Company
1111 Columbus Avenue, San Francisco, CA 94133
Telephone; (415) 771-4700

Miller Redwood Company
P.O. Box 247, Crescent City, CA 95531
Telephone: (707) 464-3144

Redwood—a renewable resource.

Redwood

Exterior
Guide

California
Redwood
Association

Cover
Resawn Clear All Heart 1 × 4 redwood lumber siding creates an unusual facade for this medical building.

This page
Top left: Strong accents of Clear grade redwood are a practical and beautiful part of the exterior of this savings and loan association.

Center left: Attractively sapwood-streaked Clear grade redwood adorns an architect's home near Cleveland, Ohio.

Bottom left: A warm Texas welcome in a wooded setting with the natural beauty of redwood.

Top right: California condominiums get added sales appeal with redwood.

Bottom right: Practically maintenance free, Clear All Heart redwood helps create a relaxed atmosphere at this California community center.

asting satisfaction is the natural result
when California redwood is specified for
exterior siding, trim, and millwork. This
remarkable and versatile wood gives
excellent service when it is exposed to the
severe conditions faced by building
exteriors.

Exterior uses require high stability, and no
other commercial softwood has a lower
volumetric shrinkage than redwood. When
properly kiln dried, redwood will resist
shrinking, cupping and checking, keeping
joints tight.

Redwood can be used on the exterior
without any finish at all and will weather
gracefully to a soft gray. The range of color
effects possible with finishes is virtually
unlimited. Natural finishes, such as water
repellents and stains, blend with the grain
and textures of the wood for either formal
or informal appearance. Colors are easily
achieved with exterior stains or paints.
Whatever the type of finish, its life will be
longer because redwood holds all finishes
longer than other woods, even under the
most severe conditions.

Redwood harmonizes visually with other
materials, such as brick, natural stone, and
glass. Or it can stand alone as the predom-
inant material for simplicity of design.

How to Specify Redwood

Specifiers of redwood can assure themselves of obtaining the exact product they
desire by including the necessary
elements in the specification. These
elements are:

Use, Grade Mark and **Species, Grade,
Grain, Moisture Condition, Size,
Surface Texture** or **Pattern, Factory
Finish***, and **Type of Fastener.**

*if desired

Example Specification: "Exterior siding
shall be CRA-RIS grade-marked redwood,
Clear, Vertical Grain, Certified Kiln Dried,
×6 Pattern 133, installed with hot-dipped
galvanized siding nails."

Grades. The two highest grades of
redwood, Clear All Heart and Clear, are
preferred for siding and trim. *Clear All
Heart* is a completely clear grade,
permitting only the reddish-brown
heartwood. *Clear* grade is similar, but
permits the white sapwood which is
frequently specified for visual interest.

Grain. Redwood siding will contain both
flat and vertical grain unless a vertical
grain selection is specified *(Clear All Heart
V.G. and/or Clear V.G.)* for even better
finish retention and weatherability.

Moisture Content. For all finish carpentry,
Certified Kiln Dried redwood should be
specified. This assures a uniformly low
moisture content, stability in place, and
better finish retention. One-inch redwood
will be dried to 10 percent moisture content

(see par. 725a of *Standard Specifications
for Grades of California Redwood Lumber,*
published by the Redwood Inspection Service, One Lombard Street, San Francisco,
Calif. 94111).

Pattern or Size. Basic siding patterns are
discussed on page 6; selected exterior
patterns are shown on page 7.

Surface Texture. Pattern lumber and
boards in finish grades are normally
supplied surfaced (planed). Most patterns
and all bevel sidings are available with a
resawn surface for a slight texture.

Technical Data

Flame spread. Fire hazard classification
tests conducted by Underwriters' Laboratories, Inc., have established a flame-
spread rating of 70 for nominal 1-inch
redwood lumber, qualifying this material as
Class II under the Uniform Building Code
and the Basic Building Code, and as
Group I under the Southern Standard
Building Code and the National Building
Code.

Fire retardant. Redwood treated with fire
retardant also qualifies as Class I (0-25)
under the above mentioned codes. Only
exterior-type fire retardants are recommended for exterior application.

Insulation value. Redwood k=0.83;
R ($^{11}/_{16}$″)=0.828; R ($^3/_4$″)=0.904.

Weight. Kiln dried redwood averages 28
lbs. per cubic ft.

Application of Redwood Siding

Apply redwood siding as recommended in
CRA Data Sheet 3A4-1. These recommendations are briefly summarized here: Apply
full vapor barrier of sheet material to inside
of exterior stud walls, beneath wall finish.
This prevents moisture condensation in
walls during cold weather. Where required,
use water repellent building paper over
sheathing on exterior walls. Apply flashing
or caulk around all wall openings, caulk or
seal all butt joints in siding. For vertical
siding patterns, install blocking at 24-inch
vertical intervals to provide nailing base.

Handling

Protect the fine quality of redwood siding
by proper handling at the job site. Store
Certified Kiln Dried redwood in a dry place,
off the ground, and protected from moisture,
including that from plaster and concrete.
Siding is available paper-wrapped to keep
it clean and dry, if so specified.

Coverage Conversion Factors

To estimate board feet or surface measure
of lumber required, multiply the area to be
covered (in square feet) by the conversion
factor of the pattern. This factor allows for
width lost in dressing or lapping. Add three
to five percent for end cutting and matching
on the job.

Note: Conversion factors for bevel siding
are based on CRA recommended
application; a 1-inch lap on courses of plain

bevel siding, and a $^1/_8$-inch expansion
clearance for rabbeted bevel between the
rabbet and the tip of the next lower course.

Width	Bevel	Rabbeted Bevel	Tongue & Groove	Shiplap & Rustic
4″	1.60	1.28	1.24	N.A.
6″	1.34	1.17	1.15	1.20
8″	1.24	1.13	1.11	1.15
10″	1.18	1.10	1.09	1.12
12″	1.15	1.08	1.07	1.09

N.A.—Pattern not available.

Nails and Nailing

Nailing methods for basic patterns of
siding are illustrated on page 2.
Noncorrosive nails should be used on
exterior siding. Recommended
noncorrosive nails are stainless steel or
aluminum alloy. *Top quality, hot-dipped*
galvanized nails will also perform well if the
galvanized coating is not damaged during
nailing. CRA experience indicates that
nails galvanized by any other process are
unsatisfactory and, like common nails, can
react with redwood's natural extractives
when wet to cause stain streaks. Nails
should be long enough to penetrate into
solid wood (studs or studs and wood
sheathing combined) at least 1$^1/_2$ inches. If
this much penetration is not possible, ring
shanked nails are recommended.

Finger-joined Redwood

Finger-joined redwood in Clear All Heart
and Clear grades is available in specific
lengths up to 20 feet for fascia, trim, soffits,
and a variety of other non-structural uses.
Manufactured from pieces usually 10 to 60
inches long, joined with finger jointing and
exterior glue, and kiln dried, finger-joined
redwood is available in nominal thicknesses from $^3/_4$ to 2 inches, and nominal
widths of 2, 3, 4, 5, 6, 8, 10, and 12 inches.
It is also available in single and double
plow fascia patterns (see page 7) and can
be run to any pattern if ordered in quantity.

Redwood Plywood for Siding

Where modular or sheet components are
desired, CRA redwood plywood is unexcelled in aesthetic and utilarian advantages.
For detailed information on redwood plywood grade and texture descriptions, applications and finishing, see Wood Book
(CRA Data Sheet 3A9).

This page

Top left: Excellent insulation qualities and weathering ability are among the reasons that redwood was the preferred material for this Idaho vacation home.

Top right: Unique designs are easily achieved with the versatility of the many patterns of redwood lumber siding. A circular facade was the architect's choice for this Michigan home.

Below, large photo: Random length end-butted Clear All Heart redwood boards create a warm and inviting exterior for the headquarters of this Massachusetts machine manufacturer.

This page

Left: A classic San Francisco home was restored with all heart redwood 1 × 6 tongue and groove siding and painted redwood trim.

Below right: Office building is accented with a wall of diagonally-applied Clear grade redwood.

Bottom: Long-lasting protection from a variety of weathering conditions is promised for this Kansas home featuring redwood siding coated with a stain.

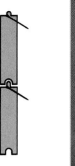

Flush Pattern

Square edge tongue and groove produces a flush surface when installed. It can be applied vertically, horizontally, or diagonally, in uniform or random widths.

Nailing: Blind nail 6-inch and narrower with one 8d finish nail diagonally into tongue. Face nail 8-inch and wider with two 8d siding nails.

V-Joint

Medium shadow patterns result from shallow V of tongue and groove or deeper V of shiplap.

Nailing; Shiplap—face nail 4- and 6-inch widths with one 8d siding nail per bearing, 1 inch from overlapping edge. On 8-inch and wider, two nails per bearing. Tongue and groove—blind nail 6-inch and narrower with one 8d finish nail diagonally into tongue. Face nail 8-inch and wider with two 8d siding nails.

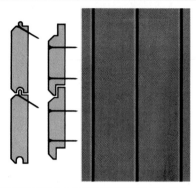

Channel Rustic

This is a shiplap variation that gives a board-on-board or inverted board and batten effect, producing strong patterns of light and shade. Usually applied vertically.

Nailing: Face nail 6-inch with one 8d siding nail per bearing, 1 inch from overlapping edge. On 8-inch and wider, two nails per bearing. Leave 1/8" clearance for expansion.

Bevel Siding

Apply horizontally. Plain bevel siding is reversible (one side surfaced for formal look or paint finish, one side resawn for natural finishes or more informal look.)

Nailing; Face nail with one siding nail per bearing (8d for 3/4-inch sidings, 7d for thinner) so nail shank clears tip of undercourse. Leave 1/8 inch above tip of rabbeted bevel siding courses for expansion. Lap plain bevel siding at least 1 inch.

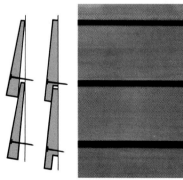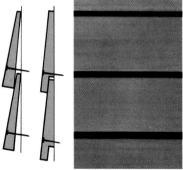

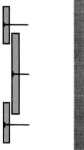

Board and Batten

Vertical siding only. Produces bold effects with many variations possible. Vary width of board, width or thickness of batten, or apply board on board to suit scale of structure.

Nailing: Space boards 1/2 inch apart; nail each underboard only **once** per bearing with 8d siding nail in center. Nail battens with 10d siding nail passing between adjacent boards.

Top: Stark angularity of a mountain setting is repeated in this vacation home of rugged redwood.

Center: A dignified, traditional look is provided by 1×6 redwood bevel siding.

Bottom: Creamy sap streaks and diagonal application of redwood add design appeal to this modern office building.

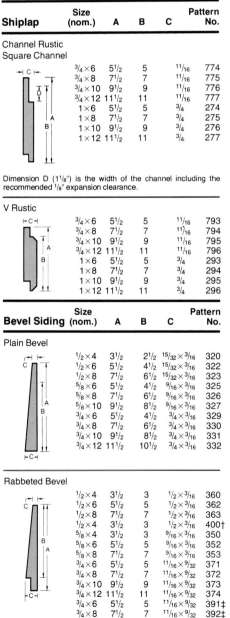

Plowed fascia (shown below before painting) and trim (left) are major uses for finger-joined redwood, because of its dimensional stability and long lengths. See "Finger-Joined Redwood" heading on page 3.

investment-conscious homeowners choose redwood for unique beauty and lasting value.

Selected Patterns

Tongue and Groove

	Size (nom.)	A*	B	C	Pattern No.
Square Edges	$3/4 \times 3$	$2^1/2$	$2^1/4$	$^{11}/_{16}$	631
	$3/4 \times 4$	$3^1/2$	$3^1/4$	$^{11}/_{16}$	632
	$3/4 \times 6$	$5^1/2$	$5^1/4$	$^{11}/_{16}$	633
	1×3	$2^1/2$	$2^1/4$	$3/4$	131
	1×4	$3^1/2$	$3^1/4$	$3/4$	132
	1×6	$5^1/2$	$5^1/4$	$3/4$	133
Eased Edges	$3/4 \times 4$	$3^1/2$	$3^1/4$	$^{11}/_{16}$	632EE
	$3/4 \times 6$	$5^1/2$	$5^1/4$	$^{11}/_{16}$	633EE
	1×4	$3^1/2$	$3^1/4$	$3/4$	132EE
	1×6	$5^1/2$	$5^1/4$	$3/4$	133EE
1S-$^3/_{32}$" V	$3/4 \times 4$	$3^1/2$	$3^1/4$	$^{11}/_{16}$	707
	$3/4 \times 6$	$5^1/2$	$5^1/4$	$^{11}/_{16}$	708
	$3/4 \times 8$	$7^1/2$	$7^1/4$	$^{11}/_{16}$	715
	$3/4 \times 10$	$9^1/2$	$9^1/4$	$^{11}/_{16}$	716
	$3/4 \times 12$	$11^1/2$	$11^1/4$	$^{11}/_{16}$	717
	1×4	$3^1/2$	$3^1/4$	$3/4$	207
	1×6	$5^1/2$	$5^1/4$	$3/4$	208
	1×8	$7^1/2$	$7^1/4$	$3/4$	215
	1×10	$9^1/2$	$9^1/4$	$3/4$	216
	1×12	$11^1/2$	$11^1/4$	$3/4$	217
1S-$^1/_4$" V	$3/4 \times 4$	$3^1/2$	$3^1/4$	$^{11}/_{16}$	709
	$3/4 \times 6$	$5^1/2$	$5^1/4$	$^{11}/_{16}$	711
	$3/4 \times 8$	$7^1/2$	$7^1/4$	$^{11}/_{16}$	712
	$3/4 \times 10$	$9^1/2$	$9^1/4$	$^{11}/_{16}$	713
	$3/4 \times 12$	$11^1/2$	$11^1/4$	$^{11}/_{16}$	714
	1×4	$3^1/2$	$3^1/4$	$3/4$	209
	1×6	$5^1/2$	$5^1/4$	$3/4$	211
	1×8	$7^1/2$	$7^1/4$	$3/4$	212
	1×10	$9^1/2$	$9^1/4$	$3/4$	213
	1×12	$11^1/2$	$11^1/4$	$3/4$	214
2S-S1S Resawn 1S	$3/4 \times 4$	$3^1/2$	$3^1/4$	$^{11}/_{16}$	709R
	$3/4 \times 6$	$5^1/2$	$5^1/4$	$^{11}/_{16}$	711R
	$3/4 \times 8$	$7^1/2$	$7^1/4$	$^{11}/_{16}$	712R
	$3/4 \times 10$	$9^1/2$	$9^1/4$	$^{11}/_{16}$	713R
	$3/4 \times 12$	$11^1/2$	$11^1/4$	$^{11}/_{16}$	714R
	1×4	$3^1/2$	$3^1/4$	$3/4$	209R
	1×6	$5^1/2$	$5^1/4$	$3/4$	211R
	1×8	$7^1/2$	$7^1/4$	$3/4$	212R
	1×10	$9^1/2$	$9^1/4$	$3/4$	213R
	1×12	$11^1/2$	$11^1/4$	$3/4$	214R

Figures in columns A, B, C and D refer to dimensions as indicated in pattern drawings.

Note: All patterns are not made by all mills.

Shiplap

	Size (nom.)	A	B	C	Pattern No.
Channel Rustic Square Channel	$3/4 \times 6$	$5^1/2$	5	$^{11}/_{16}$	774
	$3/4 \times 8$	$7^1/2$	7	$^{11}/_{16}$	775
	$3/4 \times 10$	$9^1/2$	9	$^{11}/_{16}$	776
	$3/4 \times 12$	$11^1/2$	11	$^{11}/_{16}$	777
	1×6	$5^1/2$	5	$3/4$	274
	1×8	$7^1/2$	7	$3/4$	275
	1×10	$9^1/2$	9	$3/4$	276
	1×12	$11^1/2$	11	$3/4$	277

Dimension D ($1^1/8$") is the width of the channel including the recommended $1/8$" expansion clearance.

V Rustic	Size (nom.)	A	B	C	Pattern No.
	$3/4 \times 6$	$5^1/2$	5	$^{11}/_{16}$	793
	$3/4 \times 8$	$7^1/2$	7	$^{11}/_{16}$	794
	$3/4 \times 10$	$9^1/2$	9	$^{11}/_{16}$	795
	$3/4 \times 12$	$11^1/2$	11	$^{11}/_{16}$	796
	1×6	$5^1/2$	5	$3/4$	293
	1×8	$7^1/2$	7	$3/4$	294
	1×10	$9^1/2$	9	$3/4$	295
	1×12	$11^1/2$	11	$3/4$	296

Bevel Siding

	Size (nom.)	A	B	C	Pattern No.
Plain Bevel	$1/2 \times 4$	$3^1/2$	$2^1/2$	$^{15}/_{32} \times 3/16$	320
	$1/2 \times 6$	$5^1/2$	$4^1/2$	$^{15}/_{32} \times 3/16$	322
	$1/2 \times 8$	$7^1/2$	$6^1/2$	$^{15}/_{32} \times 3/16$	323
	$5/8 \times 6$	$5^1/2$	$4^1/2$	$9/16 \times 3/16$	325
	$5/8 \times 8$	$7^1/2$	$6^1/2$	$9/16 \times 3/16$	326
	$5/8 \times 10$	$9^1/2$	$8^1/2$	$9/16 \times 3/16$	327
	$3/4 \times 6$	$5^1/2$	$4^1/2$	$3/4 \times 3/16$	329
	$3/4 \times 8$	$7^1/2$	$6^1/2$	$3/4 \times 3/16$	330
	$3/4 \times 10$	$9^1/2$	$8^1/2$	$3/4 \times 3/16$	331
	$3/4 \times 12$	$11^1/2$	$10^1/2$	$3/4 \times 3/16$	332
Rabbeted Bevel	$1/2 \times 4$	$3^1/2$	3	$1/2 \times 3/16$	360
	$1/2 \times 6$	$5^1/2$	5	$1/2 \times 3/16$	362
	$1/2 \times 8$	$7^1/2$	7	$1/2 \times 3/16$	363
	$1/2 \times 4$	$3^1/2$	3	$1/2 \times 3/16$	400†
	$5/8 \times 4$	$3^1/2$	3	$9/16 \times 3/16$	350
	$5/8 \times 6$	$5^1/2$	5	$9/16 \times 3/16$	352
	$5/8 \times 8$	$7^1/2$	7	$9/16 \times 3/16$	353
	$3/4 \times 6$	$5^1/2$	5	$^{11}/_{16} \times 9/32$	371
	$3/4 \times 8$	$7^1/2$	7	$^{11}/_{16} \times 9/32$	372
	$3/4 \times 10$	$9^1/2$	9	$^{11}/_{16} \times 9/32$	373
	$3/4 \times 12$	$11^1/2$	11	$^{11}/_{16} \times 9/32$	374
	$3/4 \times 6$	$5^1/2$	5	$^{11}/_{16} \times 9/32$	391‡
	$3/4 \times 8$	$7^1/2$	7	$^{11}/_{16} \times 9/32$	392‡
	$3/4 \times 10$	$9^1/2$	9	$^{11}/_{16} \times 9/32$	393‡
	$3/4 \times 12$	$11^1/2$	11	$^{11}/_{16} \times 9/32$	394‡

†This pattern has a round edge, $3/8$" radius.
‡Resawn face. These patterns have a square edge.

Plowed Fascia

	Size (nom.)	A	B	C	D	Pattern No.
Single Plow $5/16$" or $7/16$"	$3/4 \times 6$	$5^1/2$*	$^{11}/_{16}$	$5/16$	$5/16$	80
	$3/4 \times 8$	$7^1/4$	$^{11}/_{16}$	$5/16$	$5/16$	81
	$3/4 \times 6$	$5^1/2$*	$^{11}/_{16}$	$5/16$	$7/16$	84
	$3/4 \times 8$	$7^1/4$	$^{11}/_{16}$	$5/16$	$7/16$	85
	1×6	$5^1/2$*	$3/4$	$3/8$	$5/16$	580
	1×8	$7^1/4$	$3/4$	$3/8$	$5/16$	581
	1×6	$5^1/2$*	$3/4$	$3/8$	$7/16$	584
	1×8	$7^1/4$	$3/4$	$3/8$	$7/16$	585
Double Plow $5/16$" & $7/16$"	$3/4 \times 6$	$5^1/2$*	$^{11}/_{16}$	$5/16$		88
	$3/4 \times 8$	$7^1/4$	$^{11}/_{16}$	$5/16$		89
	1×6	$5^1/2$*	$3/4$	$3/8$		588
	1×8	$7^1/4$	$3/4$	$3/8$		589

*Also available surfaced at $5^3/8$" wide.

S4S Dry Finish

	Nominal	Dressed
	$3/4 \times 2$	$^{11}/_{16} \times 1^1/2$*
	$3/4 \times 3$	$^{11}/_{16} \times 2^1/2$
	$3/4 \times 4$	$^{11}/_{16} \times 3^1/2$
	$3/4 \times 6$	$^{11}/_{16} \times 5^1/2$
	$3/4 \times 8$	$^{11}/_{16} \times 7^1/4$
	$3/4 \times 10$	$^{11}/_{16} \times 9^1/4$
	$3/4 \times 12$	$^{11}/_{16} \times 11^1/4$
	1×2	$3/4 \times 1^1/2$*
	1×3	$3/4 \times 2^1/2$
	1×4	$3/4 \times 3^1/2$
	1×6	$3/4 \times 5^1/2$
	1×8	$3/4 \times 7^1/4$
	1×10	$3/4 \times 9^1/4$
	1×12	$3/4 \times 11^1/4$
	2×4	$1^1/2$* $\times 3^1/2$
	2×6	$1^1/2$* $\times 5^1/2$
	2×8	$1^1/2$* $\times 7^1/4$
	2×10	$1^1/2$* $\times 9^1/4$
	2×12	$1^1/2$* $\times 11^1/4$

*Also available surfaced at $1^5/8$" net.

Finish Suggestions

Unfinished redwood. When left unfinished in exterior use, redwood will gradually, naturally weather to a soft driftwood gray. This attractive result can be hastened with the application of a *bleach* which speeds the natural weathering process. Bleaching also avoids the period of darkening of the wood that naturally weathering redwood may undergo.

Water repellents. Weathering effects can be modified by applying one or more brushed-on coats (two coats on new wood) of a *water repellent.* The wood will gradually change from reddish-brown to a handsome buckskin tan. If water repellent is not renewed periodically, areas exposed to water and sun may eventually bleach to driftwood gray.

Water repellent is recommended by the California Redwood Association as the best protection for redwood, while retaining the natural redwood appearance. Water repellent effects no permanent change and any finish can be applied at any time without major surface preparations. Never use a sprayer to apply water repellents, and always follow manufacturer's instructions carefully.

Redwood siding patterns may be ordered pre-treated with water repellent. Quality water repellents contain a mildewcide to prevent discoloration of the wood by mildew.

Stains. Semi-transparent pigmented stains offer great variety of color control while not obscuring the natural character of the wood's grain and texture. Some stains are heavy-bodied and will tend to hide the grain of the wood, but not the texture. The stain finish will weather, however, and the grain will become more noticeable.

Paints. Lack of pitch and resins, plus an open cellular structure, make redwood an excellent surface for paint retention.

While flat grain lumber makes a good paint base, the very finest paint retention is achieved with vertical grain redwood.

New redwood will require a primer coat and, especially with resawn redwood, two finish coats. An oil-base primer should be used on redwood.

After priming, latex-base paints will perform well on redwood, as will traditional oil-base paints. Not recommended for use on redwood are certain low-luster alkyd resin-base top coats which absorb water easily and can cause paint problems. Since moisture is the main cause of paint failure, a vapor barrier should be installed on the *inside* face of stud walls to prevent moisture migration from inside the structure to the back of the siding.

To summarize, the best paint performance is usually achieved with two coats of latex finish paint applied over a proper alkyd- or oil-base primer on vertical grain redwood siding properly installed with an effective moisture barrier.

Related Literature

More information on redwood's many uses can be found in *Redwood Interior Guide* (Data Sheet 3A7), *Redwood Landscape Guide* (Data Sheet 3A5), and *Redwood Plywood Guide* (Data Sheet 3A9). These Data Sheets are in the Wood Book. Copies may be obtained by writing California Redwood Association at the address below.

Antique to Contemporary

Top: Clear All Heart redwood bevel siding resists the effects of weather and warms the appearance of these Utah townhomes.

Bottom: Restored Victorian homes owe their longevity in part to the lasting qualities of the redwood used in their original construction.

California
Redwood
Association

One Lombard Street
San Francisco, California 94111
Telephone: (415) 392-7880

CRA Member Company Sales Offices

Arcata Redwood Company
P.O. Box 218, Arcata, CA 95521

Georgia-Pacific Corporation
Fort Bragg Division-Redwood
90 West Redwood Ave., Fort Bragg, CA 95437

Harwood Products Company
P.O. Box 609, Willits, CA 95490

Masonite Corporation, Western Lumber Division
P.O. Box 97, Calpella, CA 95418

Miller Redwood Company
P.O. Box 247, Crescent City, CA 95531

Simpson Timber Company
900 Fourth Ave., Seattle, WA 98164

The Pacific Lumber Company
1111 Columbus Ave., San Francisco, CA 94133

Redwood—a renewable resource.

Red Cedar Shingles and Shakes

For Residences

For Interiors

For Vacation Homes

For Mobile-modules

For Commercial Buildings

Pre-stained Grooved Sidewall Shakes

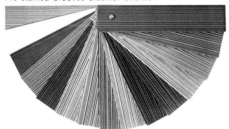

These labels under the bandstick or on cartons of red cedar shingles, handsplit shakes and grooved shakes are your guarantee of Bureau-graded quality. Insist on them.

WESTERN RED CEDAR *(thuja plicata)* is characterized by extremely fine and even grain, exceptional strength in proportion to weight, low ratio of expansion and contraction with changes in moisture content, and high impermeability to liquids.

Shingles are sawed. Shakes are split. Shingles have a relatively smooth surface, while shakes have at least one highly textured, natural grain split surface. Grooved sidewall shakes are shingles which have been rebutted and rejointed, then one face given a textured striated surface by machine process.

Shingles and handsplit shakes are generally used for roofs in the natural or unstained state. Grooved sidewall shakes are available natural too, but a majority are marketed either prime-coated or finish-coated in one of a wide range of attractive colors.

The cellular composition of Western Red Cedar—millions of tiny air-filled cells per cubic inch—provides a high degree of thermal insulation on both roof and wall applications.

Further, the wood possesses outstanding rigidity in hurricane winds and great resilience under the pounding of hail. These natural advantages are amplified by the structural strength derived from the overlapping method of application that is used.

Although most cedar roofs are not treated, the use of chemical solutions—especially in areas whose climate is characterized by a combination of heat and humidity—frequently is warranted if the ultimate in service is to be anticipated.

Red Cedar Shingle & Handsplit Shake Bureau

Suite 275, 515-116th Ave. N.E., Bellevue, WA 98004
In Canada: Suite 1500, 1055 W. Hastings St., Vancouver, B.C. V6E 2H1

APPLICATION RECOMMENDATIONS

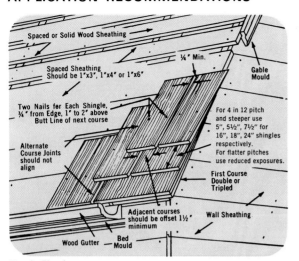

Roofs Fig. 1

Labels in Fig. 1:
- Spaced or Solid Wood Sheathing
- Spaced Sheathing Should be 1"x3", 1"x4" or 1"x6"
- Two Nails for Each Shingle, ¾" from Edge, 1" to 2" above Butt Line of next course
- Alternate Course Joints should not align
- ¼" Min.
- Gable Mould
- For 4 in 12 pitch and steeper use 5", 5½", 7½" for 16", 18", 24" shingles respectively. For flatter pitches use reduced exposures.
- First Course Double or Tripled
- Adjacent courses should be offset 1½" minimum
- Wall Sheathing
- Wood Gutter
- Bed Mould

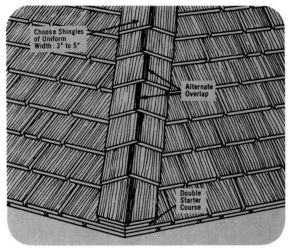

Hips and Ridges Fig. 2

Labels in Fig. 2:
- Choose Shingles of Uniform Width: 3" to 5"
- Alternate Overlap
- Double Starter Course

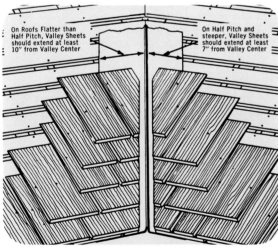

Valleys Fig. 3

Labels in Fig. 3:
- On Roofs Flatter than Half Pitch, Valley Sheets should extend at least 10" from Valley Center
- On Half Pitch and steeper, Valley Sheets should extend at least 7" from Valley Center

SHINGLES: ROOF SHEATHING—Red cedar shingles may be applied over open or solid sheathing. If the former, space between boards should not be greater than the width of the board, but not more than 4". Breather-type building paper—such as deadening felt—may be applied over either type sheathing, although paper is not used in most applications.

ROOF PITCH AND EXPOSURES—Proper weather exposure is important, and depends largely on roof pitch. On roof slopes of 4/12 and steeper, the standard exposures for No. 1 grade shingles are: 5" for 16" shingles, 5-1/2" for 18" shingles and 7-1/2" for 24" shingles. On roof slopes less than 4/12, to a minimum of 3/12, reduced exposures of 3-3/4", 4-1/4" and 5-3/4", respectively, are recommended. Reduced exposures also are recommended for No. 2 and No. 3 shingles on all roof slopes. (See chart.)

ROOF APPLICATION—Shingles normally are applied in straight, single courses. But application may be varied for the sake of achieving certain effects (thatch, serrated, weave and ocean wave applications are common styles). The following applies regardless: shingles must be doubled at all eaves and butts of first-course shingles should project 1-1/2" beyond the first sheathing board. Spacing between adjacent shingles (joints) should be 1/4". Joints in any one course should be separated not less than 1-1/2 from joints in adjacent courses, and joints in alternate courses should not be in direct alignment. (See Fig. 1.)

HIPS AND RIDGES—All hips and ridges should be of the "Boston type," with protected nailing. Factory-assembled hip and ridge units are available. Be sure to use longer nails of sufficient length to penetrate the underlying sheathing. (See Fig. 2.) The 6d (2") length normally is adequate.

VALLEYS—For roofs with one-half pitch or steeper, valley flashing should extend not less than 7" on each side of the valley center. On roofs of less than one-half pitch, flashing should extend at least 10" on each side. Shingles extending into the valley should be sawed to proper miter. Do not break joints into valley, or lay shingles with grain parallel with center line of valley. Use center-crimped and painted galvanized or aluminum valleys. (See Fig. 3.)

NAILING—Apply each shingle with two (only) rust-resistant nails (hot-dipped zinc or aluminum). Each nail should be placed not more than 3/4" from the side edge of the shingle and not more than 1" above the exposure line. Use 3d (1-1/4") nails for 16" and 18" shingles, and 4d (1-1/2") for 24" shingles. Drive the nails flush, but not so the head crushes the wood.

SIDEWALL APPLICATION—There are two basic methods of shingle sidewall application—single-course and double-course. In single-coursing (see Fig. 4a) shingles are applied much as in roof construction, but greater weather exposures are permitted. Shingle walls have two layers of shingles at every point, whereas shingle roofs have 3-ply construction. Double-coursing allows for the application of shingles at extended weather exposures over under-coursing-grade shingles. Double-coursing (see Figs. 4b and 4c) gives deep, bold shadow lines. When double-coursed, a shingle wall should be tripled at the foundation line (by using a double underlay). When the wall is single-coursed, the shingles should be doubled at the foundation line.

NAILING—For double-coursing (see Figs. 4b and 4c) each outer course shingle should be secured with two 5d (1-3/4") small-head, rust-resistant nails driven about two inches above the butts, 3/4" in from each side, plus additional nails about four inches apart across the face of the shingle. *Single-coursing* (see Fig. 4a) involves the same number of nails, but they can be shorter (3d 1-1/4") and should be driven not more than 1" above the butt line *of the next course.* Never drive the nail so hard that its head crushes the wood.

CORNERS—Outside corners (see Figure 4d) should be constructed with an alternate overlap of shingles between successive courses. Inside corners (see Fig. 4e) should be mitered over a metal flashing, or they may be made by nailing an S4S 1-1/2"- or 2"-square strip in the corner, after which the shingles of each course are jointed to the strip.

REBUTTED - AND - REJOINTED SHINGLES—These are shingles whose edges have been machine-trimmed so as to be exactly parallel, and butts retrimmed at precisely right angles. *They are used on sidewalls with tight-fitting joints to give a strong horizontal line.* Available with the natural "sawed" face, or with one face sanded smooth, they may be applied single or double-coursed.

PAINT/STAIN—Rebutted-rejointed shingles weather beautifully in the natural state. But they are often stained—or painted—with excellent results. For suggestions on nailing (single and double course) and making corners (inside and outside) see shingle sidewall instructions above.

GROOVED SIDEWALL SHAKES—Since grooved sidewall shakes are basically a rebutted-rejointed shingle with a machine-grooved surface, many of the requirements for shingle sidewall application apply. *But grooved sidewall shakes are always applied double-coursed.* This procedure yields a deep shadow line nearly 1" at the butt and greater coverage at lower cost, since extended weather exposures are possible over the undercourse of low-grade shingles.

Labels in Figs. 4a–4e:
- Wood Sheathing
- Building Paper
- Sidewalls Fig. 4a
- Unsaturated Building Paper between Shingles & Sheathing.
- Tight Joints
- Outer course ½" lower than Undercourse.
- No. 3 or Undercoursing Grade Shingles.
- Apply nails in straight line 2" above Shingle Butts.
- Fig. 4b
- Studs
- Non-wood Sheathing
- Wood Strips Nailed to Studs
- Fig. 4c
- Alternate Overlap
- Fig. 4d
- Mitered Flashing Behind
- Fig. 4e

As with shingle sidewalls, the double-course application requires an extra under-course at the foundation line. Grooved sidewall shakes are also available in 4-ft. and 8-ft. wide panels, for even faster application.

NAILING—Each outer course grooved shake should be secured with 5d (1-3/4") small-head, rust-resistant nails; these are driven about two inches above the butt, one nail about 3/4" from each edge and additional nails spaced about four inches apart across the shake face. Each undercourse shingle is fastened with staples or one or more nails. Nails that match the factory-applied color of the grooved sidewall shakes are available from some manufacturers.

CORNERS—Corners for grooved sidewall shakes should be constructed in the same manner as outlined above for shingle sidewalls. Patented metal corner units also are available.

PAINT/STAIN—Grooved sidewall shakes are marketed in a wide variety of factory-applied colors, ranging from delicate pastels to dark browns and greens. They also are available prime-coated, for finish treatment after they are applied.

HANDSPLIT SHAKES: ROOF SHEATHING—Red cedar handsplit shakes may be applied over open or solid sheathing. When spaced sheathing is used, 1 x 6s (or wider) are spaced on centers equal to the weather exposure at which the shakes are to be laid—but never more than 10 inches. In areas where wind-driven snow conditions prevail, a solid roof deck is recommended.

ROOF PITCH AND EXPOSURES—Proper weather exposure is important. As a general rule, a 7-1/2" exposure is recommended for 18" shakes and 10" exposure for 24" shakes. (See shake coverage chart.) The minimum recommended standard roof pitch for handsplit shakes is 4/12, but there have been numerous satisfactory installations on lesser slopes, climatic conditions and mode of application being mitigating factors.

ROOF APPLICATION—A 36-inch wide strip of 15-lb. minimum roofing felt should be laid over sheathing boards at the eave line. The beginning or starter course of shakes should be doubled; for extra texture it can be tripled. The bottom course or courses can be 15" or 18" shakes—the former being made expressly for this purpose. After applying each course of shakes, an 18" wide strip of 15-lb. minimum roofing felt should be laid over the top portion of the shakes, extending onto the sheathing. Position the bottom edge of the felt above the butt at a distance equal to twice the weather exposure. For example, 24" shakes laid with 10" exposure would have felt applied 20" above the shake butts; thus the felt will cover the top four inches of the shakes, and will extend out 14" onto the sheathing. (See Fig. 5.): Spacing between shakes (joints) should be about 1/2", and joints of adjacent courses should be offset at least 1-1/2". When straight-split shakes are used, the "froe-end" (the end from which the shakes have been split and which is smoother) should be laid uppermost, i.e. toward the ridge. Roofing felt interlay is not necessary when straight-split or taper-split shakes are applied in snow-free areas at weather exposures less than one-third the total shake length (3-ply roof).

VALLEYS—Valley and flashing metals that have proved reliable in a particular region should be selected. It is important that valley metals be used whose longevity will match that for which cedar is renowned. Metal valley sheets should be center-crimped, of 20-inch minimum width, and for maximum life should be either underlaid with a strip of 30-lb. roofing felt applied over the sheathing or painted with a good grade metal paint. (See Fig. 6.)

HIPS AND RIDGES—Either site-applied or pre-formed factory-made hip and ridge units may be used. Weather exposures should be the same as roof shakes. Be sure to use longer nails, sufficient to penetrate the underlying sheathing. Advisable to use two 8d nails on each side of shake. (See Fig. 7.)

NAILING—Secure each shake with two (only) rust-resistant nails (hot-dipped zinc or aluminum) driven about one inch from each edge, and one or two inches above the butt line of the course to follow. Adequate nail penetration into sheathing boards is important. The two-inch length (6d) normally is adequate, but longer nails should be used if shake thickness or weather exposure dictates. Do not drive nailheads into shakes.

SIDEWALL APPLICATION—Maximum recommended weather exposure with single-course wall construction is 8-1/2" for 18" shakes and 11-1/2" for 24" shakes. The nailing normally is concealed in single-course applications—that is, nailing points slightly above the butt line of the course to follow. Double-course application requires an underlay of shakes or regular cedar shingles. Weather exposures up to 14" are permissible with 18" shakes, and 20" with 24" shakes. If straight-split shakes are used, the double-course exposure may be 16" for 18" shakes and 22" for 24" shakes. Butt nailing of shakes is required with double-course application. Do not drive nailheads into the shake surface. (For corners, see Fig. 8.)

FINISHES AND WEATHERING QUALITIES—If not treated, red cedar shingles, grooved sidewall shakes and handsplit shakes will eventually weather to silver, dark gray or dark brown. The speed of change and final shade depend mainly on atmosphere and climate conditions. Bleaching agents may be applied, in which case the wood will turn an antique silver gray. So-called natural finishes, which are lightly pigmented and maintain the original appearance of wood, are available commercially. Stains, whether heavy or semi-transparent, are excellent for cedar. Paints are suitable, too, on exterior walls but not on roofs.

TREATMENT—The majority of cedar roofs remain untreated and are known to provide excellent service. Chemical treatment is desirable, however, when cedar roofing is installed in areas whose climate combines heat and humidity for considerable portions of the year. Fungicidal chemicals will inhibit bacteria such as moss, fungus and mildew, and will contribute to roof life service. Extreme care should be taken in applying some chemicals, such as penta-chlorophenol solutions, because of their toxicity. Follow manufacturer's directions! Cedar roofs should be cleaned periodically, normally on an annual basis, of any accumulation of debris such as leaves, needles, etc., as such foreign matter can adversely affect roof service. ·

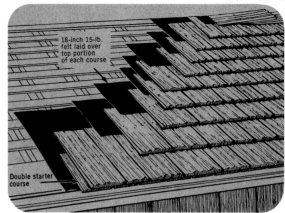

Roofs Fig. 5

Valleys Fig. 6

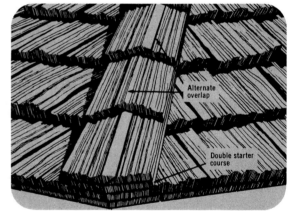

Hips and Ridges Fig. 7

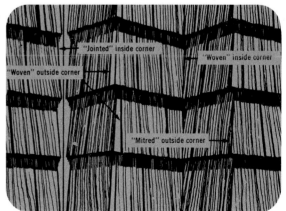

Sidewalls Fig. 8

CERTIGRADE RED CEDAR SHINGLES

GRADE	Length	Thickness (at Butt)	No. of Courses Per Bundle	Bdls/Cartons Per Square		Description
No. 1 BLUE LABEL	16" (Fivex) 18" (Perfections) 24" (Royals)	.40" .45" .50"	20/20 18/18 13/14	4 bdls. 4 bdls. 4 bdls.	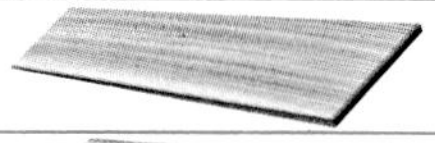	The premium grade of shingles for roofs and sidewalls. These top-grade shingles are 100% heartwood . . . 100% clear and 100% edge-grain.
No. 2 RED LABEL	16" (Fivex) 18" (Perfections) 24" (Royals)	.40" .45" .50"	20/20 18/18 13/14	4 bdls. 4 bdls. 4 bdls.		A proper grade for some applications. Not less than 10" clear on 16" shingles, 11" clear on 18" shingles and 16" clear on 24" shingles. Flat grain and limited sapwood are permitted in this grade.
No. 3 BLACK LABEL	16" (Fivex) 18" (Perfections) 24" (Royals)	.40" .45" .50"	20/20 18/18 13/14	4 bdls. 4 bdls. 4 bdls.		A utility grade for economy applications and secondary buildings. Not less than 6" clear on 16" and 18" shingles, 10" on 24" shingles.
No. 4 UNDER-COURSING	16" (Fivex) 18" (Perfections)	.40" .45"	14/14 or 20/20 14/14 or 18/18	2 bdls. 2 bdls. 2 bdls. 2 bdls.	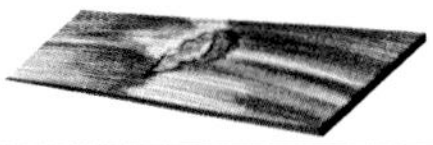	A utility grade for undercoursing on double-coursed sidewall applications or for interior accent walls.
No. 1 or No. 2 REBUTTED-REJOINTED	16" (Fivex) 18" (Perfections) 24" (Royals)	.40" .45" .50"	33/33 28/28 13/14	1 carton 1 carton 4 bdls.	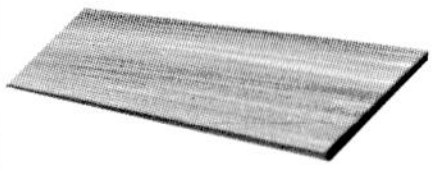	Same specifications as above for No. 1 and No. 2 grades but machine trimmed for exactly parallel edges with butts sawn at precise right angles. For sidewall application where tightly fitting joints are desired. Also available with smooth sanded face.

| PITCH | Maximum exposure recommended for roofs: | | | | | | | | |
| | NO. 1 BLUE LABEL | | | NO. 2 RED LABEL | | | NO. 3 BLACK LABEL | | |
	16"	18"	24"	16"	18"	24"	16"	18"	24"
3 IN 12 TO 4 IN 12	3¾"	4¼"	5¾"	3½"	4"	5½"	3"	3½"	5"
4 IN 12 AND STEEPER	5"	5½"	7½"	4"	4½"	6½"	3½"	4"	5½"

| LENGTH AND THICKNESS | Approximate coverage of one square (4 bundles) of shingles based on following weather exposures | | | | | | | | | | | | | | | | | | | | | | | | | | |
	3½"	4"	4½"	5"	5½"	6"	6½"	7"	7½"	8"	8½"	9"	9½"	10"	10½"	11"	11½"	12"	12½"	13"	13½"	14"	14½"	15"	15½"	16"
16" x 5/2"	70	80	90	100*	110	120	130	140	150‡	160	170	180	190	200	210	220	230	240†	....	....	....	....	....	....	....	....
18" x 5/2¼"	....	72½	81½	90½	100*	109	118	127	136	145½	154½‡	163½	172½	181½	191	200	209	218	227	236	245½	254½†	....	....	....	....
24" x 4/2"	....	....	....	....	....	80	86½	93	100*	106½	113	120	126½	133	140	146½	153‡	160	166½	173	180	186½	193	200	206½	213†

NOTES: *Maximum exposure recommended for roofs. ‡Maximum exposure recommended for single-coursing No. 1 grades on sidewalls. Reduce exposure for No. 2 grades.
†Maximum exposure recommended for double-coursing No. 1 grades on sidewalls.

CERTIGROOVE GROOVED RED CEDAR SIDEWALL SHAKES

GRADE	Length	Thickness (at Butt)	No. Courses Per Carton	Cartons Per Square*		Description
No. 1 BLUE LABEL	16" 18" 24"	.40" .45" .50"	16/17 14/14 12/12	2 ctns. 2 ctns. 2 ctns.		Machine-grooved shakes are manufactured from shingles and have striated faces and parallel edges. Used exclusively double-coursed on sidewalls.

NOTE: *Also marketed in one-carton squares.

CERTI-SPLIT RED CEDAR HANDSPLIT SHAKES

| GRADE | Length and Thickness | 18" Pack** | | | Description |
		# Courses Per Bdl.	# Bdls. Per Sq.		
No. 1 HANDSPLIT & RESAWN	15" Starter-Finish 18" x ½" Mediums 18" x ¾" Heavies 24" x ⅜" 24" x ½" Mediums 24" x ¾" Heavies	9/9 9/9 9/9 9/9 9/9 9/9	5 5 5 5 5 5		These shakes have split faces and sawn backs. Cedar logs are first cut into desired lengths. Blanks or boards of proper thickness are split and then run diagonally through a bandsaw to produce two tapered shakes from each blank.
No. 1 TAPERSPLIT	24" x ½"	9/9	5	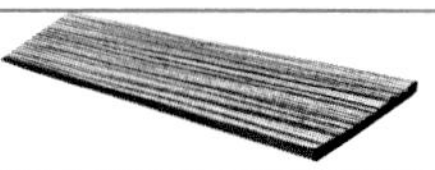	Produced largely by hand, using a sharp-bladed steel froe and a wooden mallet. The natural shingle-like taper is achieved by reversing the block, end-for-end, with each split.
No. 1 STRAIGHT-SPLIT	18" x ⅜" True-Edge* 18" x ⅜" 24" x ⅜"	20" Pack 14 Straight 19 Straight 16 Straight	4 5 5	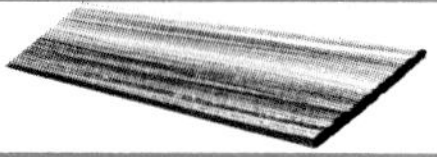	Produced in the same manner as tapersplit shakes except that by splitting from the same end of the block, the shakes acquire the same thickness throughout.

NOTE: * Exclusively sidewall product, with parallel edges.
      ** Pack used for majority of shakes.

| SHAKE TYPE, LENGTH AND THICKNESS | Approximate coverage (in sq. ft.) of one square, when shakes are applied with ½" spacing, at following weather exposures, in inches (h): | | | | | | |
	5½	7½	8½	10	11½	16	
18" x ½" Handsplit-and-Resawn Mediums (a)	55(b)	75(c)	85(d)	100	....	....	(a) 5 bundles will cover 100 sq. ft. roof area when used as starter-finish course at 10" weather exposure; 6 bundles will cover 100 sq. ft. wall area at 8½" exposure; 7 bundles will cover 100 sq. ft. roof area at 7½" weather exposure; see footnote (h).
18" x ¾" Handsplit-and-Resawn Heavies (a)	55(b)	75(c)	85(d)	100	....	....	(b) Maximum recommended weather exposure for 3-ply roof construction.
24" x ⅜" Handsplit	....	75(e)	85	100(f)	115(d)	....	(c) Maximum recommended weather exposure for 2-ply roof construction.
24" x ½" Handsplit-and-Resawn Mediums	....	75(b)	85	100(c)	115(d)	....	(d) Maximum recommended weather exposure for single-coursed wall construction.
24" x ¾" Handsplit-and-Resawn Heavies	....	75(b)	85	100(c)	115(d)	....	(e) Maximum recommended weather exposure for application on roof pitches between 4-in-12 and 8-in-12.
24" x ½" Tapersplit	....	75(b)	85	100(c)	115(d)	....	(f) Maximum recommended weather exposure for application on roof pitches of 8-in-12 and steeper.
18" x ⅜" True-Edge Straight-Split	....	....	....	....	....	112(g)	(g) Maximum recommended weather exposure for double-coursed wall construction.
18" x ⅜" Straight-Split	65(b)	90(c)	100(d)	....	....	....	(h) All coverage based on ½" spacing between shakes.
24" x ⅜" Straight-Split	....	75(b)	85	100(c)	115(d)	....	
15" Starter-Finish Course	Use supplementary with shakes applied not over 10" weather exposure.						

For detailed information on all cedar products, write to: Red Cedar Shingle & Handsplit Shake Bureau, Suite 275, 515-116th Ave. N.E., Bellevue, WA 98004
(In Canada: Suite 1500, 1055 W. Hastings St., Vancouver, B.C. V6E 2H1)

The**Wood**Book **Finishes**

Redwood

Interior Guide

3A7

California Redwood Association

Cover:
Exciting splashes of sapwood contrast with vertical and flat grain heartwood in this entrance to an office building.

This page
Top left: Dramatic diagonals of Clear grade redwood form an accent wall and emphasize a fireplace in a modern Arizona condominium.

Bottom left: Even-toned Clear All Heart redwood milled in a 1 × 6 V-joint tongue and groove pattern and applied in a continuous sweep from floor to ceiling peak in this Texas home.

Top right: Warm rustic beauty of sapwood-streaked Clear grade redwood enhances the atmosphere of this California restaurant.

Bottom right: Redwood creates a rich, relaxed atmosphere in this Midwestern hotel and club featuring rough-sawn Clear All Heart for planters, walls, and ceiling accents.

Interior walls and ceilings of California redwood have much to recommend them to designers of residential and commercial buildings. In addition to redwood's warm colors and rich grains and textures, very practical considerations soundly confirm its choice. Redwood's suitability for millwork, decorative screens, window walls, molding, and built-ins, as well as handsome structural uses, all make redwood a logical material for well integrated interiors.

Redwood overcomes some of the design limitations of other wood paneling materials because it is available in lengths up to 20 feet. Redwood, being both an interior and an exterior material, may be used for walls which pass through windows, uniting interior and outdoors. When the natural colors of redwood are modified by stain, the range of color effects is virtually unlimited. Redwood complements glass, stone, metals, fabrics, and other woods.

Specifying Redwood Interiors

Specifications for redwood should include grade, moisture content, size, and texture, and may include grain and pattern number if appropriate.

Redwood lumber for interior use is generally available in widths of 4 to 12 inches, lengths up to 20 feet, and in kiln dried thicknesses up to 2 inches. Pieces in excess of these limits may occasionally be available, but their availability should be determined before final selections are made. A limited amount of 3- and 4-inch material is available kiln dried for structural millwork.

Grades. The two highest grades of redwood, Clear All Heart and Clear, are preferred for use as paneling and trim. *Clear All Heart* is a completely clear grade, permitting only the cinnamon-brown heartwood. *Clear* grade is similar, but permits the light-colored sapwood which is frequently specified for visual interest.

Moisture content. For all interior uses, Certified Kiln Dried redwood should be used. This insures a uniform low moisture content which will, with redwood's high dimensional stability, permit joinery and cabinet work to keep its fine appearance. One-inch redwood is dried to 10 percent moisture content (see par. 725a of *Standard Specifications for Grades of California Redwood Lumber*, published by the Redwood Inspection Service, One Lombard Street, San Francisco, California 94111).

Size and pattern. Dimensions of standard interior patterns and finish lumber are given on page 7. If a special profile is to be used, a drawing with exact dimensions should be provided. Specify size, pattern description, and pattern number (e.g., ×10 Square Channel Pattern 276).

Surface texture. Pattern lumber and boards in finish grades are normally supplied surfaced (planed). Most patterns and all 3/8-inch panelings are available with a resawn surface, a medium saw texture for greater visual interest.

Grain. Redwood lumber for interior use will include both flat and vertical grain pieces unless a vertical grain selection is specified. Flat grain is the more highly figured, and its decorative swirls produce bold effects for paneling. Vertical grain is visually more subdued, more uniform, its grain running in more or less parallel lines.

Redwood Grain Patterns

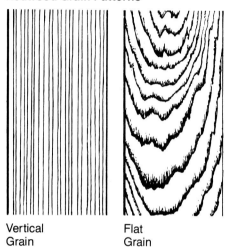

Vertical   Flat
Grain   Grain

Technical Data

Flame spread. Fire hazard classification tests conducted by Underwriters' Laboratories, Inc., have established a flamespread rating of 70 for nominal 1-inch redwood lumber, qualifying this material as Class II under the Uniform Building Code and the Basic Building Code, and as Group I under the Southern Standard Building Code and the National Building Code.

Fire retardant treatment. Redwood treated with fire retardant qualifies as Class 1 (0-25) under the above-mentioned codes. Some interior fire retardant treatments darken redwood appreciably.

Insulation value. Redwood $k = 0.83$; $R (3/8'') = 0.45$; $R (11/16'') = 0.828$; $R(3/4'') = 0.904$.

Weight. Kiln dried redwood averages 28 lbs. per cubic foot.

Installation

Interior redwood should not be installed until exterior doors and windows are in place, and any plaster, masonry, or wallboard joint tape has thoroughly dried. The heating system may be used to help dry out the interior. All plumbing and electrical work should be in place to avoid damage to paneling. Keep lumber covered to prevent soiling.

Prepare the wall for vertical paneling by installing blocking or furring strips at 24-inch intervals. Horizontal paneling may be applied directly to studs. On perimeter walls, apply sheet vapor barrier to the inner face of the stud wall or masonry wall. Care should be taken to avoid damaging the vapor barrier once it has been installed. Furring strips of 3/8-inch plywood are recommended under paneling to avoid piercing the vapor barrier and to provide a better surface for adhesives. Panelings may be applied with nails or adhesive to walls; nails are normally used for ceiling installations.

Nail carefully according to diagrams shown with pictures on page 6. Use 8-penny finish nails for face nailing, 6-penny for blind nailing 3/4-inch and 1-inch panelings. Use proportionately smaller nails for 3/8-inch and 5/8-inch panelings. If adhesive is used, it may be desirable to nail at top and bottom of each piece to give the adhesive a chance to set thoroughly.

This page

Top left: Cream-colored sapwood, a characteristic of Clear grade redwood, adds warm informality to this dining room.

Bottom left: Contemporary Mississippi home uses redwood lumber to frame ceiling skylights, bringing the outdoors inside.

Top right: A cozy bathroom of V-grooved redwood applied horizontally and diagonally.

Bottom, both pages: Country club lounge invites relaxed conversation. Walls are 1 × 6 all heart redwood; planter box dividers are 2 × 6 rough-sawn redwood with horizontal 1 × 8 forming the planter.

This page

Top left: Cinnamon heartwood and lighter sapwood have strong design appeal in this California home.

Top right: Diagonals of 1 × 4 V-grooved tongue and groove redwood create a modern, yet dignified wall treatment.

Bottom right: Kitchen seen through pass-through wall of 2 × 2 redwood lumber. Ceiling beams are 2 × 6 redwood, and kitchen cabinets are faced with rough-sawn redwood plywood.

Flush Pattern

Square edge tongue and groove produces a flush surface when installed. It can be applied vertically, horizontally, or diagonally, in uniform or random widths.

Nailing: Blind nail 6-inch and narrower with one 8d finish nail diagonally into tongue.

V-Joint

Medium shadow patterns result from shallow V of tongue and groove or deeper V of shiplap.

Nailing: *Shiplap*—face nail 4- and 6-inch widths with one 8d finish nail per bearing, 1 inch from overlapping edge. On 8-inch and wider, two nails per bearing. *Tongue and groove*—blind nail 8-inch and narrower with one 8d finish nail diagonally into tongue. Face nail 10-inch and wider with two 8d finish nails.

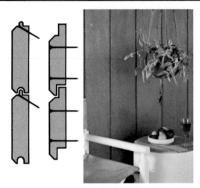

Channel Rustic

This is a shiplap variation that gives a board-on-board or inverted board and batten effect, producing strong patterns of light and shade. Usually applied vertically.

Nailing: Face nail 6-inch with one 8d finish nail per bearing, 1 inch from overlapping edge. On 8-inch and wider, two nails per bearing.

Spaced Boards

Simple but effective wall and ceiling treatment obtained by using redwood boards, surfaced or resawn, with spacing appropriate to width. On ceiling, use over wallboard or sound-absorbent material; on walls use over wallboard or plywood backing. Backing may be painted for color harmony or contrast.

Nailing: Face nail with two finish nails per bearing using 12d finish nails for 2 inch thickness nominal, 8d for 1 inch and 6d for less than 1 inch.

Finger-Joined Redwood

Selected clear pieces of redwood, usually 10 to 60 inches long, are jointed and end-glued into long boards in Clear All Heart or Clear Grades. This randomly-jointed wood, available in standard thicknesses and widths and in specific lengths up to 20 feet, makes highly decorative paneling, and can be ordered run to any pattern in quantity.

Nailing: Face nail with two finish nails per bearing using 12d finish nails for 2 inch thickness nominal, 8d for 1 inch and 6d for less than 1 inch.

A restful, quiet feeling in a hospital intensive care suite resulted from specifying Clear All Heart redwood. Horizontally-applied boards were milled in a rabbeted bevel pattern.

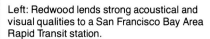
Left: Redwood lends strong acoustical and visual qualities to a San Francisco Bay Area Rapid Transit station.

Below left: Sports-themed restaurant picks up the visual variety of Clear grade redwood ribboned with sapwood.

Below: Natural beauty of V-joint 1×4 redwood ceiling and diagonal redwood walls was preferred by the owners of this Idaho home.

Selected Patterns

Tongue and Groove

	Size (nom.)	A	B	C	Pattern No.
Square Edges					
	³/₄×3	2¹/₂	2¹/₄	¹¹/₁₆	631
	³/₄×4	3¹/₂	3¹/₄	¹¹/₁₆	632
	³/₄×6	5¹/₂	5¹/₄	¹¹/₁₆	633
	1×3	2¹/₂	2¹/₄	³/₄	131
	1×4	3¹/₂	3¹/₄	³/₄	132
	1×6	5¹/₂	5¹/₄	³/₄	133
Eased Edges					
	³/₈×4	3¹/₂	3¹¹/₃₂	¹¹/₃₂	220
	³/₈×6	5¹/₂	5¹¹/₃₂	¹¹/₃₂	221
	³/₈×8	7¹/₂	7¹¹/₃₂	¹¹/₃₂	222
	³/₄×4	3¹/₂	3¹/₄	¹¹/₁₆	632EE
	³/₄×6	5¹/₂	5¹/₄	¹¹/₁₆	633EE
	1×4	3¹/₂	3¹/₄	³/₄	132EE
	1×6	5¹/₂	5¹/₄	³/₄	133EE
V-Joint ³/₃₂″ V					
	⁵/₈×4	3⁷/₁₆	3¹/₄	⁹/₁₆	204
	⁵/₈×6	5⁷/₁₆	5¹/₄	⁹/₁₆	205
	⁵/₈×8	7⁷/₁₆	7¹/₄	⁹/₁₆	206
	³/₄×4	3¹/₂	3¹/₄	¹¹/₁₆	707
	³/₄×6	5¹/₂	5¹/₄	¹¹/₁₆	708
	³/₄×8	7¹/₂	7¹/₄	¹¹/₁₆	715
	³/₄×10	9¹/₂	9¹/₄	¹¹/₁₆	716
	³/₄×12	11¹/₂	11¹/₄	¹¹/₁₆	717
	1×4	3¹/₂	3¹/₄	³/₄	207
	1×6	5¹/₂	5¹/₄	³/₄	208
	1×8	7¹/₂	7¹/₄	³/₄	215
	1×10	9¹/₂	9¹/₄	³/₄	216
	1×12	11¹/₂	11¹/₄	³/₄	217

V-Joint ¹/₄″ V

Size (nom.)	A	B	C	Pattern No.
³/₄×4	3¹/₂	3¹/₄	¹¹/₁₆	709
³/₄×6	5¹/₂	5¹/₄	¹¹/₁₆	711
³/₄×8	7¹/₂	7¹/₄	¹¹/₁₆	712
³/₄×10	9¹/₂	9¹/₄	¹¹/₁₆	713
³/₄×12	11¹/₂	11¹/₄	¹¹/₁₆	714
1×4	3¹/₂	3¹/₄	³/₄	209
1×6	5¹/₂	5¹/₄	³/₄	211
1×8	7¹/₂	7¹/₄	³/₄	212
1×10	9¹/₂	9¹/₄	³/₄	213
1×12	11¹/₂	11¹/₄	³/₄	214

Shiplap

	Size (nom.)	A	B	C	Pattern No.
V Rustic ⁷/₃₂″ V					
	⁵/₈×6	5¹/₂	5	⁹/₁₆	290
	⁵/₈×8	7¹/₂	7	⁹/₁₆	291
V Rustic ¹/₄″ V					
	³/₄×6	5¹/₂	5	¹¹/₁₆	793
	³/₄×8	7¹/₂	7	¹¹/₁₆	794
	³/₄×10	9¹/₂	9	¹¹/₁₆	795
	³/₄×12	11¹/₂	11	¹¹/₁₆	796
	1×6	5¹/₂	5	³/₄	293
	1×8	7¹/₂	7	³/₄	294
	1×10	9¹/₂	9	³/₄	295
	1×12	11¹/₂	11	³/₄	296

Channel Rustic Square Channel

Size	A	B	C	Pattern No.
³/₄×6	5¹/₂	5	¹¹/₁₆	774
³/₄×8	7¹/₂	7	¹¹/₁₆	775
³/₄×10	9¹/₂	9	¹¹/₁₆	776
³/₄×12	11¹/₂	11	¹¹/₁₆	777
1×6	5¹/₂	5	³/₄	274
1×8	7¹/₂	7	³/₄	275
1×10	9¹/₂	9	³/₄	276
1×12	11¹/₂	11	³/₄	277

Dimension D (1″) is the width of the channel.

S4S Dry Finish

Nominal	Dressed
³/₄×2	¹¹/₁₆ × 1¹/₂*
³/₄×3	¹¹/₁₆ × 2¹/₂
³/₄×4	¹¹/₁₆ × 3¹/₂
³/₄×6	¹¹/₁₆ × 5¹/₂
³/₄×8	¹¹/₁₆ × 7¹/₄
³/₄×10	¹¹/₁₆ × 9¹/₄
³/₄×12	¹¹/₁₆ × 11¹/₄
1×2	³/₄ × 1¹/₂*
1×3	³/₄ × 2¹/₂
1×4	³/₄ × 3¹/₂
1×6	³/₄ × 5¹/₂
1×8	³/₄ × 7¹/₄
1×10	³/₄ × 9¹/₄
1×12	³/₄ × 11¹/₄
2×4	1¹/₂ × 3¹/₂
2×6	1¹/₂ × 5¹/₂
2×8	1¹/₂* × 7¹/₄
2×10	1¹/₂* × 9¹/₄
2×12	1¹/₂* × 11¹/₄

*Also available surfaced at 1⁵/₈″ net.

Finishes

Redwood is usually preferred for interior use to take design advantage of the beautiful, natural characteristics of the wood. For this reason, interior redwood is usually unfinished except for the application of a clear sealer.

Sealers. Clear, flat penetrating sealers, such as an alkyd resin or clear polyurethane, will protect both resawn and smooth redwood. It is important to use sealers on wood surfaces which may be subject to soiling or cleaning. Sealers will darken redwood appreciably, but the grain and texture will remain visible.

In any area that is exposed to moisture, such as kitchens and bathrooms, it is important to seal the wood with at least two coats of a clear polyurethane or alkyd resin varnish, sanding between coats. Varnishes are available in flat, satiny semi-gloss, and gloss finishes.

Wax finishes. For other interior use, an attractive, soft luster can be added to natural redwood by applying a wax finish. Waxes are available with a stain tint if an added color effect is desired.

Wax finishes are easy to touch up, but are difficult to remove or paint over if another finish is desired later. Wax can be applied over a sealer, making the wax easier to remove.

Stains. Special decorative effects can be achieved by coloring the wood. For interior redwood, it's best to use a pigmented stain rather than paint. The stain will not seal the wood, so an overcoat of wax, lacquer, or varnish will be needed to protect the wood from grease, dirt, and liquids.

Finish Suggestions

General rules for application of interior finishes are (1) keep wood clean and dry, (2) follow manufacturer's directions for application and thinning, (3) do not mix incompatible finishes, (4) keep room well ventilated when applying finish, and (5) when mixing colors or when unfamiliar with the finish, experiment with separate sample piece of wood to be sure of final finished effect.

Complete instructions and recommendations for finishing are contained in *Redwood Interiors,* available from CRA.

Redwood Plywood for Interiors

Redwood plywood for interior paneling is increasing in popularity among architects and interior designers seeking large panels with interesting grains and textures.

For detailed information on redwood plywood grade and texture descriptions, applications and finishing, see CRA Data Sheet 3A9 (in Wood Book).

Related Literature

For detailed information on redwood sidings and other exterior architectural uses, see CRA Data Sheet 3A4, *Redwood Exterior Guide* (in Wood Book). For information on redwood's uses in landscape structures, see CRA Data Sheet 3A5, *Redwood Landscape Guide* (in Wood Book).

Other literature available from CRA includes:

Redwood Interiors (12 pages, color)

Re-Siding & Paneling with Redwood (6 pages, color)

Redwood Homes (12 pages, color)

Redwood Insulation (Data Sheet 2D2-6)

Redwood Exterior Finishes (Data Sheet 4B1-1)

Brand List of Exterior Finishes (Data Sheet 4B1-2)

The CRA trademark is your assurance of quality. The California Redwood Association is a non-profit organization maintained by the principal redwood producers. Its interests extend from the growth and protection of quality timber for the future and the best utilization of current forest crops, to research, and the dissemination of information on the use of redwood.

California Redwood Association

One Lombard Street
San Francisco, California 94111
Telephone: (415) 392-7880

CRA Member Company Sales Offices

Arcata Redwood Company
P.O. Box 218, Arcata, CA 95521
Georgia-Pacific Corporation
Fort Bragg Division-Redwood
90 West Redwood Ave., Fort Bragg, CA 95437
Harwood Products Company
P.O. Box 609, Willits, CA 95490
Masonite Corporation, Western Lumber Division
P.O. Box 97, Calpella, CA 95418
Miller Redwood Company
P.O. Box 247, Crescent City, CA 95531
Simpson Timber Company
900 Fourth Ave., Seattle, WA 98164
The Pacific Lumber Company
1111 Columbus Ave., San Francisco, CA 94133

Redwood—a renewable resource.

The**Wood**Book **Index**

(Continued on next page.)

(Continued on next page.)

TheWoodBook 78

ORDER CARD

Send _____ copies of TheWoodBook at $9.50 each: Total $ _____

Please enclose payment with order.

Signed _____

Name _____

Company _____

Address _____

City _____ State _____ Zip _____

TheWoodBook 78

ORDER CARD

Send _____ copies of TheWoodBook at $9.50 each: Total $ _____

Please enclose payment with order.

Signed _____

Name _____

Company _____

Address _____

City _____ State _____ Zip _____

TheWoodBook 78

ORDER CARD

Send _____ copies of TheWoodBook at $9.50 each: Total $ _____

Please enclose payment with order.

Signed _____

Name _____

Company _____

Address _____

City _____ State _____ Zip _____

TheWoodBook 78

ORDER CARD

Send _____ copies of TheWoodBook at $9.50 each: Total $ _____

Please enclose payment with order.

Signed _____

Name _____

Company _____

Address _____

City _____ State _____ Zip _____

Place
Stamp
Here

Wood Products Publications
P.O. Box 1752
Tacoma, Washington 98401

Wood Products Publications
P.O. Box 1752
Tacoma, Washington 98401

Place
Stamp
Here

Wood Products Publications
P.O. Box 1752
Tacoma, Washington 98401

Wood Products Publications
P.O. Box 1752
Tacoma, Washington 98401

Place
Stamp
Here

Place
Stamp
Here

The**Wood**Book 78

ORDER CARD

Send _____ copies of TheWoodBook at $9.50 each: Total $ _____

Please enclose payment with order.

Signed _____

Name _____

Company _____

Address _____

City _____ State _____ Zip _____

The**Wood**Book 78

ORDER CARD

Send _____ copies of TheWoodBook at $9.50 each: Total $ _____

Please enclose payment with order.

Signed _____

Name _____

Company _____

Address _____

City _____ State _____ Zip _____

The**Wood**Book 78

ORDER CARD

Send _____ copies of TheWoodBook at $9.50 each: Total $ _____

Please enclose payment with order.

Signed _____

Name _____

Company _____

Address _____

City _____ State _____ Zip _____

The**Wood**Book 78

ORDER CARD

Send _____ copies of TheWoodBook at $9.50 each: Total $ _____

Please enclose payment with order.

Signed _____

Name _____

Company _____

Address _____

City _____ State _____ Zip _____

Wood Products Publications
P.O. Box 1752
Tacoma, Washington 98401

Wood Products Publications
P.O. Box 1752
Tacoma, Washington 98401

Wood Products Publications
P.O. Box 1752
Tacoma, Washington 98401

Wood Products Publications
P.O. Box 1752
Tacoma, Washington 98401